Transistor Fundamentals

Volume 1

Basic Semiconductor and Circuit Principles

by

ROBERT J. BRITE

**Under the direction of
Training & Retraining, Inc.**

Howard W. Sams & Co., Inc.

4300 WEST 62ND ST. INDIANAPOLIS, INDIANA 46268 USA

Preface

In 1948 the transistor was announced. Less than 10 years later it had supplemented the vacuum tube in most electronic circuits. A decade after that we find that the transistor is replacing the vacuum tube in electronics. In those 20 years there has not been one attempt to change the approach to the teaching of electronics. The system remains the same: teach basic electricity, then vacuum tubes, then electronic circuits, and finally introduce the concept of the transistor by comparing it to vacuum-tube operation.

Why should a device like the vacuum tube that is becoming obsolete be used as the major vehicle for explaining electronics? The answer must be "tradition." This series breaks with tradition and faces the real world—the world of semiconductor electronics. Immediately, in the first volume of the series, semiconductor theory is introduced with the study of basic electricity. The second volume finds basic transistor circuits as the major topic of discussion. Volume three goes through radio and television solid-state circuits and finally, in volume four, digital circuits are explored. The result is a true *transistor* series.

The material is presented so that the student will gain a firm background in "solid-state" electronics, including troubleshooting techniques. This, coupled with the unique modified linear-programming technique, makes this a complete *self-instructional* course. The summary questions and answers at the end of each chapter and the final examination allow the student to check his progress and understanding of the material.

TRAINING & RETRAINING, INC.

791231

ABOUT THE AUTHOR

Robert J. Brite is currently Data Manager for ITT Defense Communications, in Nutley, New Jersey. He studied engineering at Monmouth College and the Cooper Union for the Advancement of Science and Art. His electronics career dates back to 1949 when he was a troubleshooter for a major television manufacturer. His background includes: teaching radar for the Signal School at Fort Monmouth; field engineering in both radar and computer fields; and writing in the area of computers, missile guidance, communications, and electronic training devices. A two year stint at the Kilmer Job Corps Center has been his most challenging and rewarding experience. Serving in the capacities of Director of the Reception Center and Management Development Coordinator, he was one of the pioneers in the development of the unique techniques employed to wage the war on poverty. He was a member of the visitors and speakers bureau at the center and has appeared as a guest chairman and moderator for the Society of Technical Writers and Publishers. He is coauthor of *Basic Electricity and Electronics*, a five-volume programmed learning course, as well as *Synchros and Servos*. Mr. Brite has also been editorial and technical consultant for the various volumes of the Space Technology Series also published by Howard W. Sams & Co., Inc.

Acknowledgments

Grateful acknowledgment is made to all those who participated in the preparation, compilation, and editing of this series. Without their valuable contributions this series would not have been possible.

In this regard, prime consideration is given to Robert J. Brite, Data Manager for International Telephone and Telegraph Defense Communications Division. The selection of the content of the volumes, the initial preparation and organizational work, the writing contributions across the board, editing and final review, and the finalization as to technical content and educational value are due principally to his tireless and conscientious effort.

Credit for the initial concept of the programmed learning technique goes to Stanley B. Schiffman, staff member of Training & Retraining, Inc.

Finally, special thanks are due to the publisher's editorial staff for invaluable assistance beyond the normal publisher-author relationship.

SEYMOUR D. USLAN, Editor-in-Chief
and
HERMAN SCHIFFMAN, President
Training & Retraining, Inc.

Introduction

This book carefully explains the principles of basic electrical circuits and those of semiconductors. Following a unique method of presentation these principles are related through simple analogies to devices with which you are familiar. This volume first supplies the building blocks necessary for progressing to the more complex materials presented toward the end of the volume and the material found in the subsequent volumes of the series. The constant reviewing and application of the material presented in this book will give the student the background that will allow him to proceed through the remainder of the series.

WHAT YOU WILL LEARN

The book begins with an introduction to the transistor and immediately offers the student a firm understanding of voltage and current. The next chapter contains a detailed explanation of resistance and its effect on current and voltage and presents the student with the manipulation of Ohm's and Kirchhoff's laws. A chapter entirely devoted to semiconductor principles prepares the student for the next volume on transistor circuits. The volume ends with a detailed study of the nature of inductance, capacitance, and resistance in a-c circuits.

WHAT YOU SHOULD KNOW
BEFORE YOU START

The only requirements for studying this series are a firm background in simple mathematical techniques, including powers of ten, basic algebra, and trigonometry (a review of this is offered in this volume). For the most part, simple mathematical expressions are used. All new terms are defined fully.

WHY THE PROGRAMMED TEXT FORMAT WAS CHOSEN

During the past few years, new concepts of learning have been developed under the common heading of programmed instruction. Although there are arguments for and against each of the several formats or styles of programmed textbooks, the value of programmed instruction itself has been proved to be sound. Most educators now seem to agree that the style of programming should be developed to fit the needs of teaching the particular subject. To help you progress successfully through this volume, a brief explanation of the programmed format follows.

Each chapter is divided into small bits of information presented in a sequence that has proved best for learning purposes. Some of the information bits are very short—a single sentence in some cases. Others may include several paragraphs. The length of each presentation is determined by the nature of the concept being explained and by the knowledge the reader has gained up to that point.

The text is designed around two-page segments. Facing pages include information on one or more concepts, complete with illustrations designed to clarify the word descriptions used. Self-testing questions are included at the end of each of these two-page segments. Most of these questions are in the form of statements requiring that you fill in one or more missing words; other questions are either multiple-choice or simple essay types. Answers are given at the top of the succeeding page, so you will have the opportunity to check the accuracy of your response and verify what you have or have not learned before proceeding. When you find that your answer to a question does not agree with that given, you should restudy the information to determine why your answer was incorrect. As you can see, this method of question-answer programming ensures that you will advance through the text as quickly as you are able to absorb what has been presented.

HOW YOU SHOULD STUDY THIS TEXT

Naturally, good study habits are important. You should set aside a specific time each day to study, in an area where you can concentrate without being disturbed. Select a time when you are at your mental peak, a period when you feel most alert.

Here are a few pointers you will find helpful in getting the most out of this volume.

1. Read each sentence carefully and deliberately. There are no unnecessary words or phrases; each sentence presents or supports a thought which is important to your understanding of the technology.
2. When you are referred to or come to an illustration, stop at the end of the sentence you are reading and study the illustration. Make sure you have a mental picture of its general content. Then continue reading, returning to the illustration each time a detailed examination is required. The drawings were especially planned to reinforce your understanding of the subject.
3. At the bottom of most right-hand pages you will find one or more questions to be answered. Some of these contain "fill-in" blanks. In answering the questions, it is important that you actually do so in writing, either in the book or on a separate sheet of paper. The physical act of writing the answers provides greater retention than merely thinking the answer. Writing will not become a chore since most answers are short.
4. Answer all questions in a section before turning the page to check the accuracy of your responses. Refer to any of the material you have read if you need help. If you do not know the answer, even after a quick review of the related text, finish answering any remaining questions. If the answers to any questions you skipped still have not come to you, turn the page and check the answer section.
5. When you have answered a question incorrectly, return to the appropriate paragraph or page and restudy the material. Knowing the correct answer to a question is less important than understanding why it is

correct. Each section of new material is based on previously presented information. If there is a weak link in this chain, the later material will be more difficult to understand.

6. Carefully study the Summary Questions at the end of each chapter. This review will help you gauge your knowledge of the information in the chapter and actually reinforce your knowledge. When you run across questions you do not completely understand, reread the sections relating to these statements, and recheck the questions and answers before going to the next chapter.

7. Complete the final test at the end of the book. This test reviews the complete text and will offer you a chance to find out just what you have learned. It also permits you to discover your weaknesses and initiate your own review of the volume.

This volume has been carefully planned to make the learning process as easy as possible. Naturally, a certain amount of effort on your part is required if you are to obtain maximum benefit from the book. However, if you follow the pointers just given, your efforts will be well rewarded, and you will find that your study will be a pleasant and interesting experience.

Contents

CHAPTER 1

CHAPTER 2

CHAPTER 3

CHAPTER 4

CHAPTER 5

CHAPTER 6

1

Introduction to Transistors

What You Will Learn

In this chapter you will learn of some of the applications of transistors. You will discover why they have all but replaced the vacuum tube as the major component in electronic equipment. You will learn that the principles that explain the operation of the transistor are the same principles that explain the operation of all basic electrical circuits—voltage, current, and impedance. You will see that the transistor is nothing more than a current-controlling device. This chapter closes with a summary of the material covered in this volume.

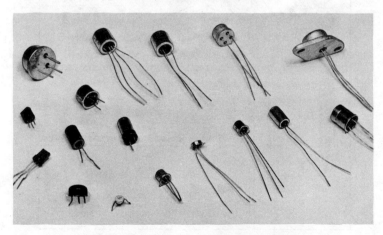

Fig. 1-1. Transistors vary in size and shape.

TRANSISTOR APPLICATIONS

Probably the greatest single advance in electronics since the invention of the vacuum tube by Dr. Lee de Forest in 1907 was the invention of the transistor. Oddly enough, the development of the transistor started one year before the invention of the vacuum tube. In the year 1906, a silicon crystal was used as a crystal detector, the cat whisker of the early crystal radio. However, through a quirk of fate, the transistor did not reach the electronic world until 1948.

Fig. 1-2 shows a few of the many applications that have become almost the exclusive property of the transistor. One of the major reasons for the success of the transistor is its small size. This has resulted in its extensive use in portable equipment, such as radios and television sets, as well as in medical equipment, such as the pacemaker—a device that has saved the lives of many heart patients. In the field of space exploration, where there is a premium on room in every package delivered, the transistor has led the field. Weather satellites give us a better picture of the world we live in and communication satellites make it possible for us to transmit television signals even around the world. Radar sets search the skies for planes, missiles, and weather information, while sonar devices map the ocean floor, search

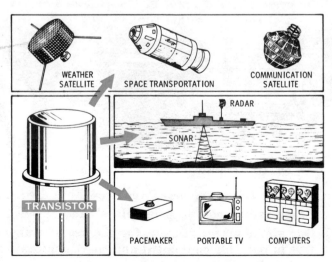

Fig. 1-2. Transistor applications.

for submarines, or locate schools of fish. All around us in office buildings all over the world, computers plug away at problems turning out in millionths of a second data that formerly took hours.

WHY ARE TRANSISTORS USED?

What is it about the transistor that has caused it to be used in the electronics industry almost to the exclusion of all other devices? Four of these reasons—size, power requirements, life, and cost—are discussed in the following paragraphs.

Size

Prior to the development of the transistor, the component used in most electronic applications was the vacuum tube. Compared to this component you can see in Fig. 1-3 how the transistor is one of the greatest space savers of all time.

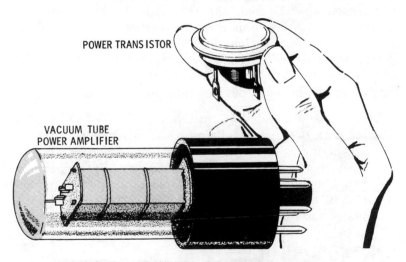

POWER TRANSISTOR

VACUUM TUBE
POWER AMPLIFIER

Fig. 1-3. Transistors are smaller than tubes.

Q1-1. Vacuum tubes are being replaced by _____.

Q1-2. Early radios used a principle of the _____.

Q1-3. One of the major reasons for the use of transistors in portable equipment and space exploration is their _____ _____.

15

Power Requirements

Due to its size and construction (Fig. 1-4) the transistor requires very little power to operate. Where a vacuum tube

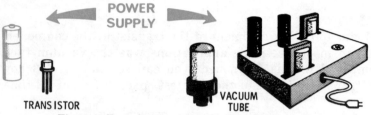

Fig. 1-4. Transistor power requirements are low.

may require a complicated power supply, a comparable transistor will only need a small dry cell battery.

Life

The construction of vacuum tubes has caused them to be plagued with breakdowns. Fig. 1-5 shows some of the causes for malfunctions in vacuum tubes—low emission, broken envelopes, gassy and microphonic tubes, and open filaments. As shown in the illustration, while several tubes have been replaced in the vacuum-tube equipment, the transistorized equipment has yet to undergo a repair. The mechanical and

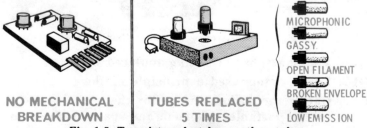

Fig. 1-5. Transistors last longer than tubes.

chemical construction of the transistor is so simple that its life under normal applications is almost unlimited.

Cost

When transistors were first developed, they were much the same price as the vacuum tubes they replaced. As soon as industry tooled up for the mass production of transistors, their price decreased rapidly, and today it is not unusual to find that for the cost of one vacuum tube you might pur-

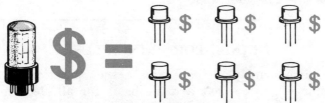

Fig. 1-6. Transistors are cheaper than tubes.

chase several transistors. By reducing the cost of transistors (as well as other electronic components), the maintenance of transistorized equipment has been simplified tremendously. Many of the components are so cheap that they are considered expendable ("throw-away items" in the jargon of the electronics industry) and can be thrown away when found faulty.

Fig. 1-7. Transistorized components are cheap enough to be expendable.

Q1-4. Transistors require much _____ power to operate than vacuum tubes.

Q1-5. The life of a _____ is much longer than that of a _____.

Q1-6. The fact that many electronic components are considered throw-away items today is due to the _____ _____ of transistors.

TRANSISTOR PRINCIPLES

The same principles that explain the operation of the transistor are those that are the basis for all electronics. They are *voltage*, *current*, and *impedance*.

Voltage

Voltage is a potential force. It is a force similar to the motor which moves a car, or the pump which propels water through pipes. Sources of voltage are batteries and generators. Like any other force voltage can cause motion—hence its name of electromotive force or emf. This force causes the electrical motion called current.

Current

The motion caused by the motor is the movement of the car. The motion caused by the pump is the flow of water. The motion caused by voltage is current, which is the motion or flow of electrical particles called electrons.

Impedance

Impedance controls the rate of current as road conditions control the movement of cars, as shown in Fig. 1-8. Even though the cars in the illustration have the same motors, the number of cars passing down the dirt road in one hour will be less than the number passing down the highway. The dirt road offers a higher *resistance* to the flow of traffic than does the concrete highway, thus *impeding* the flow of traffic. Thus the cars must adjust their speed to the different road conditions even though they are all capable of the same

Fig. 1-8. A dirt road offers high resistance to traffic.

speed. Now look at the pumps in Fig. 1-9. Each of these pumps has the same capacity to pump water, but one pumps through a straight pipe and the other must pump through a curved pipe (of the same length). Note that the number of gallons per minute leaving one pipe will be less than that leaving the other.

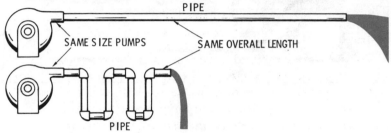

Fig. 1-9. Which pipe offers the least resistance to water flow?

Q1-7. In the preceding illustration the curved pipe offers a(n) _____high_____ _____Resis.____ to the flow of water than the straight pipe.

Q1-8. More water per minute will flow through the _____S_____ pipe than through the _____C_____ pipe.

Q1-9. In the illustration below, system (one, two) will have the most current.

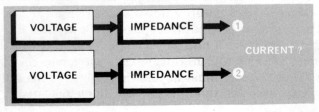

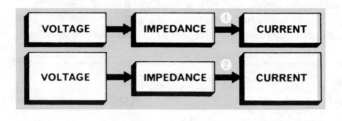
A TRANSISTOR IS A
CURRENT-CONTROLLING DEVICE

Just as impedance controls current, the transistor can also control current. Fig. 1-10 shows that a small current at the input to a transistor can cause a large current at the output of the transistor. Although this is not exactly the

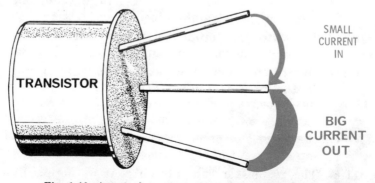

Fig. 1-10. A transistor uses current to control current.

case, it is sufficiently true for the purposes of this volume. Volume 2 will cover the transistor in detail. It is enough to know now that the transistor is an impedance device that changes its output impedance when the input current changes.

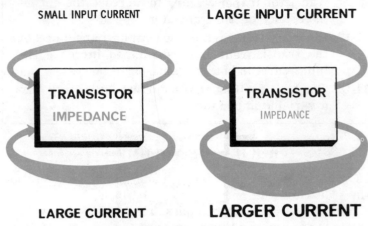

Fig. 1-11. Changing input current changes output impedance.

Fig. 1-11 shows the transistor capability that has made the device the important component that it is today. Notice how a small current in part A is applied to the transistor causing a certain large current through the output impedance of the transistor. In part B the input current has been increased, reducing the output impedance, and therefore increasing the output current.

Q1-10. The output ___Current___ of a transistor can be varied by changing the input _Current_.

Q1-11. In order to decrease the output current of a transistor it is necessary to __Incre.__ the output impedance of the transistor.

Q1-12. In order to decrease the output impedance of the transistor it is necessary to __Incre__ the input current of the transistor.

Q1-13. The transistor controls current by acting like a variable __Imped.__.

PREVIEW OF VOLUME 1

As you can see, if you wish to understand the operation of the transistor you must have a good basic knowledge of electrical and electronic principles. The rest of this volume is devoted to giving you this knowledge so that you can learn the transistor principles developed in Volume 2 of this series.

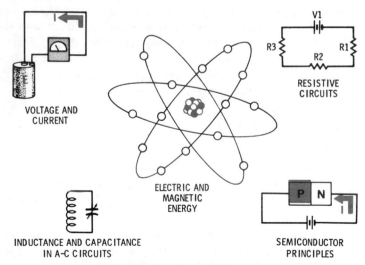

Fig. 1-12. Preview of Volume 1.

SUMMARY QUESTIONS

1. The transistor ranks as one the most significant developments in electronics since the vacuum tube.
   a. Transistors are used in portable equipment because of their _SMALL_ size and minute _power_ requirements.
   b. The low cost of transistors is made even lower when you consider the _long_ life of transistors.
2. The transistor controls current by serving as a variable impedance.
   a. Increasing the voltage in a system will _INCR_ the current.
   b. Decreasing the impedance in a circuit will _INCR._ the current.
3. A knowledge of the basic principles of electricity, voltage, current, and impedance is all that is required to understand the operation of the transistor.
   a. The transistor is a _CURR_ controlling device.
   b. Changes in the output impedance of the transistor cause changes in the output _CURR_.
   c. To increase the output impedance of the transistor you must _Dece,_ the input current to the transistor.
   d. To increase the output current of a transistor you must _INCR._ the input current.

SUMMARY ANSWERS

1a. Transistors are used in portable equipment because of their **small** size and minute **power** requirements.

1b. The low cost of transistors is made even lower when you consider the **long** life of transistors.

2a. Increasing the voltage in a system will **increase** the current.

2b. Decreasing the impedance in a circuit will **increase** the current.

3a. The transistor is a **current** controlling device.

3b. Changes in the output impedance of the transistor cause changes in the output **current.**

3c. To increase the output impedance of the transistor you must **decrease** the input current to the transistor.

3d. To increase the output current of a transistor you must **increase** the input current.

2

Electric and Magnetic Energy

What You Will Learn

In this chapter you will learn what matter is and its relationship to molecules, elements, and atoms. The structure of the atom and the functions of the electron, proton, and neutron are discussed. You will learn how atoms may be charged either positively or negatively and how free electrons may be caused to flow under the effect of a potential difference. You will learn about magnetism, static electricity, and how a magnet may be made from an iron bar and electrical energy.

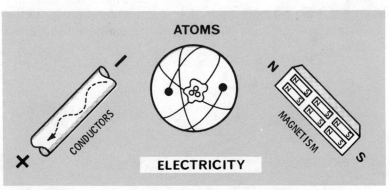

Fig. 2-1. Electricity.

MATTER

Definition of Matter

To understand transistor operation, one must first understand the structure of matter. Matter is anything that has weight. Food, water, clothing, and gold are matter. Air is matter, too. Radio waves, heat, and light are not matter; they are forms of energy.

Elements

The Element Defined—Long ago, scientists believed that all matter was composed of four basic ingredients: fire, water, earth, and air. Since they were considered the *elemental* forms of matter they were called elements. Centuries later this theory was proved wrong. Scientists were able to break matter into many pure substances. These substances could not be broken down any further and so they were called *elements*. They are identified by such properties as color, density, melting temperature, odor, and others. Today more than 100 elements have been discovered.

Elements Composed of Atoms—Many of the ancient scientists believed that these elements were composed of tiny particles called *atoms* (Fig. 2-2). It was later established that this was so—that all matter is composed of atoms. Each of these atoms consists of a *nucleus* that contains two types of particles: a *neutron* and a *proton*. Orbiting this nucleus is a third particle called an *electron*. The ancients also claimed that each of the elements was composed of the same atoms, only in different proportions and arrangements. Notice in Fig. 2-3 how each of the elements is composed of the same type and size of atom but arranged in a different fashion.

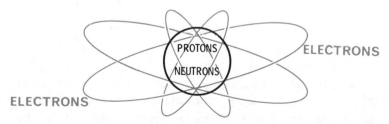

Fig. 2-2. The atom—building block of the universe.

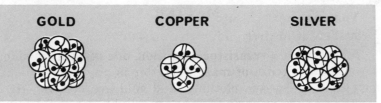

Fig. 2-3. An ancient view—elements composed of different combinations of the same atom.

Eighteenth century scientists rejected this and suggested that different kinds of atoms existed: that is, iron atoms, sulphur atoms, arsenic atoms, gold atoms, etc. Each kind of atom was supposed to have had its own size, shape, and weight. And so it was later proved that only like atoms combined to form elements (Fig. 2-4).

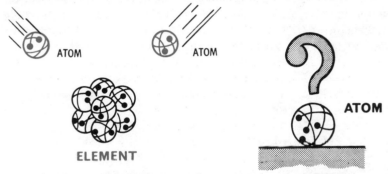

Fig. 2-4. Like atoms combine to form elements.

Q2-1. Matter is anything that has _____.

Q2-2. Radio waves, heat, and light are not _____ but are forms of _____.

Q2-3. A substance that cannot be broken down any further by chemical means is called an _____.

Q2-4. Atoms combine to form _____.

Q2-5. The particles found in the nucleus of an atom are the _____ and the _____.

Q2-6. The particle orbiting about the nucleus is the _____.

Molecules

A molecule is the smallest particle of a chemical substance capable of an independent existence. The atoms of most elements cannot exist by themselves, but they combine to form molecules (Fig. 2-5). In certain rare instances it is possible

Fig. 2-5. Atoms combine to form molecules.

for an atom to be a molecule—such is the case with helium. Helium exists in its natural state as an atom and can be classified as a molecule. When elements combine they form

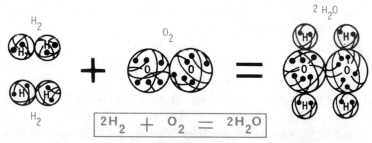

$$2H_2 + O_2 = 2H_2O$$

Fig. 2-6. Molecules combine to form compounds.

28

compounds. Fig. 2-6 shows how hydrogen and oxygen combine to form water, a compound. Four atoms of hydrogen have combined to form two molecules of hydrogen, and two atoms of oxygen have combined to form one molecule of oxygen. When the compound is formed it is the atoms of the elements that combine to form two molecules of water. The equation is:

$$2H_2 + O_2 = 2H_2O$$

STRUCTURE OF THE ATOM

Early Theories

In 1897 an Englishman discovered that a tiny unit of negative electricity was a part of every atom. Fig. 2-7 shows some of the theories of the structure of the atom that evolved from this discovery. In 1898 it was thought that

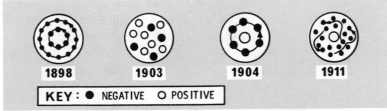

Fig. 2-7. The changing atomic theory.

an atom consisted of a large number of negatively charged particles that were contained in a ball-shaped positive field. In 1903 a theory showed pairs of positive and negative particles floating around in space. By 1904 it was thought that there was a circle of negatively charged particles surrounding a heavy positive center. Finally, in 1911 it was concluded that there was a positive charge concentrated at the center of the atom with electrons (negatively charged particles) swarming around this nucleus.

Q2-7. The smallest particle of a substance capable of independent existence is the _____.

Q2-8. Atoms cannot exist by themselves, but they combine to form _____.

Q2-9. When two or more elements combine they form a _____.

The Bohr Atom

In 1913, Niels Bohr came up with the theory of the structure of an atom that revolutionized atomic physics. Fig. 2-8 shows his model of the hydrogen atom. The electron rotates

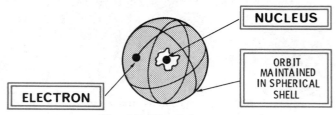

NUCLEUS

ORBIT MAINTAINED IN SPHERICAL SHELL

ELECTRON

Fig. 2-8. The Bohr atom.

about the nucleus at a specific distance from the nucleus. The distance is set by the force of attraction of the nucleus. The electron is continuously acted upon by other electrical particles in nearby atoms. It changes its orbit constantly—always maintaining the same distance from the nucleus. Because the electron travels so fast—one hundred *million billion* orbits each second—the shell seems to be solid. This shell is called an energy level.

The Bohr Model of Heavier Elements

All atoms were assigned weights. The weight assignment was based on how much they weigh in relationship to an atom of oxygen. Thus, since hydrogen, the lightest atom, weighs 1/16th of oxygen its weight is 1. These weights are called atomic weights (approximate weights used in this book). Atoms are also assigned numbers that correspond to the number of electrons they contain. All atoms are electrically neutral. That is, they have the same number of electrons (negative charges) as protons (positive charges). Thus the atomic number not only refers to the number of electrons, but also to the number of protons.

Fig. 2-9 shows the arrangement of the energy shells and electrons in the elements having atomic numbers of 2, 3, and 11. Helium, whose atomic number is 2, has two electrons orbiting in one shell. Lithium, atomic number 3, has two electrons orbiting in its first energy level (innermost shell), and one electron orbiting in its outermost energy level. Sodium, with an atomic number of 11, has two electrons in its first energy level, eight in its second energy level, and one in its third energy level. The greatest number of electrons that can be contained in one shell is 32.

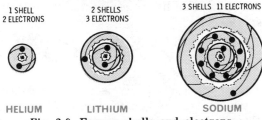

Fig. 2-9. Energy shells and electrons.

The atomic weight and atomic number of an element are not the same (except for hydrogen whose atomic weight and atomic number are both equal to 1). The atomic weight is made up of the number of protons (a figure equivalent to the number of electrons and also to the atomic number) plus the number of neutrons (the other particle contained in the nucleus). Note that the weight of these particles is almost equal and that they are more than 1840 times as heavy as an electron (which will be considered weightless for this discussion).

Q2-10. The electrons in the Bohr atom are arranged in shells or _energy   levels_.

Q2-11. Atomic weights are assigned by comparing the weight of the atom with the weight of an atom of _oxygen_.

Q2-12. All normal atoms are electrically _neutral_.

Q2-13. The atomic number corresponds to the number of _electrons_ or _protons_.

31

ELECTROSTATICS

Static Electricity

Most of you are familiar with the term static electricity. You have probably experienced a small electrical shock that can result when you walk on a thick rug and then touch a metal object. Or maybe you have seen and heard the crackle of electricity when removing a woolen sweater in a darkened room. In Fig. 2-10 are shown two ways of generating static

Fig. 2-10. Static electricity.

electricity. In one instance a glass rod is rubbed vigorously with a silk cloth. Sparks are observed in the dark and finally small pieces of paper are attracted to the glass rod. In another example a rubber rod is rubbed with a woolen cloth. Again the sparks result, and the rod is able to attract dust particles. Why does the rod take on seemingly magnetic properties?

Free Electrons

Compared to protons and neutrons, electrons are extremely mobile. They move in their orbits at tremendous speeds. In some atoms the outermost energy level is only partially occupied by electrons. For example, an atom of chlorine has seven electrons in its outer shell. The shell can hold a maximum of eight electrons. Since it lacks one electron from making its outer shell complete it tends to attract electrons to this space or hole in its shell. Sodium on the other hand has one electron in its outer shell which it would like to give up. This electron in the sodium atom is almost *free* to move about at will if the right conditions exist. Glass, like sodium, has electrons that are relatively free. Silk on the other hand is like chlorine in that it would like to receive electrons. The friction of rubbing the silk on the glass gives the free electrons on the glass enough energy to jump over the silk (Fig. 2-11). Since electrons have been removed from the glass it now has more protons than electrons and must be positively charged. The silk, having gained electrons, must be negatively charged.

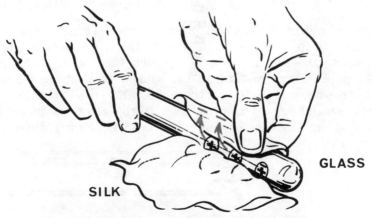

Fig. 2-11. Glass gives up electrons to silk.

Q2-14. The particle with the most mobility in an atom is the ___electron___.

Q2-15. When a material loses electrons it is _positively_ **charged.**

Attraction and Repulsion of Charges

How does the glass pick up materials? First let us understand how charges react to each other. If two electrons are brought close together they will repel each other. If a proton is brought close to an electron it will attract the electron. Or, as you can see in Fig. 2-12, like charges repel and unlike charges attract. Now we can see how the glass attracts a

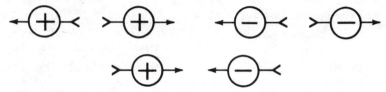

Fig. 2-12. Like charges repel—unlike charges attract.

neutral object like a small piece of paper (Fig. 2-13). The glass, which has a positive charge due to the loss of electrons to the silk, is allowed to touch the paper. Although the paper is neutral, it still has some free electrons. These electrons are attracted to the glass, and since they do not have enough energy to cross over to the glass, the paper is picked up. The case of the rubber rod is slightly different

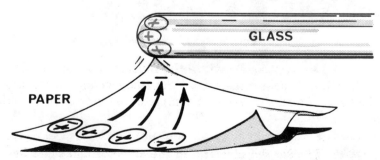

Fig. 2-13. Neutral paper attracted to positively charged glass.

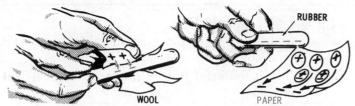

Fig. 2-14. Negatively charged rubber rod attracts neutral paper.

although the same principles are used. Fig. 2-14 shows that wool tends to give up electrons, while rubber tends to accept electrons. When the rubber rod is touched to the paper it tends to repel free electrons. They migrate to the other end of the paper leaving the end touching the rod positively charged. The paper is then picked up by the negatively charged rod.

Formation of Ions

Now let us return to sodium and chlorine. Fig. 2-15 shows the pertinent facts about the elements sodium (Na) and chlorine (Cl). When they are combined to form salt, they

| ELEMENT | SYMBOL | ATOMIC. | | PROTONS - ELECTRONS | NEUTRONS |
		WT	NO		
SODIUM	Na	23	11	11	12
CHLORINE	Cl	35	17	17	18

SODIUM
CHLORIDE

SHARED ELECTRON

Fig. 2-15. Sodium shares an electron with chlorine.

share an electron as shown in the illustration. This satisfies both sodium's desire to give up the free electron in its outer shell and chlorine's desire to complete its outer shell of only seven electrons.

Q2-16. Like charges _repel_ and unlike charges _ATTRACT_.

Q2-17. The shared electron in the above illustration belongs to _Na_.

sodium

35

If sodium chloride in its molten state (heated until it is a thick liquid) is placed in a container and then has electricity passed through it, an interesting phenomenon occurs (Fig. 2-16). The molecules of sodium chloride separate. The chlorine takes the electron that was being shared with it,

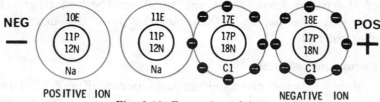

POSITIVE ION   NEGATIVE ION

Fig. 2-16. Formation of ions.

thus completing the outer shell, but adding an extra electron. It is therefore negatively charged, and it is called a *negative ion*. The sodium has given up one electron to the chlorine and is therefore positively charged. It is called a *positive* ion. The negative ions will migrate to the positive terminal of the source of electricity. The positive ions (sodium) will migrate to the negative terminals of the source of electricity. When the negative ion arrives at the positive terminal it will give up the extra electron in its outer shell. This electron will pass around to the negative terminal where it will be reunited with the positive sodium ion. These two atoms (the chlorine at the positive terminal and the sodium at the negative terminal, may now join together and share the electron as before. By constantly repeating this process, electricity is caused to flow through the molten salt. We may say that molten salt *conducts* electricity.

Conductors, Semiconductors, Insulators

For the purposes of electronics we must consider materials as either good conductors of electricity, poor conductors of electricity, or not conductors of electricity at all. Consider a good conductor of electricity such as copper; most electrical wire is made from copper.

A conductor is a substance through which electrons will move readily. The conditions for such movement are simple. We have seen that an electron placed in the vicinity of a proton will move in that direction. Thus the electron has the *potential* for movement. However, we can improve that potential by placing a lot of protons nearby and also by one

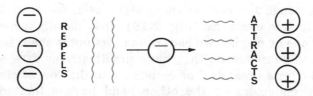

Fig. 2-17. Electron moves due to difference of potential.

other method; that is, by placing negative charges (electrons or ions) on the other side of the electron (Fig. 2-17). The bigger the difference is between the positive and negative charges the faster the electron moves. This difference in the amount of charges is referred to as a *difference in potential*. When such a difference in potential is applied to a copper wire, there is a current in the wire, as shown in Fig. 2-18.

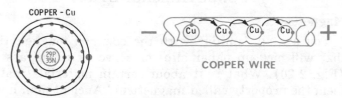

Fig. 2-18. Current in a copper wire.

Copper atoms have one electron in their outer shells. This electron, a free electron, migrates toward the positive potential by going from outer shell to outer shell.

Q2-18. When an atom gains an electron to complete its outer shell it is a _Neg_ ion.

Q2-19. The difference between the number of electrons in one place and the number of electrons in another place is called _poten_ difference.

37

A conductor can be thought of as a material that has many free electrons (Fig. 2-19). It is usually a metal, and has one or maybe two electrons in its outer shell. Insulators are those materials that have practically no free electrons and offer a great deal of resistance to the flow of electricity. Semiconductors on the other hand have a limited ability to pass electrons. There are ways to treat semiconductors so that they will or will not act like conductors under certain conditions. It is this latter capability that makes them useful in the manufacture of transistors. Note that if the potential difference across an insulator is made large enough, there will be a current; however, the material will be destroyed.

ELECTROMAGNETISM

Magnetism

You are all familiar with the common magnet, the one that will pick up paper clips or serve as a compass needle (Fig. 2-20). What is it about certain materials that gives them the property called magnetism? Ancient man had been aware that there were certain materials in nature that would attract other materials; for example, lodestone attracting iron. Modern man has made inroads into the explanation of this phenomenon.

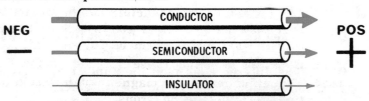

Fig. 2-19. The nature of electrical conductors.

Fig. 2-20. Magnetism.

Electrons in Motion

The motion of electrons causes magnetic fields to be set up. For example, the orbital electron shown in Fig. 2-21 generates a magnetic field as shown, with a north pole in an upward direction and a south pole in the downward direction. In the same illustration you see how the spinning

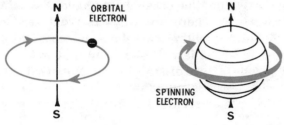

Fig. 2-21. Electron movement—source of magnetism.

of an electron causes a magnetic field. Those materials that exhibit magnetic properties owe 90 percent of this property to the spin of the electrons about their own axis and only about 10 percent to the orbiting of the electrons. All materials contain electrons that move in these fashions but there is something peculiar about the electron motion in magnetic materials.

Q2-20. A conductor has many _free_ electrons.

Q2-21. The material that offers much resistance to the flow of electrons is an _INSULATOR_.

Q2-22. The fact that semiconductors can be treated so that they act like either conductors or insulators is what makes them useful as _TRANSISTORS_.

Q2-23. Electrons in motion cause _MAGNETIC_ fields.

Q2-24. The major reason for magnetic materials is the (spin, orbiting) of electrons.

In most atoms electrons move in pairs. These pairs have spins in opposite directions, as shown in Fig. 2-22. Although each of these electrons generates a magnetic field, the results are nullified since the fields are of equal magnitudes but in opposite directions (pairs A and B in Fig. 2-22). Pair C on the other hand shows two electrons rotating in the same direction. The generated magnetic fields tend to reinforce rather than cancel each other. Electrons that are paired in this fashion are found in magnetic materials. A group of electrons like those shown in pair C join to form a magnetic *domain*. In most magnetic materials these magnetic domains are not aligned; that is, domains from different atoms face in different directions, as shown in Fig. 2-23. As a result they do not reinforce each other and the material is not yet magnetized. By methods which we will examine later, these domains may be aligned, with the result being the magnetized material. A few substances have domains already aligned and are considered permanent natural magnets.

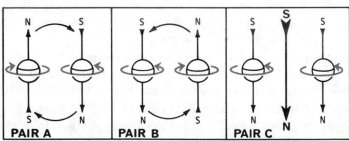

Fig. 2-22. Electrons spinning in same direction reinforce magnetic field.

Magnetic Fields

In a magnetized material such as the bar magnet shown in Fig. 2-24, the magnetic fields of all the domains line up so that the magnetic lines of force leave the north pole and

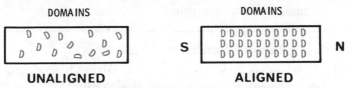

Fig. 2-23. Formation of a magnet.

enter the south pole. Note that the lines of force do not intersect each other but strain to keep their distance. The illustration shows very few of the millions of lines of force

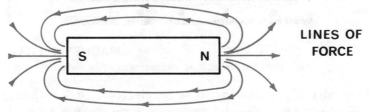

Fig. 2-24. Magnetic field around a bar magnet.

that would appear around a magnet. Just like electrical charges, magnetic poles exhibit the same behavior. That is, like poles repel and unlike poles attract (Fig. 2-25).

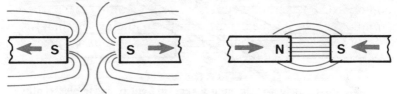

Fig. 2-25. Like poles repel—unlike poles attract.

Q2-25. The magnetic fields formed by electrons that spin in the same direction are called ___Domains___

Q2-26. In order to form a magnetic material the domains must be ___Aligned___.

41

Potential Difference Caused by Magnetism

Fig. 2-26 shows how electron flow through a conductor generates a magnetic field around the conductor. Note that this field will exist for the entire length of the conductor. Note also that it took a potential difference from one side

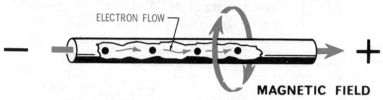

Fig. 2-26. Electron flow causes magnetic field.

of the wire to the other to cause the electrons to flow through it. Now examine what happens when we move a conductor through a magnetic field. In Fig. 2-27 we see a conductor moving through the magnetic field formed by the north and

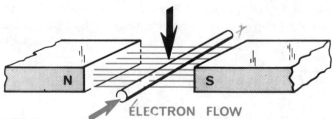

Fig. 2-27. Move conductor through magnetic field to cause electron flow.

south poles of two magnets. As it cuts through the magnetic lines of force, an electron flow is noticed in the conductor. We know that in order for electrons to flow there must be a difference of potential. Therefore, it must follow that a potential difference was generated across the wire when it was passed through the magnetic field.

SUMMARY QUESTIONS

1. The atom is the basic building block of all matter.
   a. Protons and neutrons are found in the _nucleus_ of the atom.
   b. The particle of an atom that moves in an orbit is the _electron_.

2. The structure of the atom was finally discovered by Niels Bohr.
   a. Atoms are electrically neutral because they have the same number of _electr_ and _prot_.
   b. Complete this table.

ELEMENT	ATOMIC NUMBER	ATOMIC WEIGHT	PROTONS	NEUTRONS	ELECTRONS
HYDROGEN	1	1	1	0	1
HELIUM	2	4	2	2	2
LITHIUM	3	7	3	4	3
SODIUM	11	23	11	12	11
COPPER	29	64	29	35	29

3. The nature of static electricity, when explained, gives you the basics for the understanding of electricity.
   a. Rubbing a glass rod with silk causes _free e_ electrons to collect on the silk.
   b. Like charges _repel_ and unlike charges _attract_.
   c. A material through which electrons pass readily is called a _conductor_.
   d. If it is desirable to prevent electrons from flowing from one conductor to another adjacent conductor they should be separated by an _insulator_.
   e. In order to cause electron flow through a conductor it is necessary to provide a _potential_ difference.

4. The phenomenon of magnetism is caused by electron motion.
   a. Magnets are formed by the alignment of _domains_.
   b. Show the polarity of the difference of potential generated in Fig. 2-27.

SUMMARY ANSWERS

1a. Protons and neutrons are found in the **nucleus** of the atom.

1b. The particle of an atom that moves in an orbit is the **electron.**

2a. Atoms are electrically neutral because they have the same number of **electrons** and **protons.**

2b.

ELEMENT	ATOMIC NUMBER	ATOMIC WEIGHT	PROTONS	NEUTRONS	ELECTRONS
HYDROGEN	1	1	1	0	1
HELIUM	2	4	2	2	2
LITHIUM	3	7	3	4	3
SODIUM	11	23	11	12	11
COPPER	29	64	29	35	29

3a. Rubbing a glass rod with silk causes **free** electrons to collect on the silk.

3b. Like charges **repel** and unlike charges **attract.**

3c. A material through which electrons pass readily is called a **conductor.**

3d. If it is desirable to prevent electrons from flowing from one conductor to another adjacent conductor they should be separated by an **insulator.**

3e. In order to cause electron flow through a conductor it is necessary to provide a **potential** difference.

4a. Magnets are formed by the alignment of **domains.**

4b.

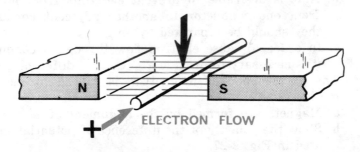

ELECTRON FLOW

3

Voltage and Current

What You

Will Learn

In this chapter you will learn about work and energy and how they are related to electronics. You will gain an understanding of the basic electrical units of voltage and current. Methods of generating electromotive force (emf) will be explained, with particular emphasis being placed on the dry cell and the alternating-current generator. A great deal of this chapter will be devoted to explaining the nature of alternating current. Such topics as the development of a voltage sine wave, voltage and current measurement, and the nature of time as related to the a-c signal will lead the student to a thorough knowledge of alternating current. The chapter concludes with a discussion of the relationship of current and voltage in a circuit, and the nature of a-c power.

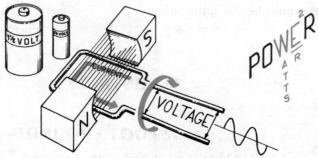

Fig. 3-1. Voltage sources.

WORK AND ENERGY

What Is Work?

Strange question? Not really! Many a man has returned from a hard day at the golf course and has had a difficult time convincing his wife that he has been "working." Once and for all we will settle this question. Whenever a *weight* is moved a *distance* by exerting a *force, work* is done. Under this definition not only does golf qualify as work, but so do bowling and many other entertaining activities. Examine Fig. 3-2. A man is shown in three stages of his approach

Fig. 3-2. When weight is moved through a distance, work is done.

to the bowling lane. As he progresses toward the foul line he raises the bowling ball (which weighs about 16 pounds) a distance of 2 feet. He does this against the force of gravity which opposes this motion. He has done some work. How much? Work is measured by determining the amount of force necessary to move the weight, and then multiplying it by the distance the weight was moved. Thus, as has been illustrated, the man moves a weight of 16 pounds a distance of 2 feet and the resultant work done is 32 foot-pounds (Fig. 3-3). If we take into account the force of gravity then the work is called the foot-pound*al*. The unit of force in this case would be the pound*al*.

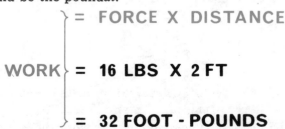

Fig. 3-3. One unit of work is the foot-pound.

Some Other Units of Work

When we deal in other systems of measurement we must consider different units of work. For example, Fig. 3-4 shows the work units associated with the gram-centimeter and kilogram-meter systems of measurement. Note here that when a gram of weight is moved a centimeter the result

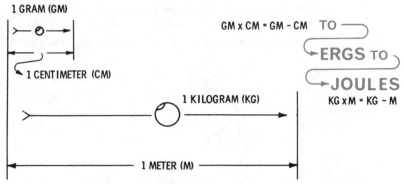

Fig. 3-4. Other units of work or energy.

is a gram-centimeter (gm-cm) of work. When we consider a gram of force used against gravity then the gram of force becomes a dyne (the unit of force in this system). The work done is then in dyne-centimeters (just like the foot-poundal). However, the dyne-centimeter is often referred to as an *erg*. Since the erg is such a small quantity of energy it is more usual to consider a work unit called the *joule* (= 10,000,000 ergs). In the same fashion, kilograms of force can be converted into *newtons* by considering the force of gravity, and the resultant unit of work, the newton-meter, can be converted into joules.

Q3-1. The factors that determine the amount of work done are _Force_ and _Distance_.

Q3-2. The most common unit of work in the gram-centimeter system is the _Joule_.

47

DIFFERENCE OF POTENTIAL

What Force Moves Electrons?

In the last chapter we found that electrons tend to move from areas where there is an excess of electrons to areas where there is a sparsity of electrons. By making the difference between two such areas great, the *potential* for the electron to move from one area to the other is increased. We call the difference in electrical charge between two points the *difference in potential,* and it is measured in a unit called the volt. Refer to Fig. 3-5. Here we consider a difference in potential between points A and B. Let us consider moving some electrons from A to B. How many should we consider?

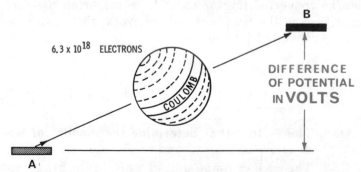

Fig. 3-5. Electrons moved by difference of potential.

Just as the erg is too small to consider as a unit of work, so is the electron too small a unit to consider moving. To consider practical motion we must take 6.3×10^{18} electrons (6,300,000,000,000,000,000), a number of electrons called a *coulomb*. For convenience we consider them bound together in the shape of a sphere. If we measure the amount of energy expended in moving them from point A to point B, and it turns out to be *1 joule*, then the difference of potential between point A and B is *1 volt*. Or another way of saying

$$\frac{JOULE}{COULOMB} = VOLT$$

Fig. 3-6. A volt is a joule per coulomb.

this is that a *volt* is a force that will cause a *joule* of energy to be expended in moving a *coulomb* of electrical charge. Or more simply—a *volt* is a *joule* per *coulomb* (Fig. 3-6).

How is Electron Flow Measured?

The movement of electrons from one place to another is called current. Just as water flow is measured in units like feet per minute, so can electrons be measured in terms of the number of electrons to pass a point in a unit of time. When a coulomb of electrons passes a point in one second, we call that a current of *1 ampere* (Fig. 3-7).

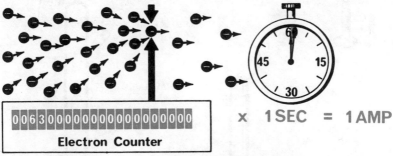

Fig. 3-7. A coulomb per second is an ampere.

Q3-3. A volt is a __joule__ per __coulomb__.
Q3-4. An ampere is a __coulomb__ per __second__.

GENERATING VOLTAGE

Friction

In Chapter 2 you were shown how rubbing a glass rod with silk created a small difference of potential which could be utilized to pick up light objects. Can the method of creating static electricity by friction be utilized to create a practical voltage? Yes! Fig. 3-8 shows the Van de Graaff artificial lightning generator. The silk belt is driven at a high velocity by a motor geared to P1. The right side of the belt is positive and passes close to the metal plate that is tied to ground. The plate has small hairlike follicles that allow electrons to be drawn up from ground and deposited on the left side of the belt. These electrons are transported up into the metal sphere where they are deposited on the metal sphere via the transfer plate, which is similar in construction to the metal plate. When the sphere is thus negatively charged it represents a very high potential difference from the objects in the surrounding area. It is then used for ex-

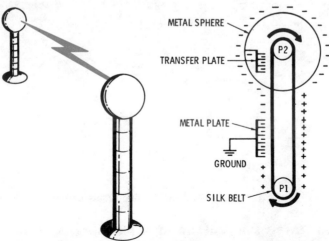

Fig. 3-8. Artificial lightning from the Van de Graaff generator.

periments involving the use of artificial lightning and for other experiments where high voltages are required.

Heat

Fig. 3-9 shows another method of generating a difference of potential. A copper wire and an iron wire are twisted together (they may be any two different conductors). Heat is then applied to them and a voltage is generated at their

Fig. 3-9. The thermocouple.

ends. This voltage is very small but may be used in certain control operations. The arrangement is called a *thermocouple*, and it is often used in commercial thermostats.

Pressure

The method of applying pressure to a quartz crystal to create a voltage is called the *piezoelectric effect* and is shown in Fig. 3-10. Note that pressure in the horizontal plane causes a potential difference in the vertical plane. The resultant voltage is very small.

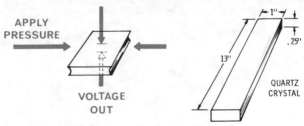

Fig. 3-10. Piezoelectric effect.

Q3-5. Two different wires twisted together and heated are called a Thermocouple.

Q3-6. The crystal pickup of a phonograph is an example of the _____ **effect.**

piezoelectric

Light

With the advent of the space age this method of generating voltage has really come into its own. Certain materials will generate a voltage when exposed to the sun's rays. On the ground this method is limited by the cycles of night and day and overcast weather. However, in space these problems do not exist. A spacecraft like that shown in Fig. 3-11 will

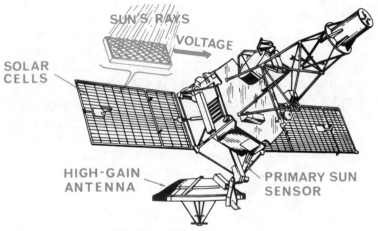

Fig. 3-11. Photoelectric effect.

have a multitude of solar cells attached to movable wings. A sun sensor will continuously point at the sun and in doing so adjust the position of the wings so that they constantly appear at right angles to the rays of the sun. The combined voltages of all the solar cells will furnish the power for the various electronic systems in the vehicle.

Chemical

Another method of generating electrical energy is through the use of chemical energy. Fig. 3-12 shows a simple voltaic cell of the type invented by Alessandro Volta in 1789. He noticed that if two dissimilar metals were placed in an acid solution a potential difference existed between them. He further noted that if a wire were connected between them

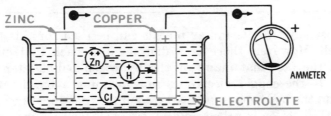

Fig. 3-12. Voltaic cell.

there was current in the wire. When hydrochloric acid is poured into water, the resultant solution is called an *electrolyte*—that is, a solution that contains ions. In this case we have positive ions, Hydrogen (H+), and negative ions, Chlorine (Cl−). When the copper and zinc electrodes are placed in this solution, the zinc dissolves. As the zinc atom enters the solution it leaves two electrons behind which makes the zinc atoms positive and the zinc electrode negative. The positive zinc ions repel the positive hydrogen ions forcing them back to the copper electrode where they capture an electron and are bubbled off as gaseous hydrogen. With an excess of electrons at the zinc electrode and a sparsity of electrons at the copper electrode there will be a current which will register on the ammeter. This process continues until the zinc strip completely dissolves. The electromotive force developed by this cell is approximately 1 volt and does not depend on the size of the cell but rather on the materials.

Q3-7. Light energy is converted into electrical energy in a _Solar cell_.

Q3-8. A solution that contains ions is called an _electrolyte_.

Q3-9. The voltaic cell converts _Chemical_ energy into _electrical_ energy.

Almost any two dissimilar metals can be used for this type of cell. However, there is a distinct drawback that stems from the fact that many of the hydrogen bubbles tend to cling to the copper electrode, thus forming a barrier that rejects the hydrogen ions in the solution and stops the reaction. The action is called *polarization* and may be prevented by using a carbon rod instead of the copper and placing the rod in a porous cup containing manganese dioxide. The cup doesn't prevent the bubbles from forming but the atoms of hydrogen combine with the maganese dioxide. The manganese dioxide is called a *depolarizer.* Another disadvantage of this cell is that it is a wet cell and its liquid electrolyte can be spilled easily. This disadvantage is overcome by the dry cell shown in Fig. 3-13. The zinc can is the negative electrode. Lining the can is a blotter soaked with electrolyte. In the center is the carbon rod that serves as the positive

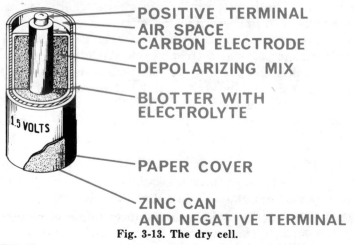

POSITIVE TERMINAL
AIR SPACE
CARBON ELECTRODE

DEPOLARIZING MIX

BLOTTER WITH ELECTROLYTE

1.5 VOLTS

PAPER COVER

ZINC CAN
AND NEGATIVE TERMINAL

Fig. 3-13. The dry cell.

electrode. It is surrounded by the depolarizing mix which carries both sal ammoniac (a combination of ammonia and chlorine) which serves as an electrolyte, and manganese dioxide which serves as the depolarizing agent. The air space allows for the collection of gases generated in the cell. Wax or pitch seals the top of the can which has a metal cap to serve as the positive electrode. The entire cell is enclosed in a cardboard container. The cell generates approximately 1.5 volts. This type of voltage source can be used only when small amounts of current are required, as in flashlights and transistor radios.

Magnetic

The most common method of generating large voltages is by rotating a coil of wire through a magnetic field, as seen in Fig. 3-14. This method is commonly used wherever electrical power is required.

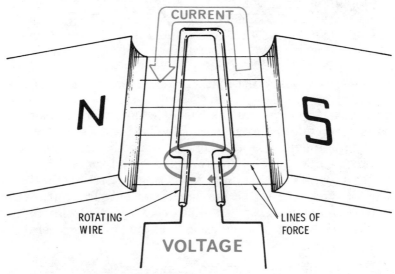

Fig. 3-14. Magnetism + motion = emf.

Q3-10. In a dry cell manganese dioxide is used to prevent POLARIZATION.

Q3-11. The generator in a car is an example of changing mechanical energy into electrical energy.

Let us examine the factors that affect current generation through this method. Fig. 3-15 shows a magnetic field with two wires moving through it. Note that the direction of motion of the wire determines the direction of the current.

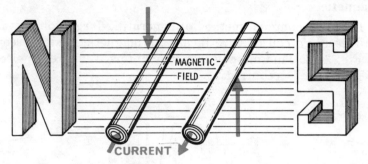

Fig. 3-15. Direction of motion affects direction of current.

In Fig. 3-16 you can see that the direction of motion affects the amount of current generated. The first wire shown is moving parallel to the lines of force and therefore does not cut through any of the lines of force. The resultant current is zero. The next wire moves perpendicularly to the lines of force and generates a maximum current. The third wire moves at an angle θ to the lines of force. The closer this angle is to 90 degrees, the greater is the current generated.

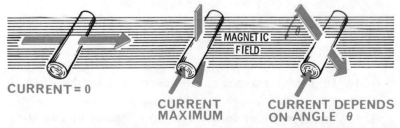

Fig. 3-16. Direction of motion affects amount of current.

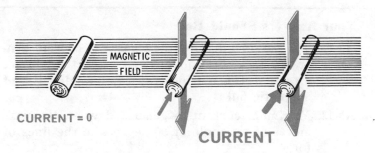

CURRENT = 0

CURRENT

Fig. 3-17. Speed of motion affects amount of current.

Another factor affecting the amount of current generated is the speed of motion, as shown in Fig. 3-17. With no motion at all, the current generated is zero. As the speed is increased, current is generated. The amount of current depends on the number of lines of force cut in a unit of time. Thus, if the speed is increased, there will be more current.

Fig. 3-18. Density of magnetic field affects amount of current.

In a similar fashion Fig. 3-18 shows the result of increasing the strength, and therefore the density, of the magnetic field. Two wires moving at the same speed through these fields will generate different amounts of current, since the wire on the right in the illustration will cut more lines of force per unit time than the one on the left.

Q3-12. The factors affecting the amount of current generated by a wire moving in a magnetic field are Direction, speed, and Density.

Q3-13. Maximum current is generated when the wire moves at an angle of ___90___ degrees to the lines of force.

Fig. 3-19 shows two wires moving through fields of equal density at the same speed, yet the current induced in the wires moves in opposite directions. Can you see why this is

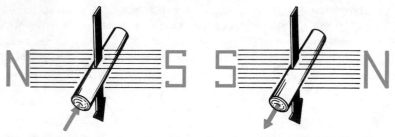

Fig. 3-19. Location of north and south poles affects current direction.

so? Note that in one instance the wire moves through a field with the north pole on the left and south pole on the right, while in the other case the fields are reversed. Thus you see that the direction of current is also dependent on the location of the north and south poles. Now let us consider what happens as a wire makes a circular path through a

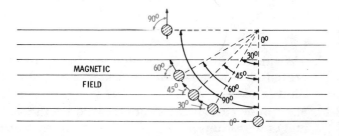

Fig. 3-20. Angles assumed as wire rotates in magnetic field.

magnetic field. Fig. 3-20 shows various positions of the wire as it rotates through its first 90 degrees. We know now that the amount of current induced in the wire when its direction is 0 degrees with respect to the magnetic field will be 0. We further know that when the angle is 90 degrees we will in-

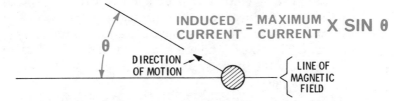

$$\frac{\text{INDUCED}}{\text{CURRENT}} = \frac{\text{MAXIMUM}}{\text{CURRENT}} \times \text{SIN } \theta$$

Fig. 3-21. Induced current depends upon sine of angle.

duce a maximum current. Between the zero and maximum values the current induced will depend on the angle, as shown in Fig. 3-21. That is, the induced current is equal to the maximum current multiplied by the sine of θ (theta), which is the angle that the wire makes with the magnetic field. To better understand this concept a brief review of simple trigonometry follows.

Trigonometry

Trigonometry is the branch of mathematics that considers the measurement of the angles and sides of triangles. For our purposes we will consider only those triangles that have a 90-degree angle. We will be concerned with the ratios of the various sides in these triangles to each other. The three ratios of concern to us will be those called *sine*, *cosine*, and *tangent*. It will be found that these ratios for a particular angle do not change no matter what the length of the sides of the triangle are. It is this fact that makes them such powerful tools in the study of electronics.

Q3-14. If the current induced at 90 degrees is 3 amperes and the sine of θ (30 degrees for this problem) is 0.5 what is the current induced at 30 degrees? Show work. *I.SA   3 . 0.5*

Q3-15. The three significant ratios that we will study in trigonometry are ___*Sine*___, ___*cosine*___, and ___*Tangent*___.

3

59

Sine—This ratio is shown in Fig. 3-22. Let us review some of the terminology of triangles. First consider the legs of the triangle. They are the sides that include the right angle. The third side of the triangle, the one opposite the

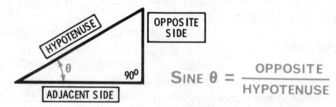

$$\text{SINE } \theta = \frac{\text{OPPOSITE}}{\text{HYPOTENUSE}}$$

Fig. 3-22. The sine function.

right angle is called the *hypotenuse*. If we select either of the other angles and call it arbitrarily θ (as in the illustration), then we refer to the leg opposite angle θ as the opposite side. The leg that encloses the angle θ is then the adjacent side. The hypotenuse retains its name no matter which angle is selected. If the other angle is selected then its oppo-

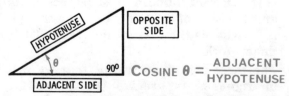

$$\text{COSINE } \theta = \frac{\text{ADJACENT}}{\text{HYPOTENUSE}}$$

Fig. 3-23. The cosine function.

site side becomes the adjacent side of the angle θ shown in the illustration. The sine of the angle θ is given as the ratio of the length of the opposite side to the length of the hypotenuse. This is abbreviated $\sin \theta = \dfrac{\text{opp}}{\text{hyp}}$.

Cosine—The cosine of angle θ is shown in Fig. 3-23. It is given as the ratio of the adjacent side to the hypotenuse. This is abbreviated as $\cos \theta = \dfrac{\text{adj}}{\text{hyp}}$.

Tangent—The tangent of the angle θ is shown in Fig. 3-24. It is the ratio of the opposite side to the adjacent side and is abbreviated $\tan \theta = \dfrac{\text{opp}}{\text{adj}}$.

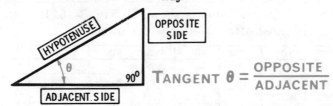

$$\text{TANGENT } \theta = \frac{\text{OPPOSITE}}{\text{ADJACENT}}$$

Fig. 3-24. The tangent function.

Common Sine Functions—Since we will initially be concerned with the sine of the angle let us generate a simple table of these functions. Fig. 3-25 shows a 30-60-90-degree triangle whose sides are of the lengths shown. From this triangle we get two of the ratios—sine 30 degrees and sine 60 degrees.

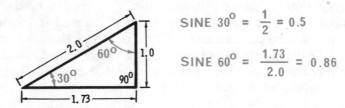

$$\text{SINE } 30^{\circ} = \frac{1}{2} = 0.5$$

$$\text{SINE } 60^{\circ} = \frac{1.73}{2.0} = 0.86$$

Fig. 3-25. Sine functions of 30 degrees and 60 degrees.

Q3-16. In the triangle above compute cos 30 degrees = $\dfrac{1.73}{2}$
0.86 .

Q3-17. Compute tan 30 degrees = 0.58 . $\dfrac{1}{1.73}$

Q3-18. The sine of 30 degrees and the cosine of 60 are equal.

You now have some facility with calculating trigonometric functions. This familiarization is all that is needed, as values for these functions are usually obtained from prepared tables. Such a table is shown in Fig. 3-26. It contains some of the most often used sine functions.

ANGLE	SINE	ANGLE	SINE	ANGLE	SINE	ANGLE	SINE
0^0 -360^0	0			180^0	0		
30^0	0.5	120^0	0.86	210^0	0 -0.5	300^0	-0.86
45^0	0.707	135^0	0.707	225^0	-0.707	315^0	-0.707
60^0	0.86	150^0	0.5	240^0	-0.86	330^0	-0.5
90^0	1.0			270^0	-1.0		

Fig. 3-26. Table of common sine functions.

ALTERNATING CURRENT

We can now return to the rotating wire and calculate current values at various angles of rotation. Fig. 3-27 shows the first 90 degrees of the rotation. To simplify matters let us consider that the maximum current induced is 1 ampere. Thus the current induced will be equal to the sine of the angle. Five points have been selected. From the table shown in Fig. 3-26 obtain the values of sine 0 degrees, 30 degrees, 45 degrees, 60 degrees, and 90 degrees. The result is the

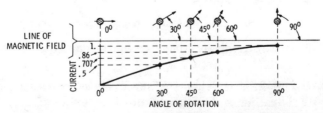

Fig. 3-27. Current variation with angle of rotation.

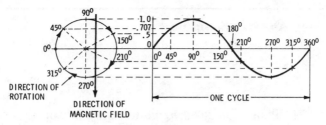

Fig. 3-28. Generation of sine wave.

curve shown in the illustration. Now consider the rest of the rotation through 360 degrees. From Fig. 3-28 we can see how some of the points are placed on a graph. The horizontal axis is a plot of the angle of rotation while the vertical axis is a plot of the current. The curve starts at 0 degrees whose sine is 0. The next point is at 45 degrees whose value from the table is 0.707. Then 90 degrees whose value is 1.0, 150 degrees whose value is 0.5, and then 180 degrees whose value is 0 since the wire is again moving parallel to the magnetic field. From this point the wire is moving through the field in the opposite direction and the resultant current is negative from 180 degrees through 360 degrees. The current alternates from positive to negative and is known as *alternating current*. Since this curve varies as the sine of the angle it is known as a *sine wave*. The plot of current from 0 degrees to 360 degrees is known as one cycle. Fig. 3-29 shows some of the nomenclature associated with a sine wave. As you will see it is common to other wave forms, too.

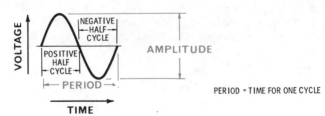

Fig. 3-29. Sine wave nomenclature.

Q3-19. The vertical height of the waveshape is the
Amplitude

Q3-20. The time it takes for one cycle is known as the
period.

Q3-21. Time is measured along the horizontal axis.

63

Note that the amplitude of the waveshape may be representative of either voltage or current. Further note that the positive portion of the wave is known as the positive half-cycle and the negative as the negative half-cycle.

Frequency

Frequency is a measure of the number of cycles that take place in one second. For example, Fig. 3-30 shows one wave that completes a cycle in one second. The frequency of this

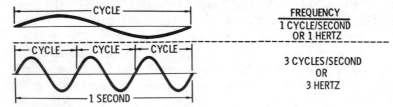

Fig. 3-30. Number of cycles per second is called frequency.

sine wave is said to be 1 cycle per second, more recently called 1 *hertz*. Beneath this sine wave is one that completes 3 cycles in the same time. Its frequency would be 3 hertz.

Frequency Versus Period

Fig. 3-31 shows the relationship between frequency and period. Two cycles of a 2-Hz waveshape are shown. The period is therefore 0.5 second as shown. Thus the frequency is equal to the reciprocal of the period or $1 \div 0.5 = 2$ hertz. Since most of the periods we will deal with will be in the order of thousandths and millionths of a second and many of the frequencies will be in the order of thousands and millions of hertz it is necessary to introduce some of the shorthand symbols that are used in electronics. The table

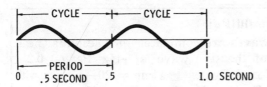

FREQUENCY = 2 CYCLES/SECOND

$$\text{FREQUENCY}\ (f) = \frac{1}{\text{PERIOD}\ (T)} = \frac{1}{.5\ \text{SEC}} = 2\ \frac{\text{CYCLES}}{\text{SECOND}}$$

Fig. 3-31. Relationship of frequency to period.

in Fig. 3-32 shows some of the most often used prefixes and their abbreviations. Two of the prefixes we will use very often when dealing with frequencies are k and M—as in kHz (kilohertz) and MHz (megahertz).

PREFIX	GIGA	MEGA	KILO	DECI	MILLI	MICRO	NANO	PICO
ABBREVIATION	G	M	k	d	m	μ	n	p
MULTIPLIER	10^9	10^6	10^3	10^{-1}	10^{-3}	10^{-6}	10^{-9}	10^{-12}

Fig. 3-32. Commonly used prefixes.

Q3-22. If 20 sine waves are completed in 4 seconds the frequency of the sine wave is _____. Period _____

Q3-23. The period of a sine wave is 4 milliseconds. The frequency is _____.

Q3-24. The frequency of a sine wave is 500 kHz. The period is _____ microseconds. _____ milliseconds.

Your Answers Should Be:

A3-22. If 20 sine waves are completed in 4 seconds the frequency of the sine wave is **5 Hz**. Period **0.2 sec.** F = No. of Cycles ÷ Time = 20 ÷ 4 sec = 5 cps (Hz) T = 1 ÷ F = 1 ÷ 5 Hz = 0.2 sec.

A3-23. The period of a sine wave is 4 milliseconds. The frequency is **250 Hz.**

$$F = 1 \div 4 \text{ msec} = \frac{1}{4 \times 10^{-3} \text{ sec}} = \frac{10^3}{4}$$

$$= \frac{1000}{4} = 250 \text{ Hz}$$

A3-24. The frequency of a sine wave is 500 kHz. The period is **2** microseconds (μsec). **0.002** millisec.

$$T = \frac{1}{F} = \frac{1}{500 \times 10^3 \text{ Hz}} = \frac{1}{0.5 \times 10^6 \text{ Hz}}$$

$$= \frac{10^{-6}}{0.5} = 2 \ \mu\text{sec}.$$

Note that the symbol μ is the greek letter mu.

Fig. 3-33 shows how to manipulate 1000 Hz to obtain the period of 1 millisecond. It is assumed that the student has a good working knowledge of the powers of ten.

$$T = \frac{1}{f} = \frac{1}{1000 \text{ Hz}} = \frac{1}{10^3 \text{ Hz}} = 10^{-3} \text{ SEC} = 1 \text{ millisecond} = 1 \text{ ms}$$

Fig. 3-33. Period in milliseconds.

Wavelength

Wavelength is defined as the distance a radio wave travels in the time for one cycle. Fig. 3-34 shows the formula for this relationship. To obtain the wavelength in meters (the Greek letter lambda is used to represent wavelength) divide the velocity of radio waves in meters/sec (same as the speed of light) by the frequency in hertz. An example of such a calculation is shown in Fig. 3-35. The frequency of the wave shown is 2 Hz since two cycles take place in 1 second. The velocity of radio waves is a constant of 300,000,000 meters per second. Thus the wavelength is 150,000,000 meters. Calculations like these are used to determine the

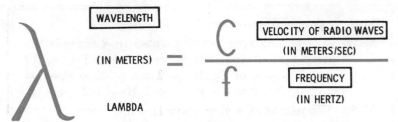

Fig. 3-34. The wavelength of a radio wave is the distance the wave travels in the time for one cycle.

proper lengths for antennas. Most antennas are cut to either half- or quarter-wavelengths for the transmitted frequency. For example, the frequency of television Channel 2 (upper end) is 60 MHz. Its wavelength would be 300,000,000 meters/sec ÷ 60 MHz = 5 meters. If the antenna were cut to a half-wavelength it would be 2.5 meters long. By folding it

Fig. 3-35. Wavelength—sample calculation.

in half you would have an antenna of about 1.25 meters long which is about 4.1 feet long. A glance at your television antenna will verify this.

Q3-25. The distance that a wave travels in the time for one cycle is called _wavelength_

Q3-26. If the frequency in the formula for wavelength is given in kHz then the wavelength will be in _Millimet_.

Q3-27. Channel 2 has a frequency range of 54 to 60 MHz and Channel 7 has a frequency range of 174 to 180 MHz. Channel __7__ will require the shorter antenna.

Your Answers Should Be:

A3-25. The distance that a wave travels in the time for one cycle is called **wavelength.**

A3-26. If the frequency in the formula for wavelength is given in kHz then the wavelength will be in **millimeters.**

A3-27. Channel 2 has a frequency range of 54 to 60 MHz and channel 7 has a frequency range of 174 to 180 MHz. Channel 7 will require the shorter antenna. That is, the higher the frequency, the shorter the period. The shorter the period the shorter the distance traveled in the time for one cycle (wavelength) and the shorter the antenna.

Voltage and Current Measurement

Until now we have spoken mainly about the time relationships in the sine wave. Now let us concern ourselves with the methods of measuring the voltage and current of the sine wave. The following measurements work equally well with voltage and current. Only the instruments used will vary.

Peak Voltage—As shown in Fig. 3-36, this peak voltage is the same as E_{MAX} (or I_{MAX} in a current waveform). It is

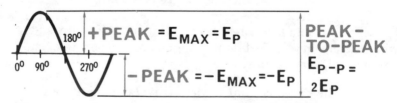

Fig. 3-36. Peak and peak-to-peak voltages.

therefore the maximum voltage of the sine wave (half-cycle). The voltage measured from this positive peak to the negative peak is known as the peak-to-peak voltage, and in a sine wave of the type we have been discussing it would be equal to twice the maximum voltage of one half-cycle. Peak-to-peak voltages can be measured visually on an instrument called an oscilloscope, and on some voltmeters that have a scale that is appropriately calibrated.

Average Voltage—The concept of average voltage is best shown through the use of a simpler waveform than the sine wave. Such a waveform is the square wave, shown in Fig. 3-37. In this square wave you see a constant positive 4 volts

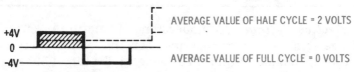

Fig. 3-37. Average value of a simple square wave.

for half a cycle and a constant negative 4 volts for half a cycle. This square wave is similar to the voltage we would obtain if we were to run a direct current (say from a 4-volt battery) through a circuit for a short period of time and then run it through in the reverse direction (thus obtaining the negative half-cycle). It is obvious upon inspection that the average voltage for a full cycle of such a waveform is zero, providing the time for each half cycle is the same.

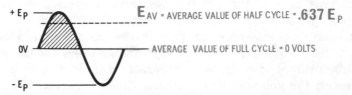

Fig. 3-38. Average value of a sine wave.

However, the average voltage for the positive half-cycle will be +2 volts. In Fig. 3-38 see a sine wave whose average full-cycle voltage is also zero. However, because the half-cycles are not composed of constant voltages, the average voltage for a half-cycle of a sine wave will turn out to be 0.637 of the peak voltage, instead of half the peak voltage as in the square wave.

Q3-28. If the maximum voltage of a sine wave is 7 volts, the peak-to-peak voltage is ___14 V___.

Q3-29. If the peak voltage of a square wave is 8 volts, the average full-cycle voltage is ___0 V___.

Effective Voltage—To understand the nature of effective voltage it is necessary to remember that when there is a current through a wire, heat is generated (Fig. 3-39). Your toaster and electric iron are applications of this phenome-

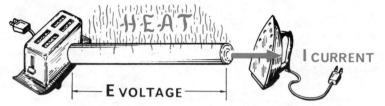

Fig. 3-39. Current through wire generates heat.

non. This heat is not always desirable as you may have noticed if you have touched an electric light bulb after it had been on for some time. In talking about a d-c voltage you will find that all of the current drawn from the battery will be utilized *effectively* to generate heat. In a sine wave however, the voltage at any instant (*instantaneous voltage* due to an instantaneous current) is changing. Thus the heat generated at any instant is different. Thus, it is found that the effective current of a sine wave is 0.707 of the peak current (Fig. 3-40). That is, a sine wave whose peak current is 1 ampere will have the same heating effect as a d-c current of 0.707 amperes. Most instruments like the voltmeter and ammeter are designed to measure effective values.

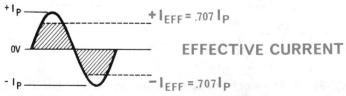

Fig. 3-40. Effective current value of a sine wave.

POWER

As you have seen, current passing through a wire generates heat. The amount of heat generated could be measured thermally if we so desired. It is more important to calculate the amount of power generated in terms of *watts*. One watt is the amount of power generated when a voltage of 1 volt causes a current of 1 ampere (Fig. 3-41). For the purposes

$$P \text{ \begin{matrix} POWER \\ (WATTS) \end{matrix}} = E \text{ \begin{matrix} VOLTAGE \\ (VOLTS) \end{matrix}} \times I \text{ \begin{matrix} CURRENT \\ (AMPERES) \end{matrix}}$$

Fig. 3-41. Power equals voltage times current.

of a-c voltages, the voltages and currents used will be the effective values. In the next chapter you will learn more of the nature of power in your studies of resistors and Ohm's law.

Q3-30. In the accompanying illustration identify the following: peak voltage, peak-to-peak voltage, effective voltage, and average voltage.

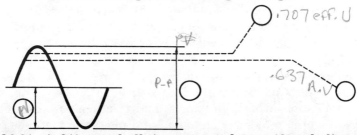

Q3-31. A 240-watt bulb is connected to a 120-volt line; the current drawn is ___2___ amperes.

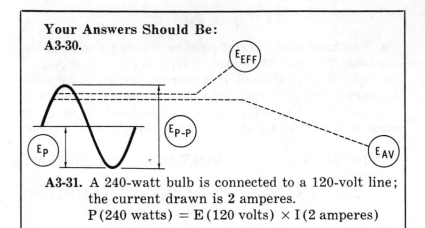

Your Answers Should Be:
A3-30.

E_{EFF}

E_{P-P}

E_P

E_{AV}

A3-31. A 240-watt bulb is connected to a 120-volt line; the current drawn is 2 amperes.

P (240 watts) = E (120 volts) × I (2 amperes)

SUMMARY QUESTIONS

1. When a weight is moved work is done and energy is expended.
   a. When a 6-pound weight is moved from a height of 14 inches to a height of 38 inches the work done is _144_ ~~inches~~ foot-pounds. *change to feet*
   b. A 50-gram weight is moved ___4___ centimeters vertically causing an expenditure of 200 dyne-cm.
2. Electrons can be caused to move by providing a difference in potential between two points. Work is done and energy is expended when electrons are moved.
   a. Difference in potential is measured in __V__.
   b. If 20 joules of energy are expended in moving 4 coulombs of electrical charge, the difference in potential is ___5 V___.
   c. When 12 coulombs of electrical charge are moved past a point in 3 seconds, the current is ___4___ amperes.
3. Voltage may be generated in several different ways. All of these ways depend on the conversion of one type of energy (heat, light, or mechanical, for example) to electrical energy. Some of the methods used have limited applications (heat, pressure, and friction, for example) while others like the chemical and magnetic methods are used to supply primary power to much of the electronic equipment in use today.

a. A solar battery converts ___light___ energy to ___electri___ energy.

b. Your car battery changes ~~elect.~~ _Chemical_ energy to ___electri___ energy.

c. A maximum current is induced in a wire when it moves (parallel, <u>perpendicular</u>) to the magnetic lines of force.

d. The induced current at any instant is equal to the product of the maximum current and the ___sine___.

4. Rotating a wire through a magnetic field causes a current through the wire first in one direction and then in the other. This is called an alternating current and because its instantaneous current is proportional to the sine of the angle of rotation, it is called a sine wave.

a. If the period of a sine wave is 4 milliseconds its frequency is ___250___ hertz.

b. The distance that a wave travels in the time for one cycle is called the ___wavelength___

c. List the following voltages associated with a sine wave in order according to magnitude (largest first): peak, effective, peak-to-peak, and average.

SUMMARY ANSWERS

1a. When a 6-pound weight is moved from a height of 14 inches to a height of 38 inches the work done is **12 foot-pounds.** ($38'' - 14'' = 24'' = 2'$ ∴ $2' \times 6$ lbs $= 12$ ft-lbs)

1b. A 50-gram weight is moved 4 centimeters vertically causing an expenditure of **200 dyne-cm.**

2a. Difference in potential is measured in **volts.**

2b. If 20 joules of energy are expended in moving 4 coulombs of electrical charge, the difference in potential is **5 volts.**

2c. When 12 coulombs of electrical charge are moved past a point in 3 seconds, the current is **4 amperes.**

3a. A solar battery converts **light** energy to **electrical** energy.

3b. Your car battery changes **chemical** energy to **electrical** energy.

3c. A maximum current is induced in a wire when it moves **perpendicular** to the magnetic lines of force.

3d. The induced current at any instant is equal to the product of the maximum current and the **sine** θ.

4a. If the period of a sine wave is 4 milliseconds its frequency is **250 hertz.**

4b. The distance that a wave travels in the time for one cycle is called the **wavelength.**

4c. **Peak-to-peak, peak, effective, average.**

4

Resistive Circuits

What You Will Learn

In this chapter you will learn about the basic circuit principles which can be used to explain virtually every electronic circuit you will come in contact with from now on. The manner in which current is developed in a simple circuit containing resistance and a source of voltage is explored, and the laws of Ohm and Kirchhoff are discussed in great detail. Much of the chapter will be devoted to using these laws in the solution of series and parallel circuits.

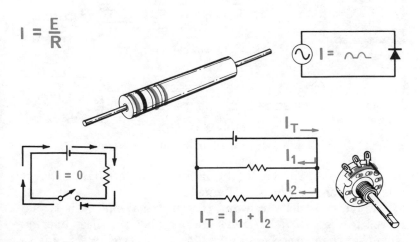

Fig. 4-1. Basic circuit principles.

BASIC CIRCUIT PRINCIPLES

Let us consider what is meant by a circuit. We would like to put the electrical energy at our command to work. To do this we must have a source of *voltage*, an object to work on (referred to as a *load*), and a method of delivering the electrical energy to the load.

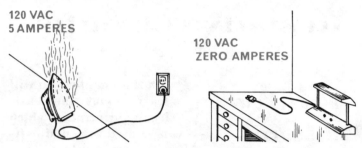

Fig. 4-2. Current delivered to a load.

Fig. 4-2 shows a typical source of voltage found in every home: the electrical outlet that delivers approximately 120 volts of alternating current. Next to it is a lamp which is not on because it has not been plugged into the outlet. That is, we have not provided a path for the electrical energy to reach the light. No current is delivered and no energy may

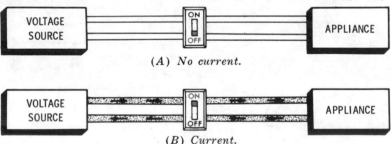

Fig. 4-3. A switch used to complete a circuit.

be expended in the load (the lamp). The left-hand side of this figure shows an iron plugged into the outlet. A current of 5 amperes is delivered and the electrical energy is transferred to the load (the iron) and expended as heat energy. Note that the method of delivering the electrical energy is to provide a path for current to the load and back to the source.

Fig. 4-3 shows another element of a complete circuit: the switch. A typical wall unit is shown that is usually arranged so that it activates the wall outlets in a room. An appliance, such as a lamp or a radio, may be plugged into such a wall outlet ready to be activated as soon as the circuit is complete. This is accomplished by flipping the switch to the ON position, thus providing a path for current to the appliance and back to the source of voltage.

SIMPLE CIRCUIT ANALYSIS

A simple circuit is shown in Fig. 4-4. It consists of two cells, a switch, and a lamp. Instead of drawing the objects in a *wiring* diagram (Fig. 4-4B), it is much simpler to draw symbols that represent the components in a circuit. Such a drawing is shown in Fig. 4-4A, and is called a *sche-*

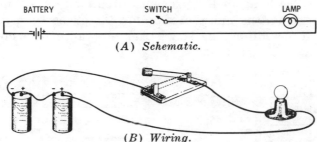

(A) *Schematic.*

(B) *Wiring.*

Fig. 4-4. Comparison of diagrams.

matic diagram. As we discuss new components we will introduce corresponding symbols for use on schematic diagrams. In Fig. 4-4 the two 1.5-volt dry cells are the source of voltage, the load is the lamp, and the switch controls the current to the load.

Q4-1. The object in a circuit that utilizes the electrical energy is called the _LOAD_.

Q4-2. There is no current in the circuit of Fig. 4-4 because it is not a (an) _closed_ circuit.

Q4-3. A diagram that shows symbols instead of the actual objects is called a (an) _SCHEMATIC_.

Q4-4. Draw a circuit diagram of a flashlight.

RESISTANCE

Definition

Resistance is the opposition offered to the current in a circuit. The lamp in the previous circuit offers an opposition to the current and therefore has the property of resistance. By definition, the larger the resistance in a circuit, the smaller the current.

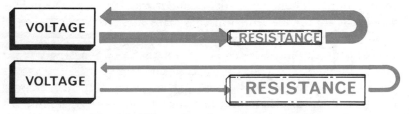

Fig. 4-5. Effect of resistance in a circuit.

Fig. 4-5 shows two circuits supplied by the same voltage source. The circuit with the greatest amount of resistance has the least amount of current. Resistance is measured in units called *ohms*.

Conductivity

In electronics you will be concerned with three types of materials. These materials are classified according to their ability to "allow the passage of" (*conduct*) electricity. Those that pass electricity readily are known as *conductors*. Materials with many free electrons fall into this category. Silver, platinum, and copper are some that you will find used

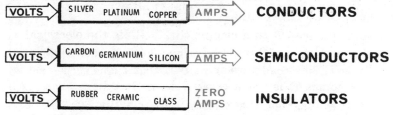

Fig. 4-6. Conductors, semiconductors, and insulators.

to make up the wires that connect the various components in a circuit. They offer very little opposition to current—that is they have little resistivity (resistance).

The materials in the next class tend to *impede* the current in a circuit. Materials such as germanium, silicon, and carbon are called *semiconductors*, and they are used in the manufacture of diodes, transistors, and *resistors*. These components all have the ability to regulate the current in a circuit. They accomplish this by varying the amount of *resistance* (also called *impedance*) in a circuit.

The next class of materials prevents the flow of electricity in a circuit. They are called *insulators*. Rubber, ceramic, and glass materials fall into this class and are used to prevent electricity from traveling undesirable paths. A simple example of this is the insulation on the common line cord, which not only prevents you from coming in contact with the high voltage in it, but also acts to separate the wires from each other, thus keeping the current from taking a short cut back to the source (an action known as a short circuit) instead of traveling through the high resistance of the appliance.

Just as the opposition to current is measured in units of resistance called ohms so may you consider the ease with which current is passed in units of *conductance*, called *mhos*. Fig. 4-7 shows the relationship between these units.

To better understand the concept of conductivity let us consider using the nation's highways as an analogy. At

$$\text{CONDUCTIVITY} = \frac{1}{\text{RESISTANCE}}$$
(MHOS)   (OHMS)

Fig. 4-7. Relationship of conductivity to resistivity.

5 P.M. the scene in industrial plants all over the country is the same. The parking lots are packed with cars as shown in Fig. 4-8. The full parking lot represents the pressure to be put on the roads. It is therefore analogous to the source of *voltage*. The roads are the *wires* that connect the factory to the homes (they represent the *load*). When the whistle blows (the *switch*) the circuit is complete. The cars move toward the driveway to enter the road. Although all of the cars can travel as fast as 100 miles per hour, they nevertheless can proceed only at the speed dictated by the resistance of the road.

Fig. 4-8. "Resistance" and "conductance" on a highway.

What are some of the factors that govern the resistance of the road? The stop sign, the S-curve, the traffic light, and the narrow bridge all are signs that tend to slow down the vehicles. However, the speed limit signs are different. They tell the vehicles how fast they may go, and you will notice that the higher the speed limit, the lower the resistance of the road. The superhighway, for example, may have a limit of 65 mph, which must mean that it has no traffic lights, no severe curves, and plenty of traffic lanes. These speed limit signs are the same as *conductance* in an electric circuit. Thus, conductance shows the speed at which electrons may move in a circuit, while resistance shows the amount of opposition to current in a circuit.

Resistivity

Factors Determining Resistance—Resistivity is a measure of the amount of resistance offered by a specific material, and is a constant that varies with temperature. It is represented by the Greek letter rho (ρ) and is measured in units like ohm-meters or ohms per circular mil-foot. Note

$$\text{OHMS} = \mathbf{R} = \rho \, \frac{\ell}{\mathbf{A}} = \text{OHM} - \text{METERS} \times \frac{\text{METERS}}{\text{METERS}^2}$$
$$\Omega \, (\text{OMEGA})$$

$$\text{RESISTANCE} = \text{RESISTIVITY} \times \frac{\text{LENGTH}}{\text{CROSS SECTIONAL AREA}}$$

Fig. 4-9. Factors determining resistance.

that the resistance depends on not only the resistivity of the material; it will increase with the length of the component and decrease as the cross-sectional area is increased. Thus, a thin wire offers a great amount of resistance just as a narrow road will prevent a great number of cars from moving between two points. A road made from concrete allows more cars per hour to pass than a dirt road. In the same fashion the material from which the wire is made affects the resistance.

Q4-5. The opposition offered to current in a circuit is called *Resistance*.

Q4-6. The unit of resistance is the *Ω ohm*.

Q4-7. Materials that pass current readily are known as *Conductors*.

Q4-8. Materials used to regulate the current in a circuit are called *Semiconductors*.

Q4-9. The rubber coating on a line cord is an example of the use of a (an) *insulator*.

Q4-10. The unit for measuring conductance is the *Mhos*.

Q4-11. The speed limit signs on the highways are analogous to the electrical circuit measurement of *conductance*.

Resistivity of Various Materials—Fig. 4-10 shows the resistivities of three types of materials. The unit of resistivity used is the ohm-centimeter which is the resistance of a wire one centimeter long whose cross-sectional area is one circular mil (mil = .001 in; circular mil = Area of .001 in²). Approximate values are used, as we are interested in the order of magnitude of the resistivities of the three types of materials that we will come in contact with in electronics.

The first of these materials is copper, the most common, and the one used in connecting wires, almost to the exclusion of all other materials. As a material with many free electrons it has an almost minuscule resistivity of .000001 ohm-centimeters. Materials such as gold and silver have much lower resistivities but because of their high cost are used only for very special applications.

MATERIAL	RESISTIVITY	CLASSIFICATION
COPPER	10^{-6} OHM - CM	CONDUCTOR
GERMANIUM	10^{2} OHM-CM	SEMICONDUCTOR
CERAMIC	10^{14} OHM - CM	INSULATOR

Fig. 4-10. Resistivity of various materials.

The next material listed is germanium, a semiconductor, used for manufacturing diodes and transistors. Note that the resistivities are in the order of 100 ohm-centimeters for semiconductor materials. The materials used for constructing resistors (carbon and carbon composition) are in this order of magnitude. Insulators such as ceramics carry resistivities in the order of 10,000,000,000,000 ohm-centimeters. Thus, they offer an almost infinite opposition to current, compared to the other materials mentioned.

The Unit of Measurement

Resistance is measured in units called ohms. Fig. 4-11 defines the ohm as the resistance offered in a circuit that allows 1 ampere of current when a voltage of 1 volt is

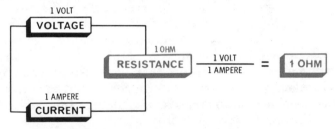

Fig. 4-11. Definition of an ohm.

applied. Another way of saying this is when 1 volt is divided by 1 ampere the result is 1 ohm. This relationship is the most important one you will study in electronics and is the basis for Ohm's law.

Q4-12. A material with many free electrons is called a(an) CONDUCTOR.

Q4-13. A material with a resistivity of 500 ohm-centimeters would most likely be a(an) SEMICONDUCTOR

Q4-14. Calculate the resistance of 1000 centimeters of copper wire whose cross-sectional area is 1 square centimeter.

Q4-15. If it takes 10 volts to develop a current of 1 ampere in a circuit, the resistance of the circuit is _____10_____ ohms.

Q4-16. If there are 20 amperes of current in a circuit with 10 volts applied, the resistance is _5_____.

Your Answers Should Be:

A4-12. A material with many free electrons is called a **conductor.**

A4-13. A material with a resistivity of 500 ohm-centimeters would most likely be a **semiconductor.**

A4-14. Using the formula given in Fig. 4-9 and taking the resistivity from the table in Fig. 4-10 we have: $R = \dfrac{1}{A} = 10^{-6}$ ohm-cm $\times \dfrac{1000 \text{ cm}}{1 \text{ cm}^2}$

$= .001$ ohm

A4-15. If it takes 10 volts to develop a current of 1 ampere in a circuit, the resistance of the circuit is **10** ohms. Referring to Fig. 4-11 we note that if it takes 1 volt to develop a current of 1 ampere through a resistance of 1 ohm, then it must mean that a circuit that requires 10 volts to develop a current of 1 ampere must have a resistance of 10 times as much or, in this case, 10 ohms.

A4-16. If there are 20 amperes of current in a circuit with 10 volts applied, the resistance is **0.5** ohm. That is $\dfrac{10 \text{ volts}}{20 \text{ amperes}} = 0.5$ ohm.

Resistor Types and Construction

Various types of resistors are used in electronics. Fig. 4-12 shows some of the most often used *fixed* resistors. A fixed resistor is one whose value may not be varied in a circuit. It is selected for a specific nonvariable function and a specific range of voltage and current conditions.

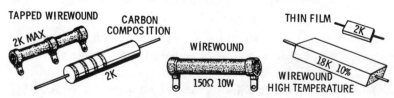

Fig. 4-12. Fixed resistors.

Fixed Composition—The most common of all resistors you will come in contact with is the carbon composition resistor. A 2000-ohm (2K) resistor of this type is shown in Fig. 4-12. The colored stripes tell its value. The use of this color coding is explained in this chapter. A simple component to construct, it has at its core a small deposit of carbon connected to the two copper leads and surrounded by an insulating material. This type of component cannot withstand high currents and it is difficult to make in exact resistance values.

Fixed Wirewound—The next most often encountered resistor is the wirewound resistor shown in Fig. 4-13. This component consists of a ceramic core around which is wound a thin copper-nickel alloy (or other moderately resistive

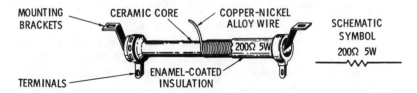

Fig. 4-13. Wirewound resistor.

material) wire. The wire is coated with an insulating material to prevent adjacent turns from coming in contact with each other. Metal clamps are placed at either end to serve as terminals for connection into a circuit. An enamel-coated insulation is molded over the whole assembly, leaving only the terminals exposed. This protects the wires from breakage and provides additional insulation from the surrounding circuits. The component is hollow to allow for heat dissipation. Mounting brackets may be placed inside the component as shown. The component is marked with its value and a wattage rating, which will be discussed later on in this chapter. The schematic symbol for this component is shown, and it is the same for all types of fixed resistive components.

Q4-17. A component whose resistance may not be varied in a circuit is called a(an) _Fixed_ resistor.

Q4-18. The most commonly used component is the _CARbon Composition_ resistor.

Tapped Resistors—Different types of wirewound resistors are available depending on the application. The 18K unit shown in Fig. 4-12 is used for high-temperature applications. The tapped wirewound resistor in Fig. 4-13 is used where a particular current division is desired in a circuit. The one shown has a flat construction and a maximum value of 2000 ohms. The tap may be placed anywhere (that is, during manufacture), depending on your needs. Center-tapping is typical. This would give you a resistance of 1000 ohms from either end to the center and 2000 ohms from end to end. Thus, by taking the output from the center-tap of such a resistor, you may select half the voltage in a particular circuit.

Thin-Film Technique—Fig. 4-14 shows the construction of a thin-film tapped resistor. As we enter the era of micro-

Fig. 4-14. Thin-film resistor, tapped.

electronics the need for smaller and smaller components becomes greater. One of the techniques used is the thin-film technique. Thin films (in the order of 50 to 100 *atoms* thick) are deposited on insulating substrata by a process called vacuum evaporation. The component in Fig. 4-14 is compared to a domino to give you an idea of its size (in the order of .01 inch square). Newer techniques used in the manufacture of integrated circuits may provide as many as 100 such components in the same space. The schematic symbol for such a component is shown in the illustration. It is very difficult to construct accurate resistors using thin-film techniques. However, as you will see, the most important factor is not the actual value of a resistor but rather its value compared to other resistors in the circuit. Thin-film techniques allow us to maintain these ratios even though particular resistance values are not met. The most accurate method for obtaining exact resistances is the wirewound technique.

Color Code

First Three Bands—Values on carbon-type resistors are not marked in numbers; they are shown with colored stripes which tell us the characteristics. Fig. 4-15 shows what the stripes stand for. The colors used start with black (the absence of light) which represents zero, and end with white (the presence of all the colors of the spectrum) which represents nine. With the exception of brown and gray the rest of the colors are the light spectrum from red to violet and

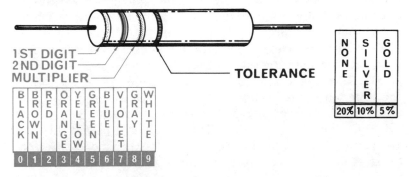

Fig. 4-15. Resistor color code.

can be committed to memory quite easily if you remember that *green* (a *five*-letter word) represents the number *five*. Facility with this code will be gained through constant usage. The first band of color on the resistor (the band right on the edge of the component no matter which way you hold it) is the first digit of the resistance value. The next band is the second digit of the resistor value. The third band is the multiplier (or number of zeros following the second digit). Thus the component shown in Fig. 4-16A has a first digit of 2 (red), a second digit of 0 (black) and a multiplier

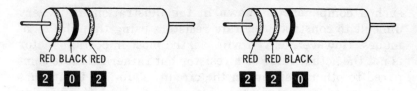

RED BLACK RED

2 0 2

(A) 2000 ohms.

RED RED BLACK

2 2 0

(B) 22 ohms.

Fig. 4-16. The order of the colors is significant.

of 100 or two zeros following the second digit (red). Therefore its value is 2000 ohms or 2K.

The Fourth Band—Tolerance—The fourth band on a resistor is used for something called *tolerance*. As we have noted, it is difficult to make carbon-composition resistors to exact values. Thus, during manufacture the resistors are measured as they come off the assembly line. All those that are within five percent of their expected value are marked with a gold stripe, those within 10 percent of their rated value are marked with a silver stripe, and those within 20 percent of their rated value have no fourth stripe. Obviously, you pay a premium for 5- and 10-percent resistors.

Standard Resistors—Note that not all values of carbon resistors are manufactured. Fig. 4-17 shows the standard 5- and 10-percent resistors manufactured. Note that only the 100-ohm range is shown. The significant digits will hold true for every range of resistor. For example, a 180-ohm resistor is shown in the table. There will also be a 1.8K and 18K, and a 1.8 Meg manufactured. Note that more different types of 5-percent resistors are made than 10-percent resistors. The reason for this is illustrated in Fig. 4-18. A 100-ohm resistor is shown with a tolerance of 20 percent. Resistors coming off the assembly line with these ratings will have a range of values as shown in the figure—that is, anywhere from 80 to 120 ohms. Consider a 100-ohm, 10-percent resistor. Its range would be 90 to 110 ohms, a total of 20

10% RESISTORS

100	120	150	180	220	270	330	390	470	560	680	820
110	130	160	200	240	300	360	430	510	620	750	910

5% RESISTORS

Fig. 4-17. Standard composition resistor values.

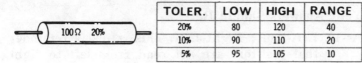

TOLER.	LOW	HIGH	RANGE
20%	80	120	40
10%	90	110	20
5%	95	105	10

Fig. 4-18. Tolerance.

ohms. The next highest resistor in the series is the 120-ohm resistor. Its range would be (based on 10 percent of 120 ohms or 12 ohms) 108 ohms through 132 ohms. Note how this overlaps the high range of the 100-ohm resistor—110 ohms. Thus, all resistor values may be taken into account using this system.

Five-percent resistors have a smaller range (10 ohms on a 100-ohm resistor) and therefore must be manufactured at closer intervals, as shown in Fig. 4-18. For special orders, resistors of 1-percent tolerance and less may be manufactured at a premium cost. Wirewound resistors are manufactured at many of the values not shown in Fig. 4-17, and at lower tolerances. The importance of the order of the colors of the resistor is shown in Fig. 4-16. Two resistors with two red bands and one black band are shown, but each has a different value.

Q4-19. Write the values of these two resistors.

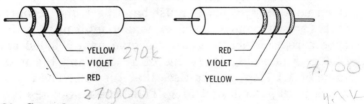

YELLOW *270k*
VIOLET
RED
270,000

RED
VIOLET
YELLOW
4,700
4.7 K

Q4-20. Complete the table below.

RESIST. NO.	1ST DIGIT	2ND DIGIT	MULT.	TOLERANCE COLOR	%	VALUE	MAX. VALUE	MIN. VALUE	RANGE
1	BROWN	RED	YELLOW	SILVER	*10*	*120 K*	*132k*	*108 K*	*24K*
2	BLUE	GRAY	ORANGE	—	*20*	*68K*	*81,600*	*54,700*	*27,24*
3	ORANGE	ORANGE	BROWN	GOLD	*5*	*330*	*346.5*	*313.5*	*33*
4	BROWN	BLACK	*Green*	*S*	*10*	1 MEG	1.1MEG		
5	*Y*	*V*	*Y*	SILVER	*10*	*470K*	*517*	423K	*94K*

Your Answers Should Be:

A4-19. Left-270K; Right-4.7K. This is just a reminder that resistors are *not* read from left to right but rather from the color nearest to the end.

A4-20. The completed table is shown below.

RESIST. NO.	1ST DIGIT	2ND DIGIT	MULT.	TOLERANCE COLOR	%	VALUE	MAX. VALUE	MIN. VALUE	RANGE
1	BROWN	RED	YELLOW	SILVER	10	120K	132K	108K	24K
2	BLUE	GRAY	ORANGE	——	20	68K	81.6K	54.4K	27.2K
3	ORANGE	ORANGE	BROWN	GOLD	5	330	346.5	313.5K	33
4	BROWN	BLACK	GREEN	SILVER	10	1 MEG	1.1MEG	0.9MEG	200K
5	YELLOW	VIOLET	YELLOW	SILVER	10	470K	517K	423K	94K

Some discussion of this table might help you understand the methods involved. The first resistor shows first and second digits of 1 and 2, respectively, followed by four zeros or 120,000 ohms, 120K. Its tolerance of 10 percent gives a ± 12K range for a maximum value of 132K and a minimum value of 108K and a range of 24K. Resistors 2 and 3 are calculated in a similar fashion except that their tolerances are 20 percent and 5 percent, respectively.

Resistor 4 requires a little more thought. Its value is given as 1 Meg; thus, it must have first and second digits of 1 (brown) and 0 (black) and a multiplier of 100,000 (five zeros), which is green, to give us 1,000,000 ohms or 1 Meg. Examining the value of 1 Meg, and the maximum value of 1.1 Meg, you can see that the difference is .1 Meg, which is 10 percent of 1 Meg. Thus, the rest of the table can be completed. Note that .1 Meg is the same as 100K.

Resistor 5 requires the most thought. The silver band indicates a 10-percent tolerance. If we consider that the minimum value is 90 percent, then we can get the actual value by dividing 423K by 90 percent to get 470K. The rest is then straightforward.

Power Considerations

You are already familiar with the fact that heat is generated when current passes through a material. The amount

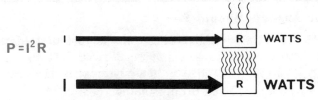

Fig. 4-19. Power dissipated increases as current increases.

of heat generated depends on two factors—the resistance of the material and the amount of current passing through it. Through the use of special constants, temperature can be converted directly into units of power called *watts*. These

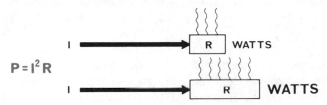

Fig. 4-20. Power dissipated increases as resistance increases.

units can be found by multiplying the resistance by the square of the current. Fig. 4-19 shows how increasing the current increases the heat generated and as a result the power dissipated in the resistor. Fig. 4-20 shows how increasing the size of the resistor (while maintaining the same

APPROX. LENGTH	2K RESISTORS	WATTAGE RATING
1/4"		1/4W
3/8"		1/2W
1/2"		1W
3/4"		2W
	COMPOSITION	

2K 10W
WIREWOUND

Fig. 4-21. Comparison of resistor size versus wattage rating.

current) increases the power dissipated. Fig. 4-21 shows how resistor size varies with typical wattage ratings. A wirewound resistor is shown for comparison.

Q4-21. Power varies directly as the square of the __*I*__.
Q4-22. Doubling the size of a resistor will __Double__ the amount of power dissipated by it.

Effect of Temperature on Resistance

As current passes through a resistor, heat is generated. The heat in turn will cause a change in resistor value. The amount of this change depends on the temperature coefficient of the material. Fig. 4-22 shows a chart of a material whose temperature coefficient is +0.55 percent per degree centigrade. The horizontal axis shows the ambient temperature while the vertical axis shows the factor by which the resistance must be multiplied for a particular temperature.

Consider a 100-ohm resistor at 25 degrees where the multiplication factor is 1.0 and therefore the resistance remains 100 ohms. At a temperature of 120 degrees the multiplication factor is 1.5 and the resistance is 150 ohms. At a temperature of 185 degrees the multiplication factor is 2.0 and the resistance will be 200 ohms. This particular chart shows an increase in resistance with temperature, or a positive temperature coefficient. Some materials exhibit a negative coefficient and can be used to compensate for circuits in which changes in resistance will seriously affect their operation.

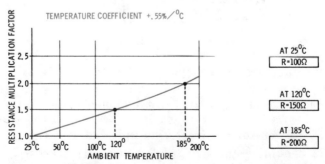

Fig. 4-22. Resistance increases with temperature.

Variable Resistors

Until now we have considered only fixed resistors. However, let us now examine the construction of those components that are made to be manually variable to answer specific circuit needs. Fig. 4-23 shows a sampling of such variable resistors, also called *potentiometers*.

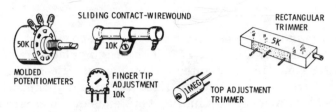

Fig. 4-23. Variable resistors—potentiometers.

Wirewound Sliding Contact—One very common type is the wirewound sliding-contact potentiometer shown in Fig. 4-24. It is constructed in the same fashion as the wirewound fixed resistor discussed previously. The difference lies in the manner in which a portion of the wires is exposed to allow the sliding contact to select any resistance. Once the proper

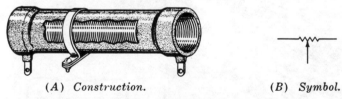

(A) *Construction.*   (B) *Symbol.*

Fig. 4-24. Sliding contact wirewound potentiometer.

resistance is selected, the screw may be tightened, which will tighten the clamp and prevent a change in the tap position. The schematic symbol for this type of resistor is shown in Fig. 4-24B. Where a high wattage resistor is required the wirewound type will be used.

Q4-23. When a material's resistance decreases as its temperature increases it is said to have a(an) _____ temperature coefficient.

Q4-24. The temperature of a material (*increases, decreases*) as the current through it increases.

Rectangular Trimmer—One of the latest types of potentiometers is shown in Fig. 4-25. This rectangular trimmer is ideal for mounting on printed-circuit boards. It consists of a screw-driven sliding contact (also called a wiper), which moves along a resistive winding, both ends of which are terminated in contact pins. At the same time that the contact moves along the resistive winding it makes contact with the collector track (usually made out of a precious metal—low resistance). The middle pin on the component is connected to the collector track.

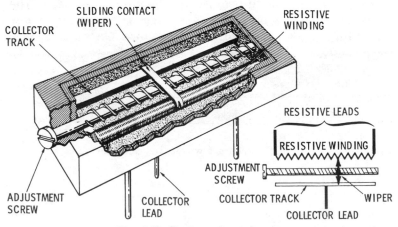

Fig. 4-25. Rectangular trimmer.

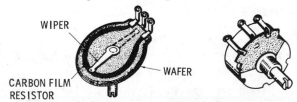

Fig. 4-26. Carbon-composition potentiometer.

Carbon-Composition Potentiometer—One of the most popular of all potentiometers is the carbon-composition type shown in Fig. 4-26. It is used in radio and tv sets for most of the variable controls such as volume, contrast, brightness, and tone. The shaft that connects to the wiper arm is made so that a control knob may be fitted over it. The shaft passes through a threaded section that may fit through a hole in a control panel, and a nut can be screwed on to hold the pot (short for potentiometer) firmly on the panel. With the back of the control removed you can easily see the construction of this component. A carbon-film resistor is bonded to the wafer (an insulating material such as ceramic). The ends of this resistor are connected to the two end contacts of the control. The middle contact is connected to the wiper arm which is formed to provide spring-tension pressure on the film resistor.

These controls cannot be made to carry large currents. Another problem with these controls is that dirt collects inside these units and deposits on the carbon film. This dirt prevents the wiper arm from making a good contact with the resistor and results in erratic operation. Perhaps you have experienced this with your radio. The problem exhibits itself as either noise when the volume control is rotated, or as positions on the volume control where nothing may be heard. This is known as a "noisy" control and can be cured by replacing the old one or cleaning it with a special cleaning compound. For higher-wattage applications a wire-wound resistor may be used in place of the carbon-film resistor.

OHM'S LAW

Basis of the Law

You have already discussed much of the basis for Ohm's law. For example you know that increasing the voltage in a

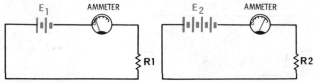

Fig. 4-27. As voltage increases current increases.

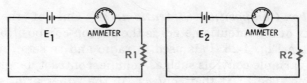

Fig. 4-28. As resistance decreases current increases.

circuit will increase the current. You also know that *decreasing* the resistance in a circuit will increase the *current*. It is very simple to show this relationship as an equation (Fig. 4-29). That is, the current measured in amperes is equal to the voltage measured in volts, divided by the resistance measured in ohms. Using I to represent current, E to represent voltage, and R to represent resistance we have the formula $I = \dfrac{E}{R}$, which is Ohm's law. Fig. 4-30 shows a sample calculation using this law. Consider a simple series circuit with a voltage of 10 volts applied to a resistor of 5 ohms. How much current is there? Applying Ohm's law we obtain $10V \div 5\Omega = 2A$.

$$\text{CURRENT}_{\text{(AMPERES)}} = \frac{\text{VOLTAGE}^{\text{(VOLTS)}}}{\text{RESISTANCE}_{\text{(OHMS)}}} \qquad I = \frac{E}{R}$$

Fig. 4-29. Ohm's law.

Circuits are not always as straightforward as this one and you may be given any two of these parameters (voltage, current, or resistance). It is important to be able to adjust the formula accordingly. Simple algebraic rules prevail here and if you are familiar with them you will not need the mnemonic device on the next page. It is known as the Ohm's law pie and simplifies the formula.

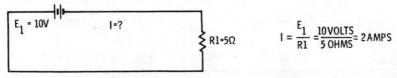

Fig. 4-30. Sample Ohm's law calculation.

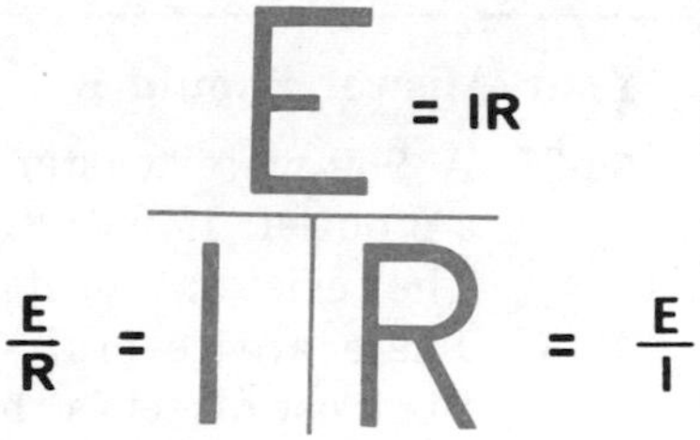

$$\frac{E}{R} = \boxed{I \,\big|\, R} = \frac{E}{I}$$

$$\overset{E}{} = IR$$

Fig. 4-31. Ohm's law pie.

Manipulation of Ohm's Law

The use of the formula is simplified in Fig. 4-31. Assume a simple circuit where you are given the current required and the voltage supplied, and you wish to calculate the resistance in the circuit. If you cover up the resistance (R) in the pie you are left with E over I, the equation for resistance. In a similar fashion you may cover I to leave E over R as the formula for the current in the circuit, and you may cover E leaving I times R as the equation for the voltage in the circuit.

Manipulation of the Power Formula

You have been introduced to the equation that says power is equal to the product of the resistance and the square of the current. Fig. 4-32 shows how to rearrange the formula to find the power when any two of the parameters are given. This is accomplished by substituting the Ohm's law parameters in the power formula.

$$P = I^2 R \quad \text{FOR } R \text{ SUBSTITUTE } \frac{E}{I}$$

$$P = I^2 \left(\frac{E}{I}\right) = IE \quad \text{FOR } I \text{ SUBSTITUTE } \frac{E}{R}$$

$$P = \left(\frac{E}{R}\right) E = \frac{E^2}{R}$$

Fig. 4-32. Manipulating the power formula.

Q4-25. **A 960-watt toaster is plugged into a 120-volt alternating-current outlet (Note that all formulas apply to ac as well as dc). It will draw a current of _____ amperes. The resistance of its heating element is _____ ohms.**

Your Answer Should Be:

A4-25. A 960-watt toaster is plugged into a 120-volt a-c outlet. It will draw a current of 8 amperes. The resistance of its heating element is 15 ohms. There are several ways to tackle this one but the most direct is the following:

Since $P = EI$, then $I = P \div E = \dfrac{960 \text{ watts}}{120 \text{ volts}} = 8$

Then $I = 8$ amperes

From Ohm's law $R = E \div I = \dfrac{120 \text{ volts}}{8 \text{ amperes}}$
$= 15$ ohms

Use of Ohm's Law Without Basic Units

Until now you have considered the solution of simple series circuit problems using the basic units of volts, ohms, and amperes. Unfortunately, it is more usual in electronics to use units like milliamps (one-thousandth of an ampere) or kilohms (one thousand ohms). Consider the table shown in Fig. 4-33. It lists some of the most often used units and shows how they behave in the Ohm's law formula. Consider the first entry in the table. If ohms and milliamperes are given then the answer will be in millivolts. Note that you may also say that when milliamps and millivolts are given the answer will be in ohms. Although this does not represent all of the combinations it does have those most often encountered in electronics. If you have a facility with the

OHMS Ω	X	AMPERES a	=	VOLTS V
OHMS Ω	X	MILLIAMPERES ma	=	MILLIVOLTS mV
OHMS Ω	X	MICROAMPERES μa	=	MICROVOLTS μV
KILOHMS KΩ	X	AMPERES a	=	KILOVOLTS KV
MEGOHMS MΩ	X	AMPERES a	=	MEGAVOLTS MV
KILOHMS KΩ	X	MILLIAMPERES ma	=	VOLTS V
MEGOHMS MΩ	X	MICROAMPERES μa	=	VOLTS V
MEGOHMS MΩ	X	MILLIAMPERES ma	=	KILOVOLTS KV
KILOHMS KΩ	X	MICROAMPERES μa	=	MILLIVOLTS MV

Fig. 4-33. Table of most often used Ohm's law expressions.

powers of ten you will not need this table, but it might still serve as a quick check on your units.

Fig. 4-34 shows some sample calculations using the table in Fig. 4-33. A current of 30 ma is passed through a 20K resistor. Thus, 20 × 30 is 600 and, from the table, K ohms × ma gives us volts. Answer 600 volts. Similarly, 80 ÷ 4 = 20, and mv and microamps gives K ohms or 20K. Once again,

20KΩ X 30ma = 600 VOLTS

$$\frac{80mV}{4\mu a} = 20 \text{ KILOHMS}$$

$$\frac{6KV}{2M\Omega} = 3 \text{ MILLIAMPS}$$

Fig. 4-34. More sample calculations using Ohm's law table.

$6 \div 2 = 3$ and Kv ÷ MΩ is milliamps—3 ma. Note how we use only the K and the M to abbreviate kilohms and Megohms. To gain an even better facility with these units you must practice. See how well you can complete the table below.

Q4-26. In completing this table make sure that your answers are in the required units. That is, if ohms and milliamps are given your answer should be in millivolts rather than in a corresponding quantity of volts.

	RESISTANCE	CURRENT	VOLTAGE
1	500Ω	3a	1500 V
2	6000Ω	5ma	30,000 mV
3	4KΩ	5ma	20V
4	12KΩ	10ma	120V
5	2MΩ	20µA	40V

Your Answer Should Be:
A4-26.

	RESISTANCE	CURRENT	VOLTAGE
1	500Ω	3a	1500V
2	6000Ω	5ma	30,000 mV
3	4KΩ	5ma	20V
4	12KΩ	10ma	120V
5	2MΩ	20μa	40V

Resistors in Series

Previously, we have considered only a simple series circuit containing a source of voltage and one resistor. What happens when there is more than one resistor in a circuit? Fig. 4-35 shows two resistors in series (R1 and R2). They

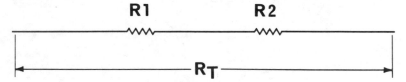

$$\text{TOTAL (SERIES) RESISTANCE} = R_T = R1 + R2$$

Fig. 4-35. Formula for calculating series resistance.

are in series because the current passing through one must also pass through the other. To find the total resistance (R_T) of this combination it is necessary only to add the two resistors together. Thus a 20-ohm resistor in series with a 30-ohm resistor would give us a total resistance of 50 ohms.

Kirchhoff's First Law

Voltage Drops—How do voltage and current behave in a series circuit containing more than one resistor? For the answer to this we must go to Kirchhoff's first law. Fig. 4-36 shows a simple series circuit containing two resistors in

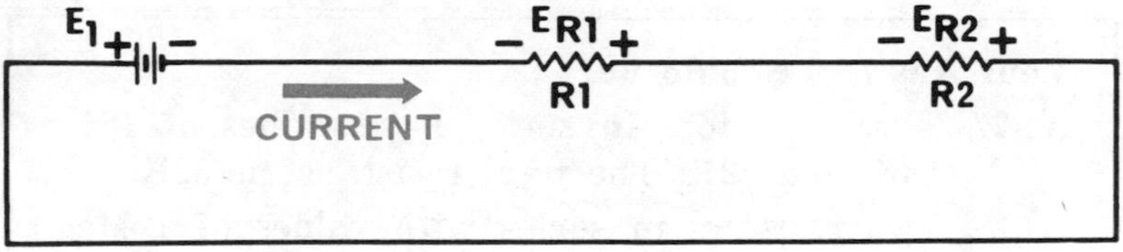

$$E_1 = E_{R1} + E_{R2} \quad \text{or}$$

$$E_1 + E_{R1} + E_{R2} = 0$$

KIRCHHOFF'S FIRST LAW

Fig. 4-36. The algebraic sum of the voltages in a series loop is zero.

series with a source of voltage. First consider the current in the circuit. Since there is only one path for it, the current measured anywhere in the circuit will be the same. Not so with the voltage! When current goes through a resistor there is a voltage developed across the resistor. This voltage is referred to as a *voltage drop*. To understand Kirchhoff's law we must consider the polarities of the voltage drops in a circuit.

You are already familiar with the polarity at the terminals of a battery as they are shown. What of the polarity of the voltage drops across the resistors? A simple rule prevails. The side of a resistor at which the *current enters* is considered *negative*. Thus if the voltage at the battery (E_1) is considered to be positive, then the voltage across the resistors (E_{R1} and E_{R2}) must be negative. Since we cannot drop any more voltage in a circuit than that which is supplied, the sum of the voltage drops in the circuit must equal the source voltage, that is, $E_1 = E_{R1} + E_{R2}$. Another way of saying this is that the algebraic sum (the sum considering the polarities of the voltages) of the voltages in a series circuit is zero. This is Kirchhoff's first law. It may be written as $E_1 + E_{R1} + E_{R2} = 0$. Note that this holds true no matter how many components there are in the circuit.

Q4-27. Three resistors in series have values of 12K, 18K and 22K. The total resistance is _____.

Q4-28. Two resistors in series with values of 1 Meg and 6.8K give us a total resistance of _____.

Q4-29. The expression for Kirchhoff's law with three series resistors is _____.

Your Answers Should Be:

A4-27. Three resistors in series have values of 12K, 18K, and 22K. The total resistance is 52K.

A4-28. Two resistors in series with values of 1 Meg and 6.8K give us a total resistance of **1006.8K.** This one is a little tricky. To add the resistors they must be in the same units. For example converting both units to ohms you get 1 Meg (1,000,000 ohms) plus 6.8K (6800 ohms) or 1,006,800 ohms. Or, converting the 1 Meg to 1000K you get 1006.8K.

A4-29. The expression for Kirchhoff's law with three series resistors is $E_1 + E_{R1} + E_{R2} + E_{R3} = 0$.

Application—Fig. 4-37 shows a sample calculation applying Ohm's and Kirchhoff's laws. Two equal resistors are shown in series with a 12-volt battery. We wish to find the current in the circuit and the voltage dropped across each of the components. To begin, we know that the current in the circuit is equal to the voltage divided by the total resistance. Therefore, it is necessary to find the total resistance. As per step 1, $R_T = 6$ ohms. Then, in step 2 we may calculate the current to be 2 amperes. To calculate the voltage drops

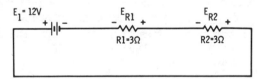

STEP:

1. $R_T = R1 + R2 = 3\Omega + 3\Omega = 6\Omega$

2. $I = \dfrac{E_1}{R_T} = \dfrac{12V}{6\Omega} = 2a$

3. $E_{R1} = I_{R1} \times R1 = 2a \times 3\Omega = 6V$

4. $E_{R2} = I_{R2} \times R2 = 2A \times 3\Omega = 6V$

5. $E_1 = E_{R1} + E_{R2} = 12V = 6V + 6V$

Fig. 4-37. Sample calculation—circuit with two equal series resistors.

we must consider the current through each resistor and its resistance. The current through resistor R1 is called I_{R1}. The voltage across it is calculated as 6 volts in step 3. Step 4 calculates the voltage across R2 as 6 volts also.

This proves something that should be obvious. That is, that two equal resistors in a series circuit will have the same voltage drops. This is due to the fact that the current through them is equal because of the series nature of the circuit. Step 5 shows that Kirchhoff's first law has been satisfied; that is, the sum of the voltages in the circuit must equal the source voltage. Note again that circuits like these can be solved no matter how many components are placed in series. The system will be the same. In the problems below try to find the simplest approach to the solutions.

Q4-30. Complete the table below.

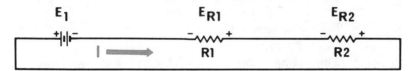

	E_1	I	R1	R2	R_T	E_{R1}	E_{R2}
1	12V	2	4Ω	2Ω	6	8 ✓	4 ✓
2	36V	3a	8Ω	4Ω	12	24 ✓	12 ✓
3	40	2	12Ω	8Ω	20	24	16V
4	100V	5a	12	8	20	60V	40
5	6000	20a	100Ω	200Ω	300	2000	4000

Q4-31. Calculate the total power dissipated and power dissipated across each resistor in problem 3 of Q4-30. $A = 80$ $R1 = $ $R_2 = $

.3 24.2 = 48   16.2 = 32

Your Answers Should Be:
A4-30.

	E_1	I	R1	R2	R_T	E_{R1}	E_{R2}
1	12V	2a	4Ω	2Ω	6Ω	8V	4V
2	36V	3a	8Ω	4Ω	12Ω	24V	12V
3	40V	2a	12Ω	8Ω	20Ω	24V	16V
4	100V	5a	12Ω	8Ω	20Ω	60V	40V
5	6KV	20a	100Ω	200Ω	300Ω	2KV	4KV

Let us examine some of the techniques applied to solve these problems. In problem 1 you find the total resistance, then the current, and finally the voltage across each of the components. In problem 2 the total resistance can be found from the voltage and current. Then the resistance of R1 can be found as well as the voltage drop across each of the components. In problem 3 the key is finding the current in the circuit by using the resistance of R2 and voltage drop across it. Then the voltage drop across R1 may be calculated and thence the total voltage.

In problem 4 the total resistance can be calculated from the applied voltage and current. The voltage drop across R1 and the current may be used to calculate the resistance of R1. The value of R2 may now be found. Using Kirchhoff's law, the value of E_{R2} could have been found immediately. In problem 5 you may find total resistance and, using the current, you may find E_1, E_{R1}, and E_{R2}.

A4-31. Using $P = EI$ we have:

$P_{RT} = E_1 \times I = 40V \times 2A = 80W$
$P_{R1} = E_{R1} \times I = 24V \times 2A = 48W$
$P_{R2} = E_{R2} \times I = 16V \times 2A = 32W$

Notice here that the sum of the power dissipated across each of the resistors is equal to the power applied. This is always true.

Resistors in Parallel

Kirchhoff's Second Law—Now we will consider what happens in a circuit where there is more than one path for current to follow. Such a circuit is called a parallel circuit and it is illustrated in Fig. 4-38. Two resistors are shown connected so that the current will leave the battery and split up at the junction and then pass through each of the resistors. Kirchhoff's second law describes the manner in which

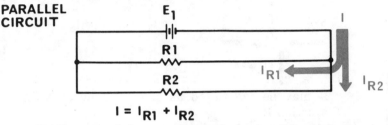

PARALLEL CIRCUIT

$$I = I_{R1} + I_{R2}$$

Fig. 4-38. The sum of the current entering a junction equals the sum of the current leaving a junction.

the current divides. It is very logical and can be readily understood. The sum of the current entering a junction must equal the sum of the current leaving a junction. The equation is shown in the figure. For example, if a current of 5 amperes enters the junction and R1 draws 3 amperes then R2 must draw 2 amperes. Which of these resistors do you suppose has the lowest resistance? It stands to reason that the resistor drawing most current has the least resistance.

Q4-32. Find the missing currents.

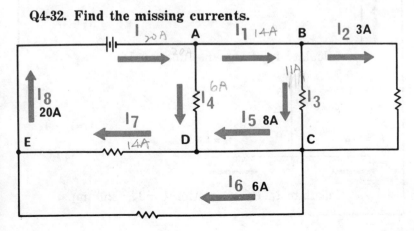

Your Answer Should Be:

A4-32. $I = 20$ amps, $I_1 = 14$ amps, $I_3 = 11$ amps, $I_4 = 6$ amps, $I_7 = 14$ amps. The methods used are described below. Examine the illustration until you find a junction where there is only one unknown current; for example, junction C.

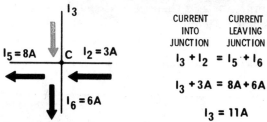

CURRENT INTO JUNCTION	CURRENT LEAVING JUNCTION

$$I_3 + I_2 = I_5 + I_6$$

$$I_3 + 3A = 8A + 6A$$

$$I_3 = 11A$$

I_3 may be calculated as shown. Now consider junction B.

$$I_1 = I_2 + I_3$$

$$I_1 = 3A + 11A = 14A$$

Calculate I_1 as shown. Now junction E.

$$I_8 = I_6 + I_7$$

$$20A = 6A + I_7$$

$$I_7 = 14A$$

Calculate I_7 as shown. Junction D.

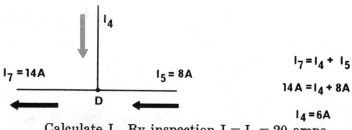

$$I_7 = I_4 + I_5$$

$$14A = I_4 + 8A$$

$$I_4 = 6A$$

Calculate I_4. By inspection $I = I_8 = 20$ amps.

Two-Path Parallel Circuit—Fig. 4-39 shows a sample Ohm's law/Kirchhoff's law calculation for a simple parallel circuit. Step 1 shows a sample observation that the applied voltage is the same as the voltage dropped across each of the resistors. Step 2 uses simple Ohm's law to calculate the current through R1. Step 3 does the same for R2. Step 4 applies Kirchhoff's law to find the total current. Using the total current in Step 5 the total resistance is calculated.

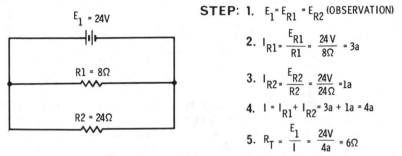

$E_1 = 24V$

$R1 = 8\Omega$

$R2 = 24\Omega$

STEP: 1. $E_1 = E_{R1} = E_{R2}$ (OBSERVATION)

2. $I_{R1} = \dfrac{E_{R1}}{R1} = \dfrac{24V}{8\Omega} = 3a$

3. $I_{R2} = \dfrac{E_{R2}}{R2} = \dfrac{24V}{24\Omega} = 1a$

4. $I = I_{R1} + I_{R2} = 3a + 1a = 4a$

5. $R_T = \dfrac{E_1}{I} = \dfrac{24V}{4a} = 6\Omega$

Fig. 4-39. Sample parallel circuit calculation.

Note that the resistance found in this manner is less than either of the resistors in the circuit. A logical explanation of this can be found if we use our highway analogy once more. Consider a superhighway (a low resistance path for cars) that is paralleled by an old dirt road (a high resistance path for cars). Even though very little traffic will travel the dirt road a few cars will be drained from the super highway thereby serving to reduce the resistance of the system below that of the highway alone. In the same fashion the parallel resistance of the circuit will always be less than the smallest resistor in the parallel system.

Q4-33. Calculate the missing values in the illustration.

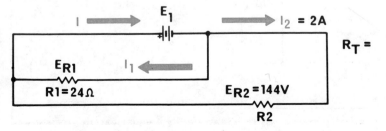

I ⟶ E_1 ⟶ $I_2 = 2A$

$R_T =$

E_{R1} I_1 ⟵

$R1 = 24\Omega$ $E_{R2} = 144V$

$R2$

Your Answer Should Be:

A4-33. Check your method against the illustration below.

STEP:

1. $R2 = \dfrac{E_{R2}}{I_2} = \dfrac{144V}{2A} = 72\,\Omega$

2. $E_1 = E_{R1} = E_{R2} = 144V$

3. $I_1 = \dfrac{E_{R1}}{R1} = \dfrac{144V}{12\,\Omega} = 6A$

4. $I = I_1 + I_2 = 6A + 2A = 8A$

5. $R_T = \dfrac{E_1}{I} = \dfrac{144V}{8A} = 18\,\Omega$

Total Parallel Resistance Calculation—Fig. 4-40 shows the method for calculating the total resistance of two resistors in parallel. The first method shows that the reciprocal

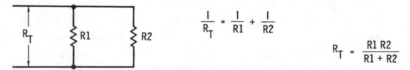

$$\frac{1}{R_T} = \frac{1}{R1} + \frac{1}{R2}$$

$$R_T = \frac{R1\,R2}{R1 + R2}$$

Fig. 4-40. Formula for calculating parallel resistance.

of the total resistance is equal to the sum of the reciprocals of each individual resistance. This formula holds true no matter how many resistors are placed in parallel. The other formula shown is a special formula used to handle only two resistors. Here the total resistance is equal to the product of the resistors divided by the sum of the resistors.

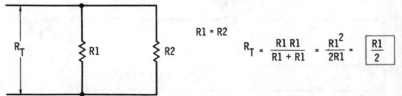

$$R1 = R2$$

$$R_T = \frac{R1\,R1}{R1 + R1} = \frac{R1^2}{2R1} = \boxed{\frac{R1}{2}}$$

Fig. 4-41. Calculating resistance for two equal parallel resistors.

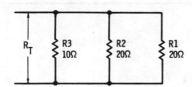

Fig. 4-42. Sample calculation—three resistors in parallel.

Fig. 4-41 shows a special case where the resistors in parallel are equal. By substituting in the equation you find that the total resistance is equivalent to half the value of one of the resistors. If you work out the equation for any number of *parallel equal* resistors you will find that the total resistance will equal the value of one resistor divided by the number of resistors in parallel. A sample calculation is shown in Fig. 4-42. Noting that R1 = R2 we see that value of $R_{R1 + R2} = \frac{R1}{2} = \frac{20}{2} = 10$ ohms. Since this is the same value of resistance as R3, then $R_T = \frac{R3}{2} = \frac{10}{2} = 5$ ohms. Using the following illustration, try calculating the resistances that are missing.

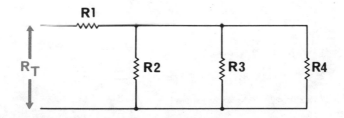

Q4-34. Complete the table below.

	R_T	R1	R2	R3	R4
1		6.8K	33K	33K	33K
2	50K		180K	90K	180K
3	100K		20K	0	20K
4		500Ω	300K	100K	75K
5		4Ω	48Ω	8Ω	48Ω

	R_T	R1	R2	R3	R4
1	17.8K	6.8K	33K	33K	33K
2	50K	5K	180K	90K	180K
3	100K	100K	20K	0	20K
4	38K	500Ω	300K	100K	75K
5	10Ω	4Ω	48Ω	8Ω	48Ω

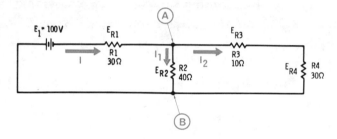

STEP:

1. R3 + R4 = 10 + 30 = 40 OHMS

2. SINCE R2 = R_{3+4}, $R_{A-B} = \frac{R2}{2} = \frac{40}{2} = 20$ OHMS

3. R_T = R1 + R_{A-B} = 50 = 30 + 20 = 50 OHMS

4. $I = \frac{E_1}{R_T} = \frac{100}{50} = 2$ AMPS

5. E_{R1} = IR1 = 2 X 30 = 60 VOLTS

6. E_{RA-B} = E_1 - E_{R1} = 100 - 60 = 40 VOLTS

7. I_{R2} = I_1 = $\frac{E_{R2}}{R2}$ = $\frac{40}{40}$ = 1 AMP

8. I_2 = I - I_1 = 2 - 1 = 1 AMP

9. E_{R3} = I_2 R3 = 1 X 10 = 10

10. E_{R4} = I_2 R4 = 1 X 30 = 30 VOLTS

Fig. 4-43. Sample calculation—series-parallel circuit.

110

Series-Parallel Circuit Calculations—Fig. 4-43 shows a sample calculation for a simple series-parallel circuit. Consider the steps that lead to its solution. First, the series resistance of R3 and R4 is found. Noting that this resistance is the same as R2, the resistance from A to B can be found.

This resistance plus R1 give us the total resistance in the circuit. In step 4 we find the current leaving E_1. Since all of this current passes through R1 we find E_{R1}. Applying Kirchhoff's first law we note that the difference between E_1 and E_{R1} is E_{R2}. Applying Ohm's law we find the current through R2 to be E_{R2} divided by R2. Applying Kirchhoff's second law we find that the current through R3 and R4 is the difference between I and I_1. Then, applying Ohm's law we find the voltage dropped across R3 and R4.

Now try your luck with a similar problem. The following illustration contains the same circuit used in the sample calculation. You are to solve the problems in the order listed below.

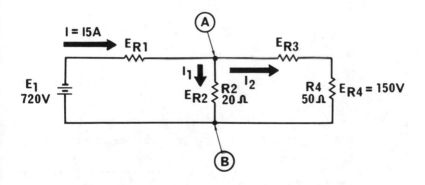

Q4-35. The value of I_2 is _____.

Q4-36. The value of I_1 is _____.

Q4-37. The value of E_{R2} _____.

Q4-38. The value of E_{R3} is _____.

Q4-39. The value of E_{R1} is _____.

Q4-40. The value of R1 is _____.

Your Answers Should Be:

For each of the answers the method is shown in an associated figure.

A4-35. The value of I_2 is **3 amperes.**

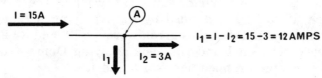

$$I_2 = \frac{E_{R4}}{R4} = \frac{150}{50} = 3 \text{ AMPS}$$

A4-36. The value of I_1 is **12 amperes.**

$I = 15A$

$I_1 = I - I_2 = 15 - 3 = 12 \text{ AMPS}$

I_1 $I_2 = 3A$

A4-37. The value of E_{R2} is **240 volts.**

E_{R2} $I_1 = 12A$ $R2 = 20\,\Omega$ $E_{R2} = I_1 R2 = 12 \times 20 = 240 \text{ VOLTS}$

A4-38. The value of E_{R3} is **90 volts.**

E_{R3} $E_{R3} = E_{R2} - E_{R4} = 240 - 150 = 90 \text{ VOLTS}$

$E_{R2} = 240V$ $E_{R4} = 150V$

A4-39. The value of E_{R1} is **480 volts.**

E_{R1} $E_{R1} = E_1 - E_{R2} = 720 - 240 = 480 \text{ VOLTS}$

E_1 720V $E_{R2} = 240V$

A4-40. The value of R1 is **32 ohms.**

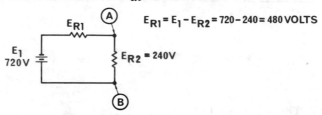

$$R1 = \frac{E_{R1}}{I} = \frac{480}{15} = 32 \text{ OHMS}$$

SEMICONDUCTOR DIODES

Front-to-Back Resistance of a Diode

Fig. 4-44 illustrates the fact that a resistor is a bilateral device. That is, it offers the same resistance to current no matter which direction the current passes through it. A semiconductor diode is a unilateral device. It is constructed

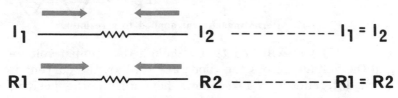

Fig. 4-44. A resistor is a bilateral device.

of materials like germanium and silicon and will be discussed in great detail in the next chapter. Here, however, we will consider only the nature of its resistance. Fig. 4-45 shows how the resistance of the diode depends on the direction of the current. Note how the current passes readily from left to right through this component while almost no

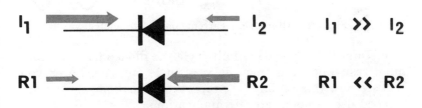

Fig. 4-45. A semiconductor diode is a unilateral device.

current passes from right to left. In a good diode the ratio of the resistance in one direction to the resistance in the other direction (known as front-to-back ratio) may be as high as 100,000 to 1.

Current and Voltage Relationship in a Circuit

When an alternating current is applied to a resistor (Fig. 4-46) the waveforms representing the applied voltage, the current, and the voltage across the resistor are similar. However, when an alternating current is applied to a diode

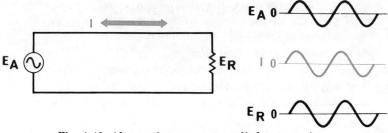

Fig. 4-46. Alternating current applied to a resistor.

(Fig. 4-47) you will find that although the applied voltage and the voltage across the diode are similar, the current is much different. Fig. 4-47 shows how during the positive half-cycle the diode offers little resistance and allows a cur-

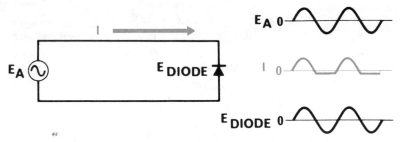

Fig. 4-47. Alternating current applied to a diode.

rent. During the negative half-cycle the diode offers a maximum resistance and there is very little current. Later you will see how this unilateral property of the diode can be put to good use in many circuit applications.

SUMMARY QUESTIONS

1. A simple circuit is composed of a source of voltage, an object to do work on, and a method of delivering the electrical energy.
   a. The object that the work is done on is called the _Load_.
   b. There is no current in a circuit when a switch is _open_.
2. Resistance is the opposition offered to the current in a circuit. It is measured in units called ohms.
   a. When there is a current of 1 ampere through a resistance of 1 ohm the voltage applied is ____1____ volt(s).

b. A variable resistor is called a(an) _POT_____.

c. The value of a resistor whose colors are brown, gray, and green is _1.8 MΩ_.   1   8 00000

d. As current increases power _INCREes_.

3. The relationship between resistance, current, and voltage in a circuit is regulated by Ohm's law.

    a. Ohm's law is stated as the current in a circuit is equal to the _VOLTAGE_____ divided by the _Resis,_____.

    b. The total resistance in a series circuit is equal to the ___SUM___ of the individual resistors.

    c. The sum of the voltages in a series loop is equal to the ___O_____.

    d. The total resistance of four 140K resistors in parallel is _35KΩ_.

    e. The sum of the current entering a junction is equal to the _SUM____ of the currents _leaving_ the junction.

    f. The voltage across two unequal parallel resistors is

    _____.

4. Semiconductor diodes allow current readily in one direction.

    a. The reason for this is that they have a high _____ resistance ratio.

    b. When alternating current is applied to a diode there is _____ current for half of each cycle.

SUMMARY ANSWERS

1a. The object that the work is done on is the **load.**

1b. There is no current in a circuit when a switch is **open.**

2a. When a current of 1 ampere flows through a resistance of 1 ohm the voltage applied is **1** volt.

2b. A variable resistor is called a **potentiometer.**

2c. The value of a resistor whose colors are brown, gray, and green is **1.8 Meg.**

2d. As current increases, power **increases.**

3a. Ohm's law is stated as the current in a circuit is equal to the **voltage** divided by the **resistance.**

3b. The total resistance in a series circuit is equal to the **sum** of the individual resistors.

3c. The sum of the voltages in a series loop is equal to the **applied voltage.** (If "algebraic sum" then equal to zero.)

3d. The total resistance of four 140K resistors in parallel is **35K.**

3e. The sum of the current entering a junction is equal to the **sum** of the currents **leaving** the junction.

3f. The voltage across two unequal parallel resistors is **the same.**

4a. The reason for this is that they have a high **front-to-back** resistance ratio.

4b. When alternating current is applied to a diode there is **almost no** current for half of each cycle.

5

Semiconductor Principles

What You Will Learn

In this chapter you are going to learn another way to tell the difference among insulators, conductors, and semiconductors. You will also study the molecular structure of some of the most widely used semiconductors. Then, you will find out how natural semiconductors can be made to operate more efficiently. Finally, you are going to study some practical applications of semiconductors.

In a previous chapter you learned how to distinguish among conductors, semiconductors, and insulators. Briefly, this distinction was a matter of the current-carrying capabilities. In this chapter, however, you will find that there is another way to distinguish among them—by energy levels. Actually, energy levels account for the difference in current-carrying capacities.

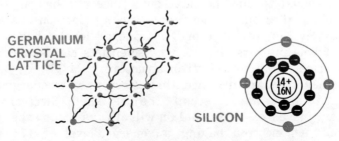

GERMANIUM CRYSTAL LATTICE

SILICON

Fig. 5-1. Molecular structures.

ATOMIC STRUCTURE

We know from Chapter 2 that electrons orbit the atom's nucleus in so-called shells. We also know that these shells have fixed numbers of electrons in them. That is, the first shell always has two electrons; the second, always eight. The third shell may have eighteen or eight (depending on the element) and so on. If we can't see an atom, how do scientists know this to be true?

Energy Levels

Scientific experiments show that the electron must have a certain quantity of energy to exist in a stable orbit in a given shell. This quantity is called the electron's *energy level*. Scientists also know that the energy level occurs in discrete amounts. In Fig. 5-2 the first electron has an energy

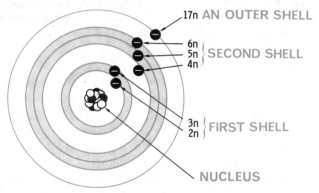

Fig. 5-2. Energy levels in electron shells.

level equal to 2n. The next outer electron has an energy level equal to 3n; the next outer electron has an energy level equal to 4n, and so forth. But, *no* electron has an energy level of, say, 2.5n or 3.5n. Energy levels always differ by whole integers. This is why scientists can so accurately describe the atom's electron structure.

They know for instance, that electrons with energy levels of 2n and 3n always occupy the first shell. Electrons with energy levels of 4n, 5n, and 6n will always occupy the second shell. An electron having an energy level of 17n would occupy a shell quite a distance from the nucleus.

Energy Bands

One of the interesting phenomena which scientists have observed is that energy levels of electrons group themselves into bands when individual atoms are combined into crystals. Valence electrons (those in the outermost shell) have energies that fall in the valence band. Above this is a *forbidden band* (or *energy gap*) and then the *conduction* band. The width of the forbidden band varies with the nature of the material; insulators have wide energy gaps, semiconductors have small gaps, and conductors have conduction and valence bands that overlap.

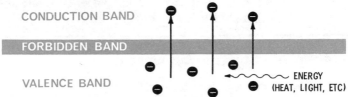

Fig. 5-3. Energy bands.

The concept of energy bands is particularly important in understanding the operation of semiconductors. An electron can exist in either the valence or the conduction band. All that is needed is the addition of the necessary energy to carry it through the forbidden band. For example, an electron in the lower band may suddenly acquire energy from external heat or radiation. It will then appear in the conduction band where it can be used for electric current.

Q5-1. Another method for distinguishing among conductors, insulators, and semiconductors is by _____ _____.

Q5-2. To exist in any shell a(an) _____ must have a certain quantity of energy.

Q5-3. Energy levels always differ by _____ integers.

Q5-4. The energy level that doesn't exist is the _____ band.

Q5-5. Energy levels group together as energy _____.

Q5-6. These energy bands are called _____, _____, and _____.

CRYSTALLINE STRUCTURE

Properties of Crystals

As you know, matter can exist in any of three states: solid, liquid, or gas. In the gas state the atoms or molecules are spread far apart and haphazardly arranged (Fig. 5-4A). In the liquid state they are packed closer together but still arranged haphazardly (Fig. 5-4B). In the solid state they take on an orderly geometric pattern in three dimensions (Fig. 5-4C). This pattern is known as a *crystal lattice*. Atoms are arranged in seven crystal-lattice systems. Semiconductors fall under the *cubic* lattice system.

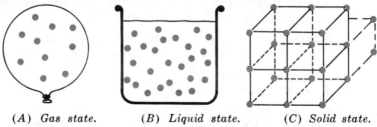

(A) Gas state.   *(B) Liquid state.*   *(C) Solid state.*

Fig. 5-4. Arrangement of atoms in matter.

Definition—A crystal is any solid whose atoms or molecules are arranged in a three-dimensional geometrical pattern. This pattern is called a *lattice* and is composed of single crystal lattice cells.

Unit Cell—A unit cell is the smallest geometrical solid from which the crystal lattice can be generated. It is often quite different from and smaller than the single crystal lattice cell. The geometrical solid is generated by using the smallest number of atoms or molecules.

Face-Centered Cube—A crystal lattice comprises many identical lattice cells going off in three dimensions and held together by atomic binding forces. One such cell is the face-centered cube shown in Fig. 5-5. Each cube face has an atom (A) which is surrounded by 12 other atoms. Copper forms this type of lattice.

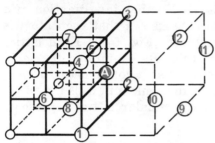

Fig. 5-5. Face-centered cube.   Fig. 5-6. Body-centered cube.

Body-Centered Cube—The body-centered cube contains a single centered atom and is surrounded by eight other atoms (Fig. 5-6). In this case, atom A is less completely surrounded than atom A of the face-centered cube. Silicon and germanium form this type of cubic crystal lattice.

Q5-7. Atoms in gases and liquids are arranged haphazardly, but in solids they are arranged in _____

_____ _____.

Q5-8. In a face-centered cube each face atom is surrounded by _____ atoms.

Q5-9. In a body-centered cube each center atom is surrounded by _____ atoms.

Diatomic Crystal Structure—Further investigation of a semiconductor face-centered cube shows that each atom is associated with four other atoms (Fig. 5-7). Each lattice cell is divided into eight unit cells. By examining the darkened unit cell shown you can see that it contains *two atoms;* that is, it is diatomic. From the diatomic unit cells the entire crystal lattice is formed. This particular lattice represents silicon.

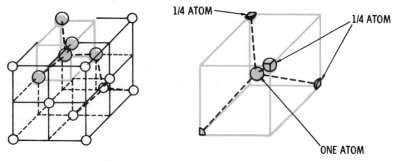

Fig. 5-7. Diatomic crystal structure.

Electrical Characteristics of Crystals

Crystal lattices are held together by electrical binding forces. These forces occur between atoms, molecules, ions, or electrons. Remember that all solids (conductors, semiconductors, and insulators) form into crystals.

Crystal Space Lattice—The crystal lattices you have studied fall under the cubic or regular crystal lattice system. In this space-lattice system the three axes are mutually perpendicular and equal in length and have five points (atoms, ions, or molecules). Other space-lattice systems have their axes at other angles and different lengths, and may have 2, 3, 4, 5, or 7 points involved. Semiconductors and some metals fall under the cubic system. The rest of the metals and all insulators fall under the space-lattice system.

Covalent Lattices—In many crystals, atoms combine with atoms to form the lattice (Fig. 5-8). When two adjacent atoms share an electron, a *covalent bond* is formed. For instance, the silicon atom has four outer shell electrons and shares these with four neighboring silicon atoms. The covalent bond tends to draw the silicon atoms together while the

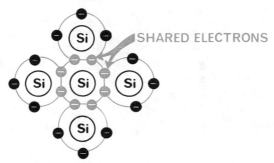

Fig. 5-8. Covalent lattice.

nuclei, being positively charged, tend to repel each other. The forces are balanced to form the crystal lattice and the entire crystal is electrically neutral. Occasionally, a shared electron gains enough energy to free itself and it drifts through the crystal. This kind of covalent lattice binding is typical of semiconductors.

Q5-10. Crystal lattices are held together by electrical binding forces between _____, _____, _____, or _____.

Q5-11. The cubic lattice system is identified by its mutually _____ axes which are _____ in length and have _____ points.

Q5-12. Covalent lattices are held together by _____ which means that two atoms _____ a single _____.

Ionic Lattices—Ions are atoms which have gained or lost electrons. In such a state they are no longer neutral. The common salt (sodium chloride) crystal is made up of such ions. Each sodium (Na) atom gives up its outer electron to a chlorine (Cl) atom. The sodium ions (Na+) become positively charged and tend to repel each other. The chlorine ions (Cl−) become negatively charged and tend to repel each other. But the sodium and chlorine ions are oppositely charged and are drawn to each other. With the ionic forces balanced, the result is the crystal lattice shown in Fig. 5-9. Each sodium ion is surrounded by chlorine ions and vice versa. Because the chlorine ions take on an electron, no free electrons exist in the crystal, hence it is an insulator. This kind of ionic-lattice binding is typical of insulators.

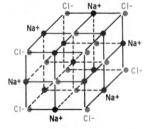

Fig. 5-9. Ionic lattice.

Metallic Crystals—When a large quantity of metallic atoms group together, as in a crystal, their valence (outer shell) electrons can travel about randomly in the metal (Fig. 5-10). These random electrons form an electron cloud around the metal atoms. The cloud, which is negatively charged, surrounds the metal ions (because they have given up an electron and are positively charged) and acts as a cement to hold the crystal lattice structure together. When the electron cloud forms, the tendency to conduct electrons increases. All metallic crystals, in which this electron cloud binding is typical, are good conductors.

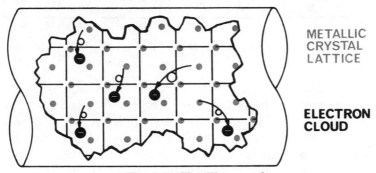

METALLIC
CRYSTAL
LATTICE

**ELECTRON
CLOUD**

Fig. 5-10. Metallic crystal.

Molecular Lattices—The unit points in the crystal lattices of compounds are atoms and not molecules. In all these solid compounds, atoms of one element do not merge with atoms of the other element. Instead, these elements are arranged in the space lattice to comprise a molecule (Fig. 5-11). Only in the vapor state do the elements actually merge, as shown with salt.

Crystalline Electric Field—The crystal electric field is actually an electrostatic field inside the crystal that holds it together. Ions, covalent bonds, or electron clouds are responsible for it. Remember that the overall crystal is electrically neutral; that is, neither positive nor negative.

(A) *Solid molecule.*   (B) *Vapor molecule.*

Fig. 5-11. Molecular lattice.

Q5-13. Ionic lattices have _____ free electrons.
Q5-14. Metallic crystals are held together by _____ _____.

TYPES OF SEMICONDUCTOR MATERIALS

Germanium

Germanium is one of the most frequently used semiconductor materials. It has an atomic weight of 73 and its outer ring contains four valence electrons. In its pure state germanium forms a single crystal structure. This means its crystal lattice is uniform and not varied as in polycrystalline materials which may have several crystal lattice systems.

Lattice Structure—The cubic lattice structure shown in Fig. 5-12 is the typical body-centered lattice cell with a diatomic unit cell. Each center germanium atom is associated with four surrounding atoms. The atoms are held together by covalent bonds and the crystal is at best only a fair conductor. Many millions of identical unit cells form the germanium crystal.

Conductivity—Because every atom in the crystal is bonded to four others, the electrons are not free to move

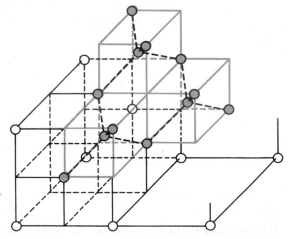

Fig. 5-12. Cubic lattice structure.

about in the crystal. This produces an electrically neutral substance. The entire crystal conducts poorly; only high electrical pressure or high thermal energy will cause a few electrons to move.

Silicon

Silicon is used as often as germanium for electronic purposes. It has an atomic weight of 14 and, like germanium, has four valence electrons. In its pure state, silicon has a single crystal structure. Its space lattice is identical with that of germanium while its conductivity slightly exceeds that of germanium.

Carbon

Fig. 5-13 shows several atoms of carbon. This element is tetravalent; that is, it has four valence electrons. It, too, has a uniform crystal structure like that of germanium and silicon.

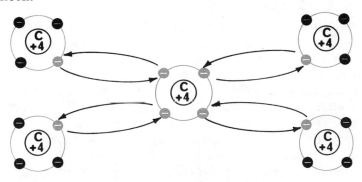

Fig. 5-13. Carbon lattice.

Q5-15. Germanium and silicon have a _____ crystal structure.

Q5-16. Both germanium and silicon are semiconductors because in the pure state they _____ poorly.

INTRINSIC CRYSTALS

The crystals we have been examining are ideal crystals; that is, they are pure. They probably never exist in nature in such a state. Ideal crystals, or *uncontaminated* crystals, are described as *intrinsic*. The manufacture of intrinsic germanium or silicon is the first step in the making of semiconductor devices such as transistors, diodes, and microelectronic circuits.

Free Electrons in Intrinsic Crystals

Earlier we learned that the current or conductivity in semiconductor crystals is poor to fair. This applies to the nearly pure crystals found in the natural state. Why is this so? Let's go back to our study of energy bands to find the reason. Remember that the energy level of the electrons in the valence band is much lower than that of the conduction band. The covalent bonds in the crystal extend out of the valence band, not the conduction band. This is why conduction is so poor. In order to free electrons, energy must be imparted to them (Fig. 5-14). This energy moves them out of the valence band and into the conduction band.

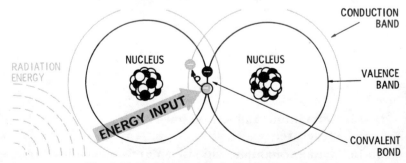

Fig. 5-14. Free electrons in intrinsic crystals.

Electron Flow in Intrinsic Germanium

Suppose we look at a particular type of crystal, like germanium, in its intrinsic state. We can assume that it has free electrons within its boundaries. These, of course, have been liberated very much as we have described. If we place a potential across this crystal we will find that an electrical current is generated but it is quite low. Remember that in metallic crystals the electron cloud essentially supplied the free electrons for current. This was so because these electrons had attained sufficient energy levels to exist in the conduction band. In semiconductor crystals, however, that is not so. Therefore, current depends on the randomly freed electrons only, and not on the valence electrons. Because the forbidden band is much smaller for semiconductors than it is for insulators, stray thermal energy or radiation often causes electrons to jump the gap into the conduction band.

Note in Fig. 5-15 how electrons flow. Thermal energy has released an electron in position 1. An electron from position 2 fills the hole left by the first electron. The one from position 3 fills the hole at position 2, and finally the electron from position 4 fills the number 3 position hole. Electrons have drifted from 4 to 3 to 2 to 1.

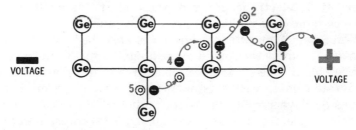

Fig. 5-15. Electron flow in intrinsic germanium.

Q5-17. Crystals without impurities are described as _____.

Q5-18. Free electrons can exist in intrinsic crystals if they absorb enough energy to move them into the _____ _____.

Q5-19. Electrons flow in intrinsic germanium when they move into _____ vacated by preceding electrons.

HOLES IN SEMICONDUCTORS

Concept of the Hole

To know how semiconductors work you must understand the concept of hole flow. For a moment, therefore, let us leave crystals and again examine a single germanium atom. You can consider the atom to be made of a nucleus and a shell of energy. For our purposes this shell may be regarded as the valence band (Fig. 5-16).

The nucleus contains 32 protons. As you know the positive effect of these 32 protons is balanced by the negative effect of 32 electrons. Four of these electrons exist in the valence band and make up the valence energy shell.

When sufficient external energy is absorbed by a valence electron it jumps the forbidden band and appears in the conduction band. The electron becomes free to move and it is no longer associated with this particular atom. The atom is left with a positive surplus due to its having one or more protons more than electrons. This *positive surplus*, represented by a missing electron, is a *hole*.

The hole in essence, may be considered a positive electron, even though it has no physical existence. It will move toward

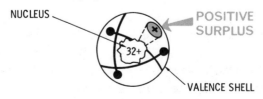

Fig. 5-16. Concept of the hole.

a negative polarity, and it will repel other holes. It is considered to have the same mass as an electron, and consequently it travels at the same velocity. A flow of holes is a flow of positive electricity.

Hole Flow in Intrinsic Germanium

Let us now return to the intrinsic germanium crystal to see how holes flow. Remember, a potential has been applied. When external energy knocked the electron out of position 1 a hole was created. A subsequent electron filled this hole (unlikes attract), but a hole appeared in position 2 from whence the electron came. This hole in turn was filled by an electron from position 3 where a new hole formed. Fig. 5-17 shows that the hole has drifted from position 1 to 2 to

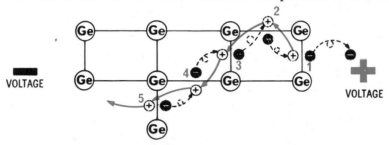

Fig. 5-17. Hole flow in intrinsic germanium.

3 to 4 to 5. Notice how the hole flows (drifts) from the positive toward the negative voltage. This is similar to the way the electron flows except that the latter flows from a negative to a positive voltage.

Q5-20. When an electron leaves the valence band a _____ is produced in the valence shell.

Q5-21. This hole has a(an) _____ electrical effect.

Q5-22. Holes may be considered positive _____.

Q5-23. Holes flow toward a _____ potential.

SEMICONDUCTOR MATERIALS

Impurities

The semiconductor crystals which we have studied are basically neutral electrically. They have no free electrons as in the case of metallic crystals. Only when external energy penetrates the lattice do electrons break free, but their number is comparatively small. Even with a large amount of thermal energy and a high potential applied, their current yield is quite low.

If certain elements are added to them, crystals can be made to pass higher currents. These additives are called impurities. The process of adding impurities to semiconductor crystals is called *doping*. There are two types of impurities. One produces free electrons, and the other produces holes. The electron-producing impurity is known as an N-type (negative) impurity and the hole-producing impurity is known as a P-type (positive) impurity.

N-Type Germanium

Look at the germanium (Ge) crystal (Fig. 5-18) which has been doped with arsenic (As). Arsenic is pentavalent, which means it has five valence electrons. You know that cubic germanium crystals are formed of body-centered cells. Each germanium atom therefore associates with four surrounding atoms. However, in the doping process the arsenic

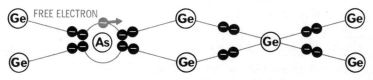

Fig. 5-18. N-type germanium crystal lattice.

atoms substitute for some of the body-centered germanium atoms. The arsenic atom joins in covalent bonds with its four neighboring germanium atoms. However, one electron remains unpaired. Sufficient thermal energy exists at room temperature to raise the electron's energy level to place it in the conduction band. Thus, it becomes free to produce current.

Donors and Majority Carriers

In the preceding example the arsenic donated an electron. The arsenic atom is called a *donor*. The entire germanium crystal is N-type, because it has a surplus of electrons to carry current. For this reason the electrons are called *majority carriers* in N-type germanium.

In the natural state, intrinsic germanium might contain one impurity atom for every 100 million germanium atoms. When it is doped, the germanium crystal might contain one donor atom for every 10 million germanium atoms. So you can see that the donor accounts for ten times the number of majority carriers that exist in the intrinsic state.

You should remember that the process of making and filling holes still goes on to produce current. Of course, their contribution is but a tiny portion of the overall current. Fig. 5-19 shows the composite effect of all the current due to the separate effects of the carriers. Note that in the case of N-type germanium, holes are the minority carriers.

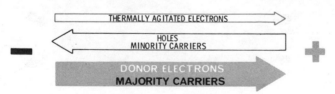

Fig. 5-19. Carriers in N-type germanium.

Q5-24. Elements added to semiconductor crystals to produce more current are called _____.

Q5-25. This process is called _____.

Q5-26. Arsenic in a germanium matrix supplies a _____ _____.

Q5-27. Doped germanium crystals with excess free electrons are called _____ crystals.

P-Type Germanium

You have just learned how arsenic makes a germanium crystal become an N type. Now, let us see how it can be doped to become a P type. This time we will dope the germanium matrix with an impurity called indium (In). This element is trivalent, that is, it has three valence electrons. Since germanium crystals form body-centered cell cubes, we find that the indium atoms substitute for some of the body-

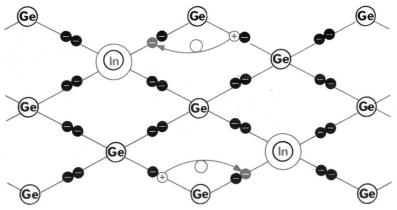

Fig. 5-20. P-type germanium crystal lattice.

centered germanium atoms. With the remaining atoms, indium forms a covalent bond by robbing an electron from the covalent pair in the next body-centered cell (Fig. 5-20). You will note that the indium now becomes completely covalent, and that the germanium is now left without an electron to form a covalent bond. This is called a *hole*. This is an unstable condition which prevails throughout the crystal.

Acceptors and Majority Carriers

In the preceding example the indium accepted an electron. The indium atom is called an *acceptor*. The entire germanium crystal is the P type, because it has a surplus of holes to carry current. For this reason these holes are called *majority carriers*.

Again, the process of making and filling holes continues to be a source of current. As in N-type crystals, the contribution to the overall current is small. Fig. 5-21 shows the composite effect of all the current due to the separate carriers. Note that in the case of P-type germanium, electrons are the minority carriers.

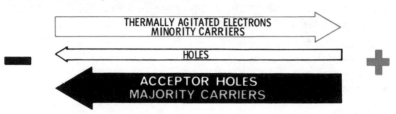

Fig. 5-21. Carriers in P-type germanium.

Q5-28. Indium in a germanium matrix robs electrons from covalent bonds to form _____ in the crystal.

Q5-29. A doped germanium crystal with an excess of free holes is known as a(an) _____-type crystal.

Q5-30. Indium is a (an) _____-type impurity.

Q5-31. The majority carriers in P-type germanium crystals are _____.

P-N JUNCTION

Although N-type germanium has an excess of free electrons, this crystal is still electrically neutral. This is so because every free electron has a corresponding positively charged atom to balance it. Also, P-type germanium crystals remain electrically neutral because excess holes are exactly balanced by the electrons which they rob.

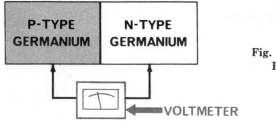

Fig. 5-22. Voltage at P-N junction.

It would seem that if you joined pieces of P-type and N-type germanium all the holes and electrons would pair up. As a result the P-N junction would simply revert to a neutral plane. But this does not happen. Instead, we find a tiny voltage in the order of a few tenths of a volt existing at the P-N junction (Fig. 5-22).

Junction Field

Let us see why this tiny voltage exists. A hole in the P type tries to diffuse into the N type. Electrons in the N type try to cross into the P type. Some holes and electrons actually pair up, but most of them encounter a barrier. This junction barrier is created by two fields.

136

One field is caused by the array of donor atoms which exist very close to the P-N junction. It has positive polarity and therefore tends to repel any hole that tries to diffuse into the N-type region. The other field is caused by the acceptor atoms near the P-N junction. This field exhibits negative polarity, and it tends to repel any electron that tries to cross into the P-type region. In essence, these fields are two poles of a battery—the donor atom layer being the positive pole and the acceptor atoms being the negative pole (Fig. 5-23). This is why the tiny voltage can be measured at the P-N junction.

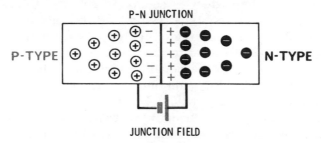

Fig. 5-23. Charge distribution at P-N junction.

The curves in Fig. 5-24 show the energy required for carriers to penetrate the junction field. Notice that for an N-type electron to diffuse into the P-type region it must absorb enough energy to buck the junction field battery. These are potential hills.

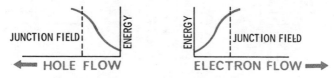

Fig. 5-24. Potential hill curves for carriers.

Q5-31. A P-N junction is evident because a tiny _____ can be measured across it.

Q5-32. Holes cannot cross into the N-type region because they are repelled by the junction _____ atoms.

Reverse Bias

What happens if we connect a battery across a P-N junction? Suppose the battery is connected so that its positive terminal contacts the N-type region, and its negative terminal contacts the P-type region (Fig. 5-25). Immediately, the electrons are attracted to the positive terminal, and the holes are attracted to the negative terminal. The effect of this is to deplete the P-N junction of carriers.

Consider the N-type region. Do you remember that we said the crystal was electrically neutral? But, if electrons are drawn from this region an electrical imbalance occurs. As a result the N-type region tends to become positive, because there are more donor atoms than electrons. Now look at the P-type region. The drawing away of holes from this crystal causes an overly negative effect. This is because more acceptor atoms exist than holes.

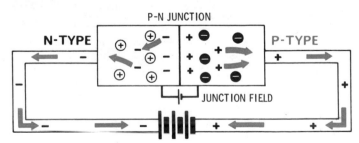

Fig. 5-25. Reverse biasing.

The increased negative effect in the P-type region repels electrons more vigorously than before. The increased positive effect in the N-type region repels holes with more vigor. This, in effect, produces a wider junction field, and current drops virtually to zero. This effect is called reverse biasing.

Forward Bias

If we reverse the battery leads, what will occur? Immediately electrons are repelled into the N-type region from the battery negative terminal, and the holes are repelled into the P-type region (Fig. 5-26). This adds energy to the electrons and holes. The absorbed energy is more than enough to surmount the potential hills. Therefore, holes and electrons combine quite readily at the P-N junction. The junction field vanishes.

Because there exists a surplus of electrons in the N-type region and because the battery positive terminal attracts them, electrons flow heavily. This way of connecting the battery to the P-N junction is known as forward biasing.

Actually, current is developed by mass hole-electron recombination. You can see this going on at the P-N junction as well as the battery positive terminal.

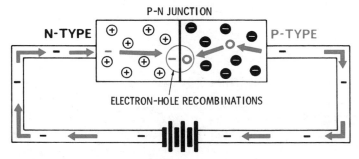

Fig. 5-26. Forward biasing.

Q5-33. When a battery connected across a P-N junction causes virtually zero current, we say that the junction is _____-_____.

Q5-34. When a battery connected across a P-N junction causes high current, we say that the junction is _____-_____.

Diodes

The unusual characteristics of the P-N junction make it useful in electronics. We use it as a diode rectifier. The electronic symbol is shown in Fig. 5-27. Notice the electron-flow direction. The cathode is the N-type material, because it is the source of electrons. The anode is the P-type material, because it is the destination of the electrons.

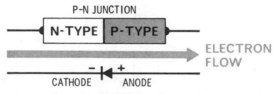

Fig. 5-27. The diode.

Remember that current generation is a matter of recombination. In the N-type region (the cathode) electrons are the majority carriers. In the P-type region (the anode) holes are the majority carriers. The absence of the junction field due to forward biasing allows the majority carriers to recombine. This is a continuous process—the battery negative terminal supplying electrons; the battery positive terminal supplying the holes.

Diodes have limitations, such as temperature. As temperature rises, resistance to current drops (negative temperature coefficient), even when the diode is reverse-biased. Current naturally depends on applied voltage. When this voltage overcomes the junction field voltage the diode acts like a conductor. When it is reverse-biased, the diode exhibits resistance but it can break down if the applied voltage is too great.

RECTIFIERS

Half-Wave Rectifier

One of the most important uses to which diodes are put is rectification. Rectification simply means changing alternating current to direct current. The diode provides this kind of current (Fig. 5-28). If, instead of a battery, an a-c generator is placed across a diode, the generator forward-biases and reverse-biases the diode at the generator frequency. When the generator voltage is positive, as in 1, the

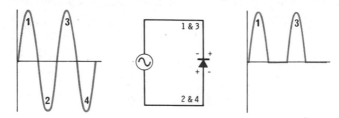

Fig. 5-28. Half-wave rectification.

diode is forward-biased and it conducts. Therefore, it puts out current which rises and falls in the same manner as the applied voltage. When the generator voltage goes negative, as in 2, it reverse-biases the diode; hence, no current. The result is a pulsating direct current every half cycle.

In Fig. 5-29 is a typical rectifier circuit. A transformer (about which you will learn in the next chapter) replaces the a-c generator. A load resistor has been added. The operating principles are identical. When point A voltage goes negative, point B is positive. This forward-biases the diode and there is current through the resistor. When the voltage reverses the diode cuts off.

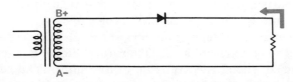

Fig. 5-29. Half-wave rectifier circuit.

Q5-35. When a-c voltage _Forward_ -biases a diode, there is current.

141

Full-Wave Rectifier

Another commonly used circuit which includes diodes is
the full-wave rectifier. In Fig. 5-30 an a-c generator has a
diode connected to each output lead. It also has a ground
line. Two load resistors have been added to complete the
circuit to ground.

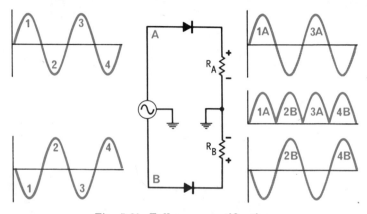

Fig. 5-30. Full-wave rectification.

When generator lead voltage A goes positive as in 1, diode
A forward-biases, and it allows electrons to flow through
its load resistor to ground, and from there back to the generator. The current through the resistor for this half cycle
is as shown as 1A. At the same time, generator B lead voltage is negative, and reverse-biases diode B to prevent electron flow through it for this half cycle.

When lead A voltage goes negative, B-lead voltage is
positive by comparison at 2. Therefore diode B forward-
biases and conducts. Electrons flow through its load resistor
to ground and back to the generator for this half cycle, as
to 2B. At the same time, diode A is reverse-biased, preventing electron flow through it for this half cycle. The sum of
the output across both load resistors is a series of half-cycle

width positive pulses of unidirectional current. This repeats for the next cycle. Note that each half-cycle, whether positive or negative, results in a positive output pulse. For this reason the circuit is called a *full-wave rectifier*.

Full-Wave Rectifier Application

Fig. 5-31 shows a practical application of this circuit. Generally, it is used as a d-c power supply. You will notice that the generator has been replaced by a transformer. However, its operation, as far as this circuit is concerned, is the same as we have described before. The load resistor is in the transformer center-tap line. The current or load is depicted by the positive d-c pulses.

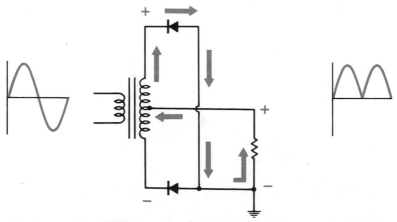

Fig. 5-31. D-c power supply.

If the load resistance varies, the load will vary in accordance with Ohm's law. For example, if a d-c power supply puts out 12 volts across a load resistor of 8 ohms, the current is found by using Ohm's law:

$$I = \frac{E}{R} \text{ or } \frac{12 \text{ volts}}{8 \text{ ohms}} = 1.5 \text{ amperes}$$

If the load resistance is changed to 12 ohms, the load becomes 1 ampere.

SUMMARY QUESTIONS

1. Energy level is another way scientists distinguish among conductors, insulators, and semiconductors.
   a. To exist in any shell, an _____ must have a certain quantity of energy.
   b. Energy levels are arranged in three bands: _____, _____, and _____.
   c. Electrons _____ exist in the forbidden band.
   d. Energy levels always differ by whole _____.

2. In a face-centered cubic lattice each face atom is surrounded by atoms.
   a. Covalent lattices are held together by _____ _____ which means that two atoms _____ a single electron.
   b. Metal crystals have many _____ electrons in the electron cloud.
   c. Germanium and silicon have _____ crystal structures.
   d. Both are semiconductors because in the pure state they conduct _____.

3. Electrons flow in intrinsic germanium when they move into holes vacated by preceding electrons.
   a. When an electron leaves the valence band, a _____ is produced in the valence shell.
   b. Holes may be considered _____ electrons.
   c. Certain elements added to semiconductor crystals to produce more current are called _____.
   d. A doped germanium crystal with an excess of free holes is known as _____ germanium.

4. A P-N junction is evident because a tiny voltage can be measured across it.
   a. When a battery connected across a P-N junction causes virtually zero current, we say that the junction is _Reverse Biased_
   b. When a battery connected across a P-N junction causes a high current we say that the junction is _forward biased_.
   c. Forward biasing is really a mass electron-hole _recombination_.

5. The rectifier circuit is a practical application of diodes.
   a. Diodes change _Alternating_ current to _Direct_ current in rectifier circuits.
   b. A half-wave rectifier gives direct current on every _other_ _half_ cycle.
   c. A full wave rectifier gives direct current on _every_ half cycle.

SUMMARY ANSWERS

1a. To exist in any shell an **electron** must have a certain quantity of energy.

1b. Energy levels are arranged in three bands: **valence, forbidden,** and **conduction.**

1c. Electrons **cannot** exist in the forbidden band.

1d. Energy levels always differ by whole **integers.**

2a. Covalent lattices are held together by **covalent bonds** which means that two atoms **share** a single electron.

2b. Metal crystals have many **free** electrons in the electron cloud.

2c. Germanium and silicon have **single** crystal structures.

2d. Both are semiconductors because in the pure state they conduct **poorly.**

3a. When an electron leaves the valence band a **hole** is produced in the valence shell.

3b. Holes may be considered **positive** electrons.

3c. Certain elements added to semiconductor crystals to produce more current are called **impurities.**

3d. A doped germanium crystal with an excess of free holes is known as **P-type** germanium.

4a. When a battery connected across a P-N junction causes virtually zero current, we say that the junction is **reverse-biased.**

4b. When a battery connected across a P-N junction causes a high current we say the junction is **forward-biased.**

4c. Forward biasing is really a mass electron-hole **recombination.**

5a. Diodes change **alternating** current to **direct** current in rectifier circuits.

5b. A half-wave rectifier gives direct current on every **other half** cycle.

5c. A full-wave rectifier gives direct current on **every** half cycle.

6

Inductance and Capacitance in A-C Circuits

What You Will Learn

In this chapter you will learn about inductance and capacitance and how components having these electrical characteristics act in alternating-current circuits. Inductance is one of the most important properties in electrical and electronic circuits. Relays, coils, transformers, and many other devices depend on inductance for their operation. Capacitance, which blocks direct current but passes alternating current is also widely used in electrical and electronic circuits.

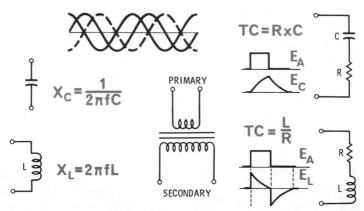

Fig. 6-1. Inductance and capacitance.

CURRENT AND MAGNETIC FIELD
IN A CONDUCTOR

When there is current through a conductor, a magnetic field builds up around the conductor. As shown in Fig. 6-2, when the magnetic field builds up, its expanding lines of force cut the conductor and generate a voltage that opposes the increasing current. After the initial surge the current

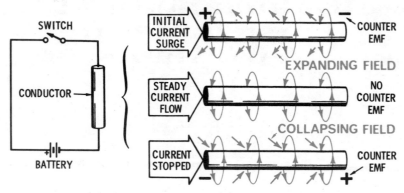

Fig. 6-2. Magnetic field in a d-c circuit.

is steady and the magnetic field is constant. Therefore, there is no counter emf generated. When the switch is opened the current stops.

This opposing voltage or *counter emf* is generated only when the current is changing. In a d-c circuit, current is changing only when the switch is either opened or closed. Therefore, the counter emf in a d-c circuit can be ignored.

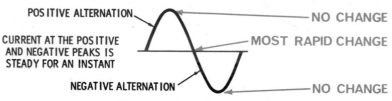

Fig. 6-3. Alternating current.

Fig. 6-3 shows that an alternating current is constantly changing. Consequently, the opposing voltage or counter emf generated by the constantly changing magnetic field is always present.

148

Relationship Between Applied Voltage, Current, and Counter EMF

Fig. 6-4 shows that when there is a sine wave of current through a conductor, the current is continually changing. At point A, the current is changing at its fastest rate; therefore the counter emf, trying to keep the current from increasing is at its negative peak. At point B, the current is at its positive peak and is not changing; the counter emf is at zero. At point C the current is decreasing at its maximum rate; the counter emf, trying to keep the current from decreasing, reaches its positive peak. At point D the current is at its negative peak; the counter emf is at zero.

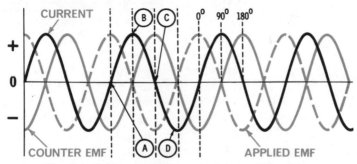

Fig. 6-4. Voltage and current phase relationships.

The following relationships exist:

1. The applied emf is 180 degrees out of phase with the induced emf. The counter emf reaches its maximum a half-cycle later than the applied emf.
2. The current lags the applied emf by 90 degrees, but leads the counter emf by 90 degrees. That is, the current reaches its maximum one quarter-cycle after the applied emf and one quarter-cycle before the counter emf.

Q6-1. The voltage generated by an expanding magnetic field is called a _Counter_ _emf_.

Q6-2. The counter emf is generated only when current is _changing_.

Q6-3. The counter emf is _180_ degrees out of phase with the applied emf.

INDUCTANCE

Inductance is the property of a circuit or component to oppose any change in the current through it. In a d-c circuit, inductance has an effect only when the direct current starts, and when attempts are made to stop it. In a-c circuits, though, the voltage is constantly changing and inductance constantly acts to retard the change in current.

All conductors have some inductance. Straight wires have very small amounts, but the *inductor* or coil has much more. The coil or inductor therefore is the component used in electronic circuits to exhibit the property of opposing a change in current. Since it serves to stop or "choke" the flow of current, it is often called a *choke.*

Symbols and Unit of Measurement

The symbols used on schematic diagrams to represent the inductor are shown in Fig. 6-5. Also shown in Fig. 6-5 is the letter L that is used to represent inductance both on schematic diagrams and in inductance formulas.

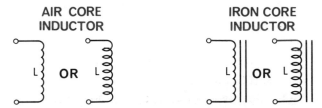

L = INDUCTANCE

Fig. 6-5. Symbols for inductance.

The unit of measurement of inductance is the *henry*. A coil is said to have an inductance of 1 henry if a current through it, changing at a rate of 1 ampere per second, produces a counter emf of 1 volt. Fig. 6-6 shows that as current increases at a rate of 1 ampere per second, a counter emf of 1 volt is generated and opposes the increase in current. As the current decreases at the same rate, a counter emf of 1 volt of the opposite polarity is generated which will tend to sustain the current. The counter emf is constantly trying to oppose any change in current.

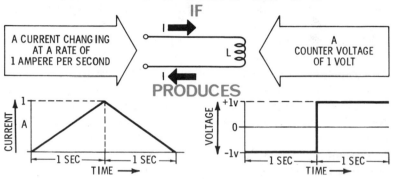

Fig. 6-6. Unit of measurement for inductance.

One henry is a very large value of inductance and will rarely be found in electronic circuits. Inductances with values in millihenrys (mh) and microhenrys (μh) are more commonly encountered in electronic equipment.

Q6-4. Inductance opposes a change in _____ in an alternating-current circuit.

Q6-5. The component that exhibits the property of inductance is the _____ or _____.

Q6-6. The unit of measurement of inductance is the _____, but the more commonly used values of inductance are _____ and _____.

Your Answers Should Be:

A6-4. Inductance opposes a change in **current** in an alternating-current circuit.

A6-5. The component that exhibits the property of inductance is the **inductor** or **coil.**

A6-6. The unit of measurement of inductance is the **henry,** but the more commonly used values of inductance are **millihenry** and **microhenry.**

FACTORS DETERMINING INDUCTANCE VALUE

Several factors determine the amount of inductance in a coil. The three most important factors are the number of turns or coil windings, the coil diameter, and the core material.

Number of Turns—The inductance of a coil is proportional to the square of the number of its turns. Fig. 6-7 shows that if one coil has twice the number of turns as another, it will have four times as much inductance; if it has three times as many turns it will have nine times as much inductance.

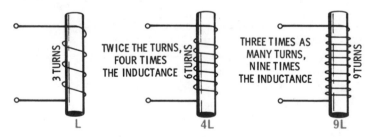

INCREASING TURNS INCREASES "L"

Fig. 6-7. Number of turns.

Coil Diameter—The larger the diameter of the coil, the more inductance it will have. Fig. 6-8 shows that if the diameter of one coil is twice the diameter of another, it will have twice the inductance value.

Core Material—A coil wound on an iron core or rod will have much more inductance than an air-core coil. Fig. 6-9

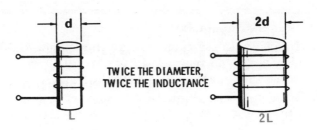

TWICE THE DIAMETER,
TWICE THE INDUCTANCE

L

2d

2L

INCREASING DIAMETER INCREASES "L"
Fig. 6-8. Coil diameter.

shows that the iron-core coil has a greater value of induc-tance than an air-core coil of the same diameter and the same number of turns. The iron core can sustain a much greater magnetic field than air, consequently it can produce a greater inductance value. It should be noted that there is no direct ratio of increase in inductance when the iron core is added as is the case with the number of turns and the coil diameter.

AIR CORE   **IRON CORE**

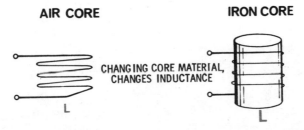

CHANGING CORE MATERIAL,
CHANGES INDUCTANCE

L

L

CHANGING CORE FROM AIR TO IRON INCREASES "L"
Fig. 6-9. Core material.

Q6-7. If a coil with ten turns has an inductance of 100 millihenrys, an increase to twenty turns will in-crease the inductance to _____ millihenrys.

Q6-8. If a coil with a diameter of one inch has an in-ductance of 800 millihenrys, a decrease to one-quarter inch will decrease the inductance to _____ millihenrys.

Q6-9. An air-core coil will have a _____ value of inductance than an iron-core coil.

PHASE RELATIONSHIP IN AN INDUCTIVE CIRCUIT

The phase relationship between the voltage applied to a circuit and the current through the circuit indicates the time interval that elapses before the applied voltage produces a current.

Resistive Circuit

If a sine-wave voltage is applied across a resistor as shown in Fig. 6-10, the current through the resistor is also a sine wave. At every instant of the voltage sine wave, the current is determined by Ohm's law and equals E/R. The two sine waves, voltage and current, are exactly in step with each other, or *in phase*. In a resistive circuit current and voltage are always in phase.

Inductive Circuit

As explained earlier, inductance opposes any change in current. The sine wave of a-c voltage is continuously changing, therefore it is trying to change the direction of the

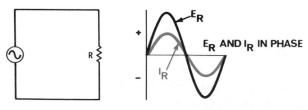

Fig. 6-10. Voltage-current phase relationship in resistive circuit.

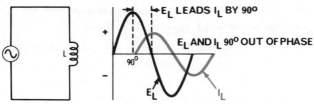

Fig. 6-11. Voltage-current phase relationship in inductive circuit.

current through an inductance. This means that inductance acts continuously to oppose any change in current when a sine wave of a-c voltage is applied. This inductive effect results in a current wave that is delayed after the applied voltage wave, as shown in Fig. 6-11. The current wave *lags* the voltage wave by exactly 90 degrees in an inductive circuit, or by one-quarter of the period of the sine wave. That is, the voltage reaches its peak 90 degrees before the current does. The two waveforms are *out of phase* by 90 degrees.

Vector Analysis

Fig. 6-12 shows the vector relationships between current and voltage in both resistive and inductive circuits. In the resistive circuit (Fig. 6-12A), it can be seen that current and voltage are in phase. In the inductive circuit (Fig. 6-12B), the current vector is 90 degrees behind the voltage vector. The length of each vector represents its magnitude.

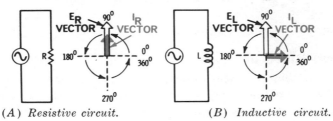

(A) *Resistive circuit.*   (B) *Inductive circuit.*

Fig. 6-12. Vector analysis.

Q6-10. The current sine wave in a resistive circuit is _____ _____ with the voltage sine wave.

Q6-11. The current sine wave in an inductive circuit _____ the voltage sine wave.

Q6-12. The current wave lags the voltage wave in an inductive circuit by _____ degrees.

155

SERIES, PARALLEL, AND SERIES-PARALLEL CONNECTED INDUCTORS

Series Inductive Circuit

When two or more inductors are connected in series, as shown in Fig. 6-13, the total value of inductance is determined by simply adding the individual inductance values. The formula for determining total inductance, it should be noted, is the same as that for determining total resistance in a series circuit.

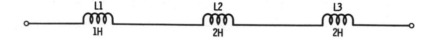

$$L_T = L1 + L2 + L3 = 1H + 2H + 2H = 5H$$

Fig. 6-13. Inductance for inductors in series.

Parallel Inductive Circuit

When two or more inductors are connected in parallel, formulas for determining total inductance are the same as those used for determining total resistance.

When two inductors are of unequal value the *product over sum* method is used, as shown in Fig. 6-14B. For inductors of equal value the method which is shown in Fig. 6-14C is used.

Series-Parallel Inductive Circuit

Fig. 6-15 shows the method used to determine total inductance in a series-parallel inductive circuit.

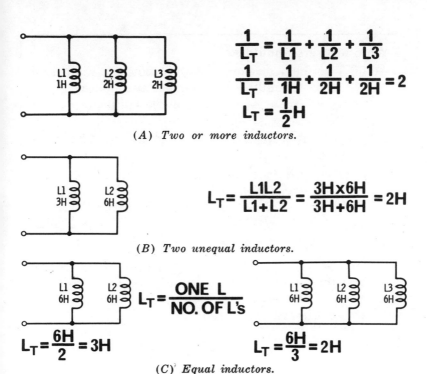

$$\frac{1}{L_T} = \frac{1}{L1} + \frac{1}{L2} + \frac{1}{L3}$$

$$\frac{1}{L_T} = \frac{1}{1H} + \frac{1}{2H} + \frac{1}{2H} = 2$$

$$L_T = \frac{1}{2}H$$

(A) *Two or more inductors.*

$$L_T = \frac{L1L2}{L1+L2} = \frac{3H \times 6H}{3H+6H} = 2H$$

(B) *Two unequal inductors.*

$$L_T = \frac{ONE\ L}{NO.\ OF\ L's}$$

$$L_T = \frac{6H}{2} = 3H$$

$$L_T = \frac{6H}{3} = 2H$$

(C) *Equal inductors.*

Fig. 6-14. Inductance for inductors in parallel.

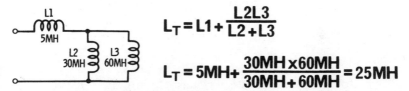

$$L_T = L1 + \frac{L2L3}{L2+L3}$$

$$L_T = 5MH + \frac{30MH \times 60MH}{30MH + 60MH} = 25MH$$

Fig. 6-15. Inductance for series-parallel inductors.

Q6-13. Two inductors, one 350 millihenrys and the other 250 millihenrys, connected in series have a total inductance value of _____ millihenrys.

Q6-14. Two inductors of 500 millihenrys connected in parallel have a total inductance of _____ millihenrys.

Q6-15. The total inductance of two parallel-connected inductors is always _____ than the inductor with the lowest value.

INDUCTIVE REACTANCE

The opposition of a resistor to current in a circuit is called resistance and is measured in ohms. The opposition of an inductor to current in an a-c circuit is called inductive reactance and is also measured in ohms.

Symbol

The symbol for inductive reactance is X_L. The letter X is used to denote reactance and the L indicates that it is the reactance offered by a coil or inductor. Reactance differs from resistance in that it is the opposition to alternating current, and the opposition will vary with the frequency of the a-c voltage applied to the coil or inductor.

Formula

The formula for inductive reactance is shown in Fig. 6-16. Inductive reactance (X_L) is measured in ohms, L is the inductance in henrys, and f is the frequency in hertz.

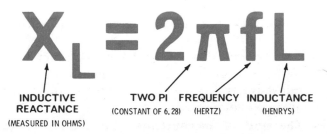

$$X_L = 2\pi f L$$

INDUCTIVE REACTANCE (MEASURED IN OHMS) TWO PI (CONSTANT OF 6.28) FREQUENCY (HERTZ) INDUCTANCE (HENRYS)

Fig. 6-16. Formula for inductive reactance.

It can be seen from the formula and from Fig. 6-17 that X_L increases when frequency increases, or decreases when frequency decreases. When the frequency of the applied voltage increases, the current through the coil is reversing faster, causing the opposition to this change in current to increase.

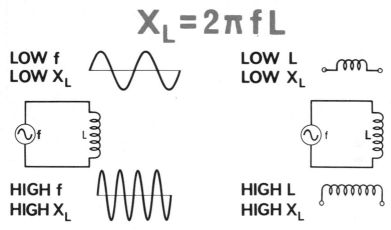

Fig. 6-17. Effect of frequency and inductance on X_L.

It can also be seen that if the value of the inductor is increased, X_L will increase, but if the value of the inductor is decreased, X_L also will decrease. With a larger value of inductance, more opposition to the change in current exists; consequently, X_L is greater.

Inductance is very useful because every inductive circuit is *frequency-sensitive*. This principle is used in filters, antennas, and many other applications. An inductive circuit passes direct current and low-frequency alternating current, but impedes the higher-frequency current.

Q6-16. The symbol used to represent inductive reactance is _____.

Q6-17. Inductive reactance depends on the value of inductance and _____.

Q6-18. The unit of measurement for inductive reactance is the _____.

FILTERS

$X_L = 2\pi FL$

Because inductive reactance depends on frequency, inductance is often used in filters—special circuits that have the property of allowing certain frequencies to pass while blocking others. There are, for example, *low-pass filters* which pass low frequencies; *high-pass filters* which pass frequencies that are above a predetermined frequency; and *band-pass filters* which pass only a certain band of frequencies.

Low-Pass Filter

The low-pass filter shown in Fig. 6-18 has an inductor in series with the input and output terminals of the circuit. When the input frequency is low, the inductive reactance of the coil is low, allowing the low input frequency to appear at the output of the circuit. As the input frequency increases, the inductive reactance of the coil increases; consequently, less and less of the input appears at the output.

High-Pass Filter

The high-pass filter shown in Fig. 6-19 has an inductor in parallel with the output terminals of the circuit. When

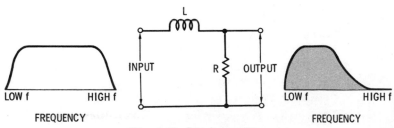

Fig. 6-18. Low-pass filter.

the input frequency is low, the inductive reactance of the coil is low, acting as a shunt across the output. Practically none of the input voltage appears at the output. As the input frequency increases, the inductive reactance of the coil increases, causing more and more of the input to appear at the output of the circuit.

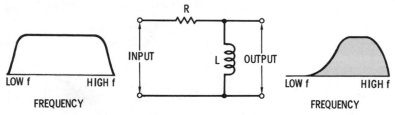

Fig. 6-19. High-pass filter.

Bandpass Filter

The bandpass filter shown in Fig. 6-20 will not be discussed here. The operation of this circuit depends on a condition called resonance which will be discussed later in this chapter.

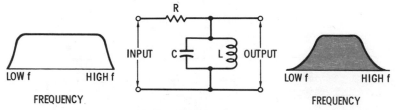

Fig. 6-20. Bandpass filter.

Q6-19. The filter that allows only high frequencies to pass is called a _____ filter.

Q6-20. The filter that blocks high frequencies and allows only low frequencies to pass is the _____ filter.

Q6-21. The filter that allows only a band of frequencies to pass is the _____ filter.

TRANSFORMERS

The device that transfers power from one voltage-current level to another voltage-current level is called the *transformer*. The transformer operates on the principle of the moving magnetic field and the fact that as the magnetic field cuts a conductor it can induce a voltage in that conductor.

Symbols

The schematic symbol used to represent the transformer will differ slightly depending on its application. Fig. 6-21

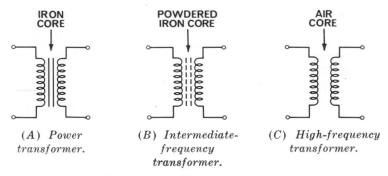

(A) *Power transformer.*

(B) *Intermediate-frequency transformer.*

(C) *High-frequency transformer.*

Fig. 6-21. Transformer symbols.

shows the three schematic symbols. The power transformer, used primarily in power applications such as power supplies, uses an iron core. The intermediate-frequency transformer, used at radio frequencies, has a powdered iron core. The high-frequency transformer, used at high radio frequencies, has an air core.

162

Transformer Operation

The transformer shown in Fig. 6-22 operates on the principle that as an a-c voltage is applied to the *primary* winding, the magnetic field will expand and collapse at the rate of the frequency of the applied voltage. As the magnetic field expands, a voltage of the opposite polarity of the primary voltage will be induced in the *secondary* winding. As the magnetic field of the primary collapses, a voltage of the opposite polarity is induced in the secondary due to the change in the direction of the collapsing magnetic field. It can be seen that the frequency of the induced voltage is exactly the same as the primary voltage and that the secondary voltage is 180 degrees out of phase with the primary voltage.

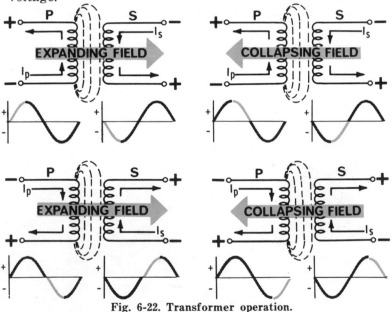

Fig. 6-22. Transformer operation.

Q6-22. The schematic symbol for a transformer can have _____ different configurations.

Q6-23. The transformer winding into which a voltage is induced is the _____ winding.

Q6-24. The transformer primary and secondary voltages are _____ degrees out of phase.

Factors Affecting Induced Voltage

One of the main advantages of using transformers is that they can change voltage. The amount of voltage induced in the secondary winding (E_S) of the transformer is not always the same as the voltage applied to the primary (E_P). The secondary voltage depends on the number of turns in

$$\frac{T_S}{T_P} = \frac{E_S}{E_P}$$

Fig. 6-23. Voltage-turns ratio.

the secondary (T_S) as compared to the number of turns in the primary (T_P). Fig. 6-23 shows the relationship between the number of turns in the secondary as compared to the primary. This ratio is called the *turns ratio*. The *voltage ratio* is the ratio of secondary voltage to primary voltage.

Step-Up Transformer

The step-up transformer shown in Fig. 6-24 has a turns ratio that induces a greater voltage in the secondary winding than is applied to the primary winding. Whenever more voltage is induced in the secondary than is applied to the primary, the transformer is called a *step-up transformer*.

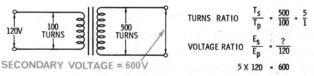

TURNS RATIO $\frac{T_S}{T_p} = \frac{500}{100} = \frac{5}{1}$

VOLTAGE RATIO $\frac{E_S}{E_p} = \frac{?}{120}$

5 X 120 = 600

Fig. 6-24. Step-up transformer.

Step-Down Transformer

The step-down transformer shown in Fig. 6-25 has a turns ratio that provides less voltage in the secondary than is applied to the primary. As with the step-up transformer, the primary-to-secondary turns ratio determines the amount of voltage induced into the secondary winding.

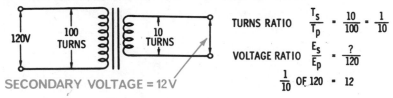

TURNS RATIO $\frac{T_s}{T_p} = \frac{10}{100} = \frac{1}{10}$

VOLTAGE RATIO $\frac{E_s}{E_p} = \frac{?}{120}$

$\frac{1}{10}$ OF 120 = 12

SECONDARY VOLTAGE = 12 V

Fig. 6-25. Step-down transformer.

Current Ratio

The *current ratio* is the relationship of primary current to secondary current. The power transfer from primary to secondary is always the same; the current ratio is the *inverse* of the voltage ratio, as shown in Fig. 6-26.

$$\frac{T_s}{T_p} = \frac{E_s}{E_p} = \frac{I_p}{I_s}$$

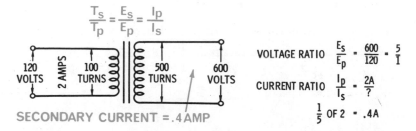

VOLTAGE RATIO $\frac{E_s}{E_p} = \frac{600}{120} = \frac{5}{1}$

CURRENT RATIO $\frac{I_p}{I_s} = \frac{2A}{?}$

$\frac{1}{5}$ OF 2 = .4A

SECONDARY CURRENT = .4 AMP

Fig. 6-26. Current ratio.

Q6-25. A transformer with more voltage induced into the secondary than is applied to the primary is a _____ transformer.

Q6-26. A transformer with six turns on the primary for each secondary winding and 120 volts applied to the primary will have a secondary voltage of _____ volts.

Q6-27. A step-up transformer will have _____ secondary current than primary current.

THE PULSE RESPONSE OF INDUCTORS

When a sine-wave voltage is applied to a circuit containing an inductor, it only delays the phase relationship of the sine-wave voltage and the circuit current. When square waves or pulses are applied, however, the inductor opposes a change of current in its usual way, and in doing so distorts the waveform of the square-wave voltage.

Analysis of Inductor Current Waveform

When a pulse voltage is applied to an inductor, as shown in Fig. 6-27, the effect of the inductor is to oppose any

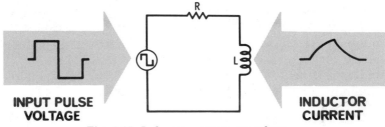

INPUT PULSE
VOLTAGE

INDUCTOR
CURRENT

Fig. 6-27. Inductor current waveform.

change in its current condition. Therefore the pulse voltage, as it increases from zero to its most positive value instantaneously, cannot produce an instantaneous change in current from zero to its maximum value. The current will increase slowly from zero to its maximum value as the pulse voltage overcomes the opposition of the inductor (X_L).

Likewise, when the pulse input voltage decreases from its maximum value to zero, the inductor will oppose this change in its current condition; consequently, the current will drop from its maximum value to zero at a much slower rate than the pulse voltage drops from maximum to zero.

Analysis of Inductor Voltage Waveform

As is true in all electronic circuits, the voltage waveform across a component is caused by the current through it. Fig. 6-28 shows that the voltage waveform across the inductor is a greatly distorted version of the pulse input wave-

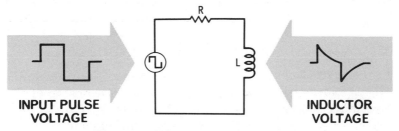

INPUT PULSE VOLTAGE
INDUCTOR VOLTAGE

Fig. 6-28. Inductor voltage waveform.

form. As the input pulse increases from zero to its maximum value, the opposition (X_L) of the inductor will be at its maximum value; consequently, the voltage across the inductor will be maximum. As the input pulse voltage remains at its maximum value, the opposition of the coil decreases, causing a decrease in the voltage drop across the inductor. As soon as the pulse voltage drops from its maximum to its minimum value, the X_L of the inductor will again increase, but because the magnetic field around the inductor is now collapsing, the polarity of the voltage across the inductor will be of the opposite polarity.

Q6-28. An inductor will _____ a square-wave input voltage.

Q6-29. The inductive reactance of the inductor is at its _____ value when the pulse input voltage is changing from zero to maximum.

Q6-30. The inductor voltage will have a _____ polarity as the pulse voltage drops from maximum to zero.

IMPEDANCE

When a circuit contains only resistance, the opposition to the current can be determined by using Ohm's law ($I = E/R$). When a circuit contains only inductance, the opposition to the current again can be determined by using Ohm's law, using inductive reactance instead of resistance ($I = E/X_L$). When a circuit contains *both* resistance and inductance, the overall opposition to the current is called *impedance*. The symbol for impedance is Z.

Impedance Formula

One simple method that can be used to determine the impedance of an RL circuit is to use vectors, as shown in Fig. 6-29. The current through the resistance in an a-c circuit is in phase with the applied voltage, while the current in the inductance lags 90 degrees behind the voltage. Just as the rms value of the inductive current cannot be used to find the overall current, the 3 ohms of resistance cannot be added directly to the 4 ohms of inductive reactance. Instead, the

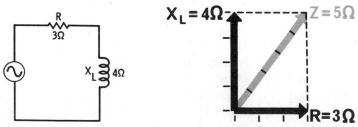

Fig. 6-29. Vector analysis to determine impedance.

overall effect of the two must be found in the same way that the overall current vector is found.

To find the overall effect of 3 ohms of resistance and 4 ohms of inductive reactance, from a point draw a vertical line 4 units long. This line represents the inductive reactance. Then from the same point draw a horizontal line 3 units long. This line represents the resistance. The two lines form two sides of a rectangle. The number of units in the diagonal of this rectangle will represent the impedance.

$$Z = \sqrt{R^2 + X_L^2}$$

IMPEDANCE = THE SQUARE ROOT OF RESISTANCE SQUARED PLUS X_L SQUARED
(OHMS)

$$\sqrt{R^2 + X_L^2} = Z$$

$R = 3\Omega; \, X_L = 4\Omega$ $\sqrt{9 + 16} = Z$

$$\sqrt{25} = Z \qquad 5\Omega = Z$$

Fig. 6-30. Impedance formula.

This method can be used only when values of R and X_L are small enough to use vectors. Another more acceptable method is the use of the formula shown in Fig. 6-30. Before trying to use this formula to determine the impedance of an RL circuit it is suggested that you review the method of finding the square root of a number.

Q6-31. When both the resistance and the inductive reactance of an RL circuit are low, impedance can be found by using _____.

Q6-32. The total impedance of an RL circuit can be found by finding the square root of _____ _____ plus _____ _____.

Q6-33. The impedance of an RL circuit with 10 ohms resistance and 7 ohms inductive reactance is _____ ohms.

INDUCTIVE CIRCUIT POWER

Inductance, unlike resistance, consumes no power. When the current in the circuit is increasing, inductance takes energy out of the circuit. It converts this energy into a magnetic field. When the current in the circuit is decreasing, however, this magnetic field collapses, and all the energy returns to the circuit.

Power in a Resistive Circuit

When an a-c voltage is applied to a resistive circuit, as shown in Fig. 6-31, the power consumed can be determined by Ohm's law. With a resistance of 20 ohms, and an applied voltage of 120 volts. the current through the circuit is 6 amperes. The power consumed is 720 watts.

The power shown in Fig. 6-31 has two positive pulses. Two important rules that you must remember are:

a. When you multiply positive values by positive values, or negative values by negative values, the results are positive values.

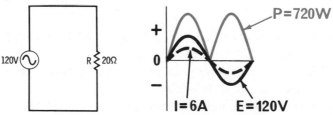

Fig. 6-31. Power in resistive circuit.

b. When you multiply positive values by negative values, the results are negative values.

Power in an Inductive Circuit

Fig. 6-32 shows the voltage, current, and power waveforms in an inductive circuit. Between points B and C both current and voltage are positive. If their values are multiplied, it appears that power is being dissipated exactly as in a resistive circuit. Between points D and E, both current and voltage are negative, and again you have exactly the same situation as in a resistive circuit—power appears to be dissipated. But, between points A and B and points C and D, there is a situation that never exists in a resistive circuit.

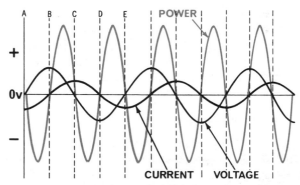

Fig. 6-32. Power in inductive circuit.

As you can see, there are pulses of negative power as well as positive power. The positive power pulses represent the time when the circuit is utilizing power to produce a magnetic field. The negative-power pulses represent the time when the circuit is absorbing power from the magnetic field. The negative pulses and the positive pulses are equal and cancel each other, so the total power dissipated is zero.

Q6-34. The voltage between points A and B of Fig. 6-32 is _____ polarity.

Q6-35. The current between points A and B of Fig. 6-32 is _____ polarity.

Q6-36. The power between points A and B of Fig. 6-32 is _____ polarity.

TIME CONSTANT IN RL CIRCUITS

As was explained previously, whenever a pulse voltage is applied to an RL circuit the waveshape of the input pulse will be distorted. The inductive effect of the coil, causing the change in current to lag behind the change in voltage, causes this distortion. The *time constant* of the RL circuit is the measure of the amount of time required for the current through the circuit to reach 63 percent of its maximum value when the voltage changes.

Time Constant Formula

The formula for determining the length of time for current to increase to 63 percent of its maximum value is shown in Fig. 6-33.

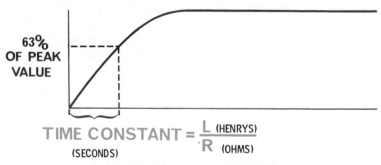

Fig. 6-33. Time constant formula.

Fig. 6-34 shows several examples of how the time constant formula is used to determine the time constant of RL networks. As the value of L increases or the value of R decreases, the time constant of the RL circuit increases.

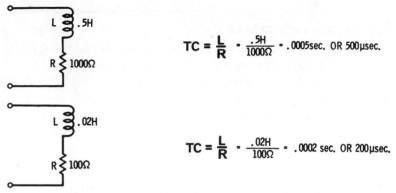

$$TC = \frac{L}{R} = \frac{.5H}{1000\Omega} = .0005\text{sec. OR } 500\mu\text{sec.}$$

$$TC = \frac{L}{R} = \frac{.02H}{100\Omega} = .0002 \text{ sec. OR } 200\mu\text{sec.}$$

Fig. 6-34. Application of time constant formula.

RL Waveforms

When a pulse of a given duration is applied to an RL circuit, the RL circuit distorts the pulse voltage waveshape. Fig. 6-35 shows waveshapes of the pulse input voltage, the inductor voltage, and the resistor voltage. The voltage across the inductor is called the *differentiated voltage;* the voltage across the resistor is the *integrated voltage.*

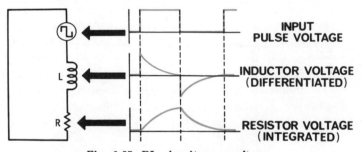

Fig. 6-35. RL circuits waveshapes.

Q6-37. The time constant of an RL circuit is the time required for current to reach _____ percent of its maximum value.

Q6-38. If the inductor value is in henrys and resistance in megohms, the time constant will be in _____ .

Q6-39. The voltage waveform across the resistor of an RL circuit is the _____ voltage .

173

Current in RL Circuits

As explained earlier, the current through the RL circuit will reach 63 percent of its maximum value in one time constant. Fig. 6-36 shows that five time constants are required for current to reach its maximum value. Assume a total circuit current of 10 amperes and an applied pulse voltage of 100 volts as an example.

a. During the first time constant, the circuit current will increase to 63 percent of 10 amperes, or 6.3 amperes. The voltage across the resistor will increase to 63 percent of the applied voltage or 63 volts, and inductor voltage will decrease 63 percent or to 37 volts.

b. During the second time constant, the circuit current will increase another 63 percent of the remaining value of 3.7 amperes, or an additional 2.3 amperes (6.3 + 2.3 = 8.6 amperes). The voltage across the re-

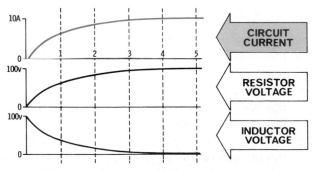

Fig. 6-36. Analysis of RL circuit current.

sistor will increase another 63 percent to 86 volts, and the inductor voltage will decrease to 14 volts.

c. During the third time constant current will increase another 63 percent or to 9.5 amperes. Resistor voltage increases to 95 volts, and inductor voltage drops to 5 volts.

d. The circuit current continues to increase 63 percent of the remaining value during the fourth and fifth time constants, until at the end of the fifth time constant, circuit current is at 10 amperes, resistor voltage is 100, and inductor voltage is zero.

Universal Time Constant Chart

The universal time constant chart shown in Fig. 6-37 can be used to calculate the rise or decay (drop) of voltage or current in any RL circuit to which a pulse voltage is applied.

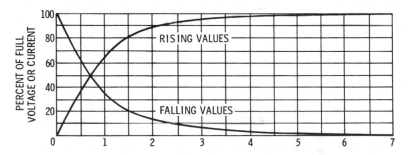

Fig. 6-37. Universal time constant chart.

The only information required to use the universal chart is the input voltage value and current value and the time constant of the circuit.

Q6-40. If L is 3 henrys and R is 5 ohms, current will reach 63 percent of its maximum value in _____ second(s).

Q6-41. If L is 2 henrys and R is 10 ohms, resistor voltage will reach 98 percent of its maximum value in _____ second(s).

Q6-42. _____ time constants are required for either circuit voltage or current to reach its maximum value.

TIME CONSTANT-TO-PERIOD RATIO IN RL CIRCUITS

The time constant-to-period ratio (TC-to-P) is the ratio of the pulse-duration time of the input pulse voltage to the time constant of the RL circuit. By knowing this ratio, the waveshape of the voltage across the resistor or inductor can be changed to the desired shape by changing the value of either R or L in the RL circuit.

TC-to-P Formula

The period of a pulse voltage is the amount of time, in seconds, that the pulse voltage remains at its maximum value, then drops and remains at its minimum value. In other words, it is the amount of time from the appearance of the leading edge of one pulse to the appearance of the leading edge of the next pulse. Fig. 6-38 shows the formulas for converting frequency of a pulse voltage to period, or period to frequency.

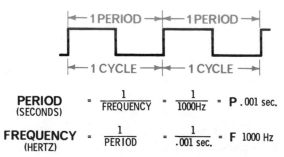

$$\text{PERIOD (SECONDS)} = \frac{1}{\text{FREQUENCY}} = \frac{1}{1000\text{Hz}} = \text{P .001 sec.}$$

$$\text{FREQUENCY (HERTZ)} = \frac{1}{\text{PERIOD}} = \frac{1}{.001 \text{ sec.}} = \text{F } 1000 \text{ Hz}$$

Fig. 6-38. Period and frequency formulas.

The relationship between the time constant of the RL circuit and the period of the pulse voltage is shown in Fig. 6-39. It can be seen that the ratio between the two is obtained by dividing the time constant by the period. It must be remembered that the time constant of an RL circuit is

$$\frac{TC}{P} \frac{\text{(TIME CONSTANT)}}{\text{(PERIOD)}} = \frac{L/R}{P}$$

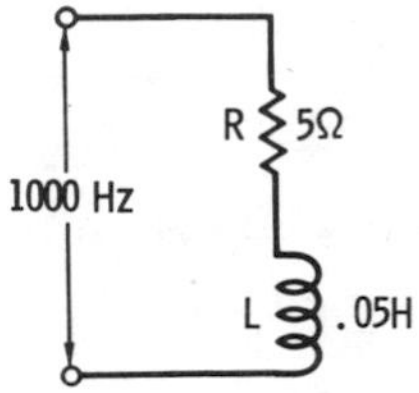

$$TC = \frac{L}{R} = \frac{.05}{5} = .01$$

$$P = \frac{1}{FREQ.} = \frac{1}{1000} = .001$$

$$\frac{TC}{P} = \frac{.01}{.001} = \frac{10}{1}$$

Fig. 6-39. Application of TC-to-P formula.

obtained by dividing the value of L by the value of R as previously explained.

The ratio of time constant to period is expressed in six general catagories as shown in Fig. 6-40.

$$\frac{1}{10} = \text{SHORT} \qquad \frac{1}{1} = \text{INTERMEDIATE}$$

$$\frac{1}{100} = \text{VERY SHORT} \qquad \frac{10}{1} = \text{LONG}$$

$$\frac{1}{1000} = \text{EXTRA SHORT} \qquad \frac{100}{1} = \text{VERY LONG}$$

Fig. 6-40. TC-to-P ratio categories.

Q6-43. The time from the appearance of the leading edge of one pulse to the appearance of the leading edge of the next is the _____ of the pulse.

Q6-44. The relationship between the time constant and the pulse time is called the _____ ratio.

Q6-45. A pulse with a frequency of 5000 hertz would have a period of _____ second(s).

RL Circuit with a Short TC-to-P Ratio

When the time constant of the RL circuit is short with respect to the period of the pulse, the following actions take place:

1. As the pulse input voltage increases from minimum to maximum, the entire input voltage is across the inductor, due to its high impedance.

2. During the long time (with respect to the TC) that the input pulse remains at its maximum value, circuit current can increase to its maximum value, causing the resistor voltage to rise to maximum, and the inductor voltage to drop to minimum.

3. As the input voltage drops to minimum, the counter emf across the inductor (due to the collapsing magnetic field) will be at its maximum negative value; resistor voltage will be at a maximum positive value.

4. As the magnetic field of the inductor collapses (during the long minimum value pulse time), the current through the resistor decreases, causing resistor voltage to drop to zero.

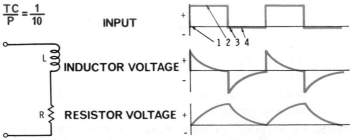

Fig. 6-41. Waveforms for short TC-to-P ratio.

RL Circuit with a Long TC-to-P Ratio

When the time constant of the RL circuit is long with respect to the period of the pulse, the following actions take place:

1. As the pulse input voltage increases from minimum to maximum, the entire input voltage is across the inductor, due to its high impedance.
2. During the short time (with respect to the TC) that the input pulse remains at its maximum value, circuit current cannot increase to its maximum value. Therefore, resistor voltage will increase to a fraction of its maximum value, and inductor voltage will drop only slightly.
3. As the input voltage drops to minimum the counter emf of the inductor will produce a voltage of negative polarity across the inductor.
4. As the magnetic field of the inductor collapses during the short time of minimum pulse value, the circuit current decreases, causing the resistor voltage to drop to zero.

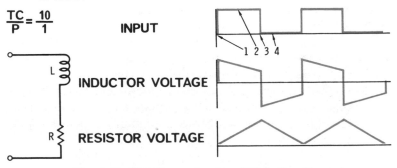

Fig. 6-42. Waveforms for long TC-to-P ratio.

Q6-46. During the input-pulse rise time (leading edge), all voltage is across the _____.

Q6-47. With a short TC-to-P ratio the resistor voltage waveshape is a _____ voltage.

Q6-48. In a long TC-to-P ratio circuit, the voltage across the resistor will be very _____.

179

Your Answers Should Be:

A6-46. During the input-pulse rise time (leading edge), all voltage is across the **inductor.**

A6-47. With a short TC-to-P ratio the resistor voltage waveshape is a **sawtooth** voltage.

A6-48. In a long TC-to-P ratio circuit, the voltage across the resistor will be very **low.**

Summary of TC-to-P Ratios

The time constant-to-period ratio (TC-to-P) is the ratio of the pulse-duration time of the input pulse voltage to the time constant of the RL circuit.

So far, only the short and long TC-to-P ratios have been discussed. Fig. 6-43 shows the resistor and inductor waveshapes for the six TC-to-P ratios when a pulse voltage is applied to the RL circuit.

Notice that the inductor voltage will always have the sharp leading edge of the pulse input voltage, but the drop in inductor voltage from its maximum to minimum value will be in direct relationship to the time constant of the circuit, with respect to the period of the pulse.

With a short ratio the drop will be slow. The very short ratio produces a much more rapid decrease, while the extremely short ratio produces a spike waveshape or a very rapid decrease. The intermediate, long, and very long ratios prevent the inductor voltage from decreasing any appreciable amount. The very long ratio produces a waveshape across the inductor that is almost identical to the pulse input voltage.

Notice also that the resistor waveshapes will always have a gradual rise from minimum to maximum value. The very long ratio produces an almost negligible resistor voltage, the intermediate ratio produces a perfect sawtooth voltage waveform, while the extremely short ratio produces a resistor waveshape that is almost identical to the pulse input voltage.

If a mirror-image of the resistor voltage waveform is superimposed on the inductor voltage waveform, the result would be the input pulse shape.

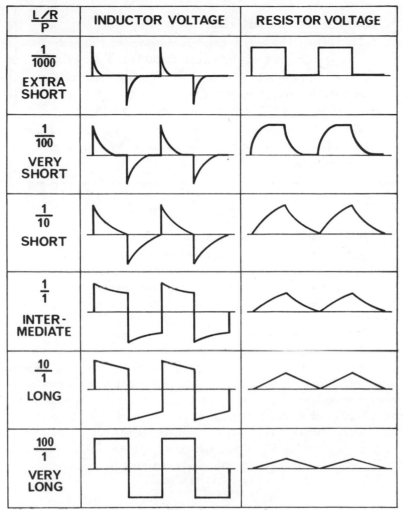

$\dfrac{L/R}{P}$	INDUCTOR VOLTAGE	RESISTOR VOLTAGE
$\dfrac{1}{1000}$ EXTRA SHORT		
$\dfrac{1}{100}$ VERY SHORT		
$\dfrac{1}{10}$ SHORT		
$\dfrac{1}{1}$ INTER-MEDIATE		
$\dfrac{10}{1}$ LONG		
$\dfrac{100}{1}$ VERY LONG		

Fig. 6-43. RL voltage waveshapes.

Q6-49. When the input pulse voltage and the inductor voltage are almost identical, the TC-to-P ratio is _____ _____.

Q6-50. When inductor voltage is an extreme spike voltage, the TC-to-P ratio is _____ _____.

Q6-51. When resistor voltage is almost identical to the input pulse voltage, the TC-to-P ratio is _____ _____.

CAPACITANCE

Capacitance is the property of an electrical circuit that opposes a change in voltage. Capacitance has the same reaction to voltage that inductance has to current. That is, when the voltage applied across a circuit is increased or decreased, capacitance resists that change.

Construction of a Capacitor

A basic capacitor, sometimes called a condenser, is shown in Fig. 6-44. It consists of two conducting metallic plates separated by a layer of air or other insulating material such as glass, mica, or oil. The insulating material between the two conducting plates is called the *dielectric*.

All capacitors have two plates with an insulator separating them. In practice, these plates are often stacked or even rolled into a compact form, as shown in Fig. 6-45.

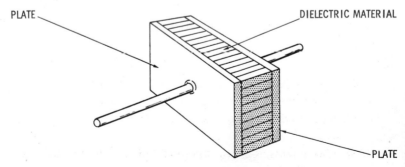

PLATE

DIELECTRIC MATERIAL

PLATE

Fig. 6-44. Basic capacitor construction.

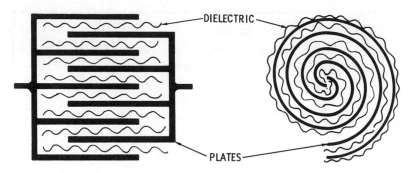

Fig. 6-45. Capacitor construction methods.

Symbols for a Capacitor

Capacitors can be classified into two categories—*fixed* or *variable*. Fig. 6-46 shows the schematic symbol for each category. The fixed capacitor, as its name implies, is made to have a definite value of capacitance, while the variable capacitor can be varied in value over a predetermined range.

The usual symbol, or alphabetical designation, used to identify capacitance is the letter *C*.

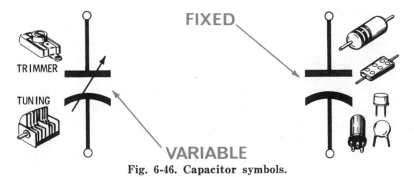

Fig. 6-46. Capacitor symbols.

Q6-52. The insulating material between the plates of a capacitor is called the _____.

Q6-53. The two types of capacitors are _____ and _____.

Q6-54. Capacitance is the property of an electrical circuit that opposes changes in _____.

CAPACITANCE MEASUREMENTS

Each electrical component must have a standard against which its value can be measured. The unit of measurement for capacitance is the *farad.*

Capacitor Action in a D-C Circuit

When a capacitor is first connected to a battery, as shown in Fig. 6-47, electrons flow to the capacitor plate and remain there, since the opposite plate is separated from the first by the dielectric. The electrons from the opposite plate are attracted to the positive battery terminal. After this initial movement of electrons one plate is filled with all of the electrons that the battery can force into it, while the other plate loses the same number of electrons. One plate is negative, the other positive. No more electrons flow; the capacitor is *charged.* The voltage between the plates is equal and opposite to the battery voltage.

Capacitor Action in an A-C Circuit

Current cannot pass through a capacitor, but alternating current appears to do so. If the voltage across the plates is continuously varied, the number of electrons on the plates

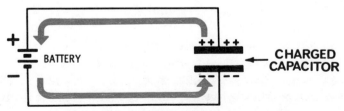

Fig. 6-47. Capacitor action in d-c circuit.

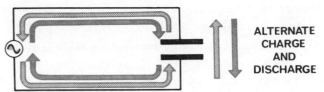
Fig. 6-48. Capacitor action in a-c circuit.

varies. As shown in Fig. 6-48, an a-c voltage can, in effect, get across the dielectric. Since the voltage is alternating, it causes an alternating current on the other side. Voltage changes are transmitted across the gap.

Unit of Measurement for Capacitors

Capacitance is measured in farads. Fig. 6-49 shows that the amount of capacitance in a capacitor is the quantity of electrical charges (in coulombs) that must be moved from one plate to the other in order to create a difference of 1 volt between the plates. The number of coulombs transferred is called the *charge*. One farad is the capacitance in which a charge of 1 coulomb produces a difference of 1 volt between the plates. The larger the capacitance of a capacitor, the more charge it will hold.

Capacitance values are usually specified in microfarads (millionths of a farad, abbreviated mfd or μf) or in picofarads (pf). Picofarads were formerly called micromicrofarads (mmf or $\mu\mu f$).

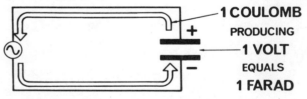
Fig. 6-49. Unit of measurement for capacitors.

Q6-55. The unit of measurement for capacitance is the
_____.

Q6-56. Common units of measurement used for capacitors are _____ and _____.

Q6-57. When one plate of a capacitor has been filled with the maximum number of electrons, it is
_____.

FACTORS AFFECTING CAPACITANCE VALUE

Plate Area

The amount of electrical charge that can be stored in a capacitor (the number of electrons that can be placed on the plate) varies with the area of the plate. Consequently, capacitance varies directly with area. When the area is doubled or twice as many plates are connected in parallel, there is twice as much area to store electrons, and the capacitance is therefore twice as great (Fig. 6-50).

Fig. 6-50. Plate area affects capacitance.

Distance Between Plates

Capacitance can also be increased by placing the plates closer together, as shown in Fig. 6-51. When the plates are closer, the attraction between the negative charges on one side and the positive charges on the other side is greater,

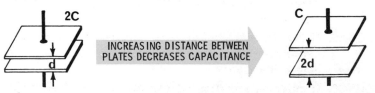

Fig. 6-51. Distance between plates affects capacitance.

and thus more charge can be stored. It is, of course, necessary to keep the plates far enough apart so that the charge does not jump the gap.

Changing Dielectric Material

Fig. 6-52 shows that higher values of capacitance can be obtained by using an insulating material (dielectric) other than air. Dielectrics such as mica, glass, oil, and *Mylar* are a few of the materials that can sustain a high electric stress

Fig. 6-52. Dielectric material affects capacitance.

without breaking down. This property is called *dielectric constant*. The higher the dielectric constant, the better the dielectric. Air has a dielectric constant of 1, glass about 5, and mica 2.5 to 6.6.

Besides allowing the plates to be placed closer together, a dielectric has another effect on capacitance. Dielectric material contains a large number of electrons and other carriers of electrical charge. Although electrons cannot flow as in a conductor, they are held rather loosely in the structure and can move slightly. The distortion of the structure of the dielectric, which is caused by charging the capacitor, has a large effect on the forces of attraction and repulsion that aid or oppose the flow of the electrons.

Q6-58. If the plate area of a capacitor is halved, the value of capacitance will be _____ its original value.

Q6-59. If the distance between the plates of a capacitor is doubled, the capacitance will be _____ its original value.

Q6-60. If mica is substituted for air as the dielectric, the capacitance will be _____.

CAPACITORS IN COMBINATION

Capacitors, like resistors and inductors, are often connected in either series, parallel, or series-parallel in electronic circuits. Therefore, the rules that must be understood for combining resistors and inductors also apply to capacitors, but for capacitors they are just the opposite.

Capacitors in Parallel

As you have previously learned, resistors and inductors in series are added. Two resistors or inductors in series have the same effect as a single, larger resistor or inductor. Capacitors *add in parallel*, as shown in Fig. 6-53. It is easy to understand why this is true if you remember that the more plates, or the larger the plate area of a capacitor, the greater the capacitance. If two or more capacitors are connected in parallel, their total capacitance can be found by adding their values.

Capacitors in Series

Capacitors connected in series can be analyzed the same way as resistors or inductors connected in parallel. Fig. 6-54

$$C_T = C1 + C2 + C3$$

Fig. 6-53. Parallel capacitor formula.

shows the two formulas that can be used to determine the total capacitance of the series-connected capacitors.

$$C_T = \frac{C1 \times C2}{C1 + C2} \text{ OR } \left\{ \begin{array}{l} \text{IF EQUAL VALUES,} \\ \dfrac{\text{VALUE OF ONE C}}{\text{NUMBER OF C's}} \end{array} \right.$$

Fig. 6-54. Series capacitor formula.

Capacitors in Series-Parallel

When capacitors are connected in series-parallel, the same method used to determine equivalent resistance or inductance can be used. Fig. 6-55 shows an example of analyzing such a circuit. Remember, just reverse the resistor-inductor formulas when working with capacitors.

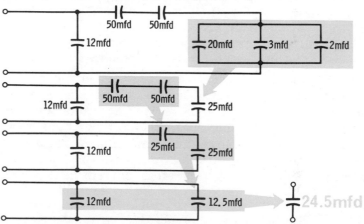

Fig. 6-55. Analysis of series-parallel circuit.

Q6-61. If three .02-mfd capacitors are connected in parallel, the total capacitance will be _____ mfd.

Q6-62. If two .05-mfd capacitors are connected in series, the total capacitance will be _____ mfd.

Q6-63. If a 25-mfd and a 100-mfd capacitor are connected in series, total capacitance will be _____ mfd.

189

CURRENT-VOLTAGE PHASE RELATIONSHIP IN A-C CAPACITIVE CIRCUITS

As with inductance, current and voltage are *not* in phase in a capacitive circuit. In a capacitive circuit, the voltage lags the current by 90 degrees.

Analysis of Current-Voltage Relationship

At any instant, the current into or out of a capacitor is proportional to the rate of change of the applied voltage. This can be seen in Fig. 6-56. The applied voltage is changing most rapidly at time A, the beginning of the sine-wave cycle; therefore, the current is at maximum. At time B the voltage across the capacitor has reached its peak and for the moment is not changing. Therefore, current at this instant

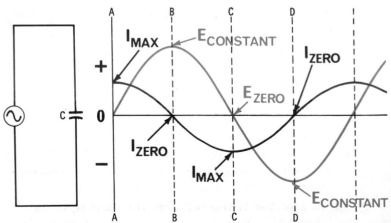

Fig. 6-56. Current-voltage relationship in capacitive circuit.

is zero. At time C, voltage across the capacitor again is changing quite rapidly (but in the negative direction), and so the current is at its negative peak. At time D, when the voltage reaches its negative peak and is momentarily not changing, the current waveform passes through zero once more.

If we trace the current from point to point along the voltage waveform, the result is a sine wave, but it is one that leads the voltage by exactly 90 degrees. This shows that if the voltage across the capacitor is a continuous sine wave with a constant amplitude, the current through the capacitor circuit is a sine wave that is 90 degrees ahead of the voltage.

Vector Analysis of Current-Voltage Relationship

Fig. 6-57 shows the vector representation of the current-voltage phase relationship in a capacitive circuit. The current vector leads the voltage vector by 90 degrees. A com-

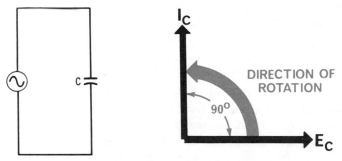

Fig. 6-57. Vector representation of current-voltage phase relationship.

parison of the vector and the current and voltage waveforms shown in Fig. 6-56 shows that at any instant of time, the voltage lags behind the current by 90 degrees.

Q6-64. In a capacitive circuit, current _____ voltage by 90 degrees.

Q6-65. The phase relationship between voltage and current is caused by _____ effects.

Q6-66. In a vector representation, the voltage vector is shown 90 degrees _____ the current vector.

CAPACITIVE REACTANCE

Capacitance has a reactance or opposition to alternating current. Unlike inductance, the reactance of the capacitor decreases as the frequency of the alternating current increases.

Capacitive Reactance Formula

The symbol for capacitive reactance is X_C. The letter X is used to denote reactance and the C indicates that it is the reactance offered by a capacitor. The formula for capacitive reactance is shown in Fig. 6-58.

$$X_C = \frac{1}{2\pi f C}$$

(OHMS)   (HERTZ) (FARADS)

Fig. 6-58. Capacitive reactance formula.

How Capacitive Reactance Operates

Because the circuit shown in Fig. 6-59 contains no resistance, the voltage across the capacitor will be the same value as the source voltage at every instant.

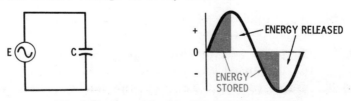

Fig. 6-59. Capacitive reactance in a-c circuits.

When a capacitor is charged up to a voltage E, it stores an amount of energy equal to the capacitance times the voltage. The capacitor will store a particular amount of energy every time the voltage reaches its positive or negative peaks. The energy depends only on capacitance and peak voltage. Fig. 6-60 shows that when the frequency of the power source is doubled and the peak voltage (E) is unchanged, the capacitor will charge every half-cycle to the same amount as before; but, it will have to do this twice as fast. This means that the same amount of energy must be supplied to the capacitor in only half the time. And since the voltage is the same, we must have twice the current to supply this same amount of total energy.

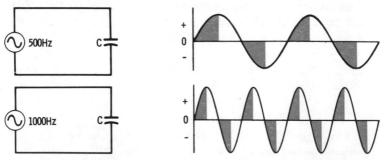

Fig. 6-60. Effect of frequency on capacitive reactance.

Capacitive reactance depends on frequency. Since it allows more current as frequency increases, capacitive reactance must decrease as the frequency increases.

Capacitive reactance also depends on the size of the capacitance. As capacitance increases, more current is needed to charge the capacitor to the same voltage (since the amount of energy stored equals $C \times E$). As a result, capacitive reactance decreases when capacitance increases.

Q6-67. The symbol used to represent capacitive reactance in formulas is _____.

Q6-68. If the frequency of the voltage applied to a capacitor decreases, capacitive reactance _____.

Q6-69. If the capacitance of a capacitor is increased, its capacitive reactance _____.

RESISTIVE-CAPACITIVE CIRCUITS

Since all circuits have some resistance, a pure capacitive circuit cannot exist. The leads of capacitors have some small value of capacitance. When the circuit contains both resistance and capacitance, the overall opposition to current is called impedance. The symbol is Z, as it was for impedance in an RL circuit.

Impedance Formula

As you already know, we cannot add resistance and capacitance because they are two different quantities (resistance is measured in ohms, capacitance in farads). Instead, it is necessary to use capacitive reactance, which was discussed previously. However, just as with inductance, to add resistance to capacitive reactance it must be remembered that resistive current is in phase with the voltage while capacitive current leads the voltage by 90 degrees. The two cannot be added directly—they must be added vectorially as shown

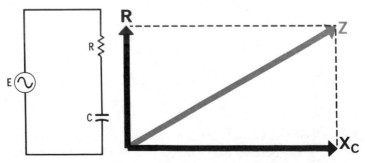

Fig. 6-61. Vector determination of impedance.

in Fig. 6-61. The capacitive-reactance vector is 90 degrees ahead of the resistance vector. The resulting quantity, an impedance, is somewhere between the two vectors and its length (quantity) is the diagonal of the reactangle they form. This is *capacitive impedance*, which is different from inductive impedance because it leads the resistance vector.

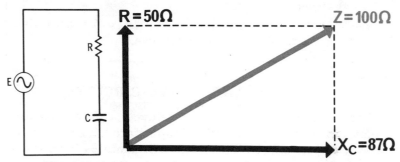

Fig. 6-62. Application of vectors to determine impedance.

Fig. 6-62 shows an example of the vector analysis of a circuit having a capacitive reactance of 87 ohms and a resistance of 50 ohms. Another formula that can be used to determine impedance of an RC circuit is shown in Fig. 6-63.

$$Z = \sqrt{R^2 + X_C^2}$$

IMPEDANCE (OHMS) = THE SQUARE ROOT OF RESISTANCE SQUARED
PLUS CAPACITIVE REACTANCE SQUARED.

Fig. 6-63. Impedance formula.

Q6-70. The overall opposition to current in an RC circuit is _____.

Q6-71. An RC circuit with a resistance of 10 ohms and capacitive reactance of 10 ohms has an impedance of _____ ohms.

Q6-72. An RC circuit with a resistance of 50 ohms and a capacitive reactance of 87 ohms has an impedance of _____ ohms.

TIME CONSTANT IN RC CIRCUITS

Whenever a pulse voltage is applied to an RC circuit, the waveshape of the input pulse is distorted. The capacitive effects of the circuit, causing the current to lead the voltage, cause this distortion. The time constant of the RC circuit is the amount of time required for the circuit current to charge the capacitor to 63 percent of the applied voltage.

Time Constant Formula

The formula for determining the length of time for the capacitor charge to reach 63 percent of its maximum value is shown in Fig. 6-64. If values of R and C are in megohms or microfarads or picofarads (micromicrofarads), the formulas are given to simplify the process of division.

Fig. 6-65 shows several examples of how the time constant formula is used to determine the time constant of the RC circuit. Notice that as the values of C or R increase, the time constant of the RC circuit increases.

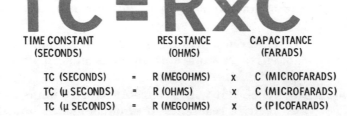

$$TC = R \times C$$

TIME CONSTANT (SECONDS)		RESISTANCE (OHMS)		CAPACITANCE (FARADS)
TC (SECONDS)	=	R (MEGOHMS)	x	C (MICROFARADS)
TC (μ SECONDS)	=	R (OHMS)	x	C (MICROFARADS)
TC (μ SECONDS)	=	R (MEGOHMS)	x	C (PICOFARADS)

Fig. 6-64. RC time constant formulas.

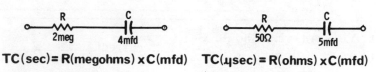

$$TC(sec) = R(megohms) \times C(mfd) \qquad TC(\mu sec) = R(ohms) \times C(mfd)$$
$$TC(sec) = 2meg \times 4mfd \qquad TC(\mu sec) = 50\Omega \times 5mfd$$
$$TC(sec) = 8sec \qquad TC(\mu sec) = 250 \mu sec$$

Fig. 6-65. Application of RC time constant formula.

RC Waveforms

When a pulse of a given time duration is applied to an RC circuit, the circuit distorts the pulse voltage as explained earlier. Fig. 6-66 shows the waveshape's pulse input voltage, the capacitor voltage, and the resistor voltage. The voltage across the capacitor is called the *integrated voltage* and the voltage across the resistor is called the *differentiated voltage*.

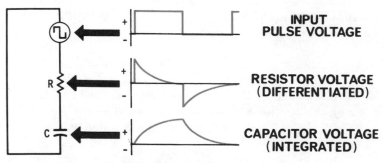

Fig. 6-66. RC waveforms.

Q6-73. The voltage across the capacitor in an RC circuit is called the _____ voltage.

Q6-74. A resistor of 10,000 ohms and a capacitor of .02 mfd would have a time constant of _____ microseconds.

Q6-75. The voltage across the resistor in an RC circuit is called the _____ voltage.

Current in RC Circuits

The current through the RC circuit, or the charge across the capacitor will reach 63 percent of its maximum value in one time constant. Fig. 6-67 shows that a total of *five* time constants are required for a capacitor charge to reach its maximum value. For this discussion, assume a total circuit current of 10 amperes and an applied pulse voltage of 100 volts as an example:

a. During the first time constant, the circuit current will decrease 63 percent of 10 amperes, to 3.7 amperes. The voltage across the capacitor will increase to 63 percent of the applied voltage or 63 volts. The resistor voltage will decrease 63 percent of the applied voltage or to 37 volts.

b. During the second time constant, the circuit current will decrease another 63 percent of the remaining value of 3.7 amperes, or an additional 2.3 amperes $(3.7 - 2.3 = 1.4$ amperes$)$. The voltage across the capacitor will increase another 63 percent to 86 volts, and the resistor voltage will decrease to 14 volts.

c. During the third time constant, current will decrease another 63 percent to 0.5 amperes. Capacitor voltage increases to 95 volts, and resistor voltage drops to 5 volts.

d. The circuit current continues to decrease 63 percent of the remaining value during the fourth and fifth time constants, until at the end of the fifth time constant, circuit current is at zero, capacitor voltage is 100 volts, and resistor voltage is zero.

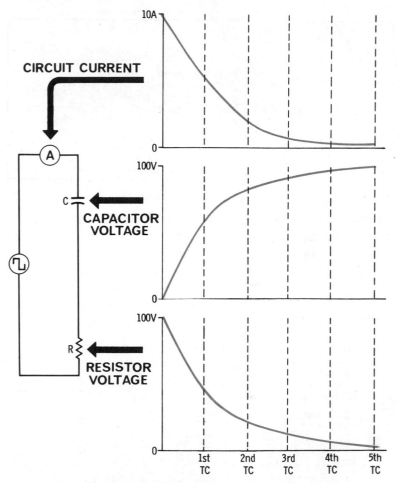

Fig. 6-67. Analysis of RC circuit current.

Q6-76. A capacitor in an RC circuit will charge to its maximum voltage in _____ time constants.

Q6-77. The resistor voltage in an RC circuit will drop 95 percent by the end of the _____ time constant.

Q6-78. If 20 volts are applied to an RC circuit, capacitor voltage will be _____ volts after the fourth time constant.

TIME CONSTANT-TO-PERIOD RATIO IN RC CIRCUITS

The time constant-to-period ratio (TC-to-P) for RC circuits is basically the same as for RL circuits except that the voltage waveform of the capacitor in the RC circuit is the same as the resistor waveform in the RL circuit, and the resistor voltage waveform in the RC circuit is the same as the inductor voltage waveform in the RL circuit.

TC-to-P Formula

It can be seen from Fig. 6-68 that the formula for determining the TC-to-P ratio is exactly the same as that for RL circuits. That is, the relationship between the time constant of the RC circuit and the period of the pulse voltage is obtained by dividing the time constant by the period. It must be remembered that the time constant of an RC circuit is obtained by multiplying the value of C by the value of R as previously explained.

$$\frac{TC}{P} \frac{\text{(TIME CONSTANT)}}{\text{(PERIOD)}} = \frac{R \times C}{P}$$

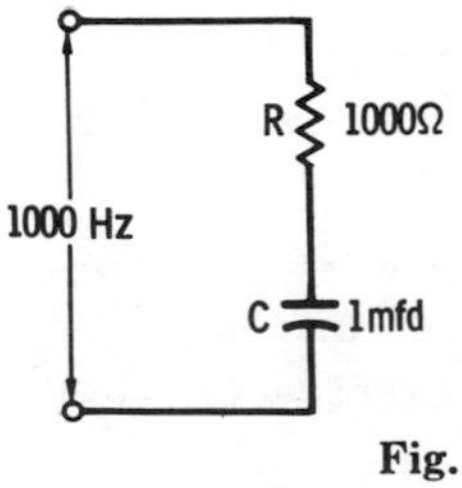

$$TC = R \times C = 1000\Omega \times 1\text{mfd} = .001\text{sec}$$

$$P = \frac{1}{FREQ.} = \frac{1}{1000} = .001\text{sec}$$

$$\frac{TC}{P} = \frac{.001}{.001} = \frac{1}{1}$$

Fig. 6-68. RC circuit TC-to-P formula.

The ratio of time constant to period is generally expressed in six general categories, as shown in Fig. 6-69. A comparison of these six categories with those given for RL circuits shows that the relationships of TC-to-P are the same.

$$\frac{1}{1000} = \text{EXTRA SHORT}$$

$$\frac{1}{100} = \text{VERY SHORT}$$

$$\frac{1}{10} = \text{SHORT}$$

$$\frac{1}{1} = \text{INTERMEDIATE}$$

$$\frac{10}{1} = \text{LONG}$$

$$\frac{100}{1} = \text{VERY LONG}$$

Fig. 6-69. RC circuit TC-to-P categories.

Q6-79. A time constant-to-period ratio of 1 to 100 is classified as _____.

Q6-80. A long TC-to-P ratio would be one with a ratio of _____ to _____.

Q6-81. A time constant-to-period ratio of 1 to 1 is classified as _____.

RC Circuit and Short TC-to-P Ratio

When the time constant of the RC circuit is short in respect to the period of the pulse, the following actions shown in Fig. 6-70 takes place:

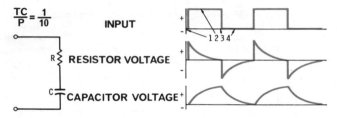

Fig. 6-70. Waveforms for short TC-to-P RC circuit.

1. As the pulse input voltage increases from minimum to maximum, the entire input voltage is across the resistor due to the low reactance of the capacitor.
2. During the long time (in respect to the TC) that the input pulse remains at its maximum value, the circuit current can charge the capacitor to the peak value of the input voltage, causing the resistor voltage to drop to its minimum value.
3. As the input pulse voltage drops to minimum, the charged capacitor (charged to the input pulse value) rapidly starts to discharge through the resistor, causing resistor voltage to be at its maximum negative value.
4. As the capacitor continues to discharge during the minimum value pulse time, capacitor voltage will drop from maximum to minimum and resistor voltage will drop from maximum negative to zero.

202

RC Circuit and Long TC-to-P Ratio

When the time constant of the RC circuit is long in respect to the period of the pulse, the following actions, as shown in Fig. 6-71, take place:

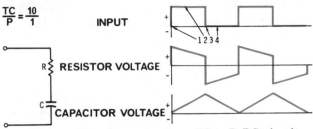

Fig. 6-71. Waveforms for long TC-to-P RC circuit.

1. As the input voltage increases from minimum to maximum, the entire voltage is across the resistor due to the low impedance of the uncharged capacitor.
2. During the short time (in respect to the TC) that the input pulse remains at its maximum value, the charge across the capacitor cannot increase to its maximum value, therefore capacitor voltage will increase only slightly, and resistor voltage will drop only slightly.
3. As the input voltage drops to minimum, the capacitor (charged to a portion of the input voltage) rapidly starts discharging through the resistor, causing resistor voltage to be at its maximum negative value.
4. The capacitor will discharge to zero during the short time of minimum pulse voltage since capacitor charge and discharge time are identical. Resistor voltage will drop from maximum negative to zero.

Q6-82. During the time that input voltage increases from minimum to maximum, the entire voltage is across the _____.

Q6-83. When input voltage changes suddenly from maximum to minimum the capacitor will _____.

Q6-84. The capacitor of the RC circuit will charge to only a small portion of the input voltage with a _____ TC-to-P ratio.

Your Answers Should Be:

A6-82. During the time that input voltage increases from minimum to maximum, the entire voltage is across the **resistor.**

A6-83. When input voltage changes suddenly from maximum to minimum the capacitor will **discharge.**

A6-84. The capacitor of the RC circuit will charge to only a small portion of the input voltage with a **long** TC-to-P ratio.

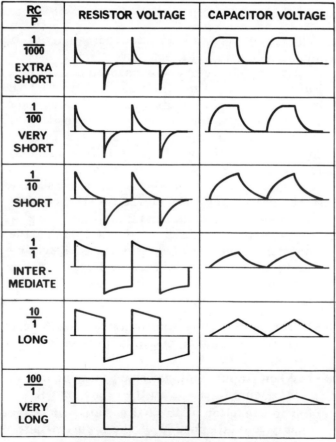

$\frac{RC}{P}$	RESISTOR VOLTAGE	CAPACITOR VOLTAGE
$\frac{1}{1000}$ EXTRA SHORT		
$\frac{1}{100}$ VERY SHORT		
$\frac{1}{10}$ SHORT		
$\frac{1}{1}$ INTER-MEDIATE		
$\frac{10}{1}$ LONG		
$\frac{100}{1}$ VERY LONG		

Fig. 6-72. RC circuit voltage waveforms.

Summary of TC-to-P Ratios

Only the short and long TC-to-P ratios have been discussed. Fig. 6-72 shows the resistor and capacitor waveshapes for the six TC-to-P ratios when a pulse voltage is applied to the RC circuit.

Notice that the resistor voltage will always have the sharp leading edge of the input pulse voltage, but the drop in resistor voltage from its maximum to minimum voltage value will be in direct relationship to the time constant of the circuit in respect to the period of the pulse. With an extremely short TC-to-P ratio, the drop in resistor voltage will be extremely rapid, while the very long ratio will produce a waveform across the resistor that is almost identical to the input pulse waveshape.

The capacitor voltage waveforms are the opposite of the resistor waveforms. The extremely short ratio will produce a capacitor waveform that is almost identical to the input pulse waveshape, while the very long ratio produces a waveshape across the capacitor that is a sawtooth voltage of very small amplitude. Notice also that the capacitor waveshapes will always have a gradual rise from minimum to maximum and then back to minimum.

Q6-85. When the input pulse voltage and the capacitor voltage are almost identical, the TC-to-P ratio is _____ _____.

Q6-86. When resistor voltage is an extreme spike voltage, the TC-to-P ratio is _____ _____.

Q6-87. When the resistor voltage is almost identical to the input pulse voltage, the TC-to-P ratio is _____ _____.

SERIES LCR CIRCUITS

When a circuit contains both inductance and capacitance in addition to resistance, the rules that apply for both inductive and capacitive circuits must apply; however, the predominant reactance, either inductive or capacitive, will determine the overall circuit characteristics.

Vector Analysis of Series LCR Circuit

When vectors, shown in Fig. 6-73, are used to represent impedance, X_C or capacitive reactance is always drawn downward (negative reactance), while X_L or inductive reactance is drawn upward (positive reactance). This vector representation shows that inductive reactance and capacitive reactance provide opposite effects.

The two reactances in series cannot be added arithmetically. X_L and X_C tend to offset each other, therefore the total effect is the difference between the two. Fig. 6-74 shows

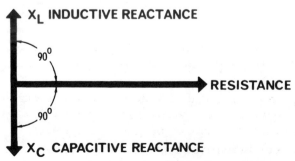

Fig. 6-73. Series LCR circuit impedance vectors.

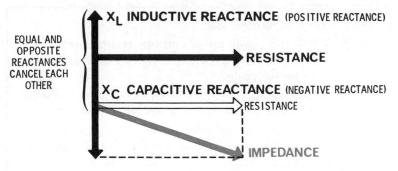

Fig. 6-74. Application of vectors to series LCR circuit.

that a circuit containing resistance, inductance, and capacitance will assume the characteristics of the predominant reactance.

LCR Circuit Impedance Formula

Fig. 6-75 shows the formula for determining the total impedance of a circuit containing X_L, X_C, and resistance. The formula can be modified to subtract the smaller reactance from the larger. The formula therefore can be $X_L - X_C$ or $X_C - X_L$ depending on which is the greater of the two reactances.

$$Z = \sqrt{R^2 + (X_L - X_C)^2}$$

IMPEDANCE
(ohms)

Fig. 6-75. Impedance formula for LCR circuit.

Q6-88. Inductive reactance (X_L) is a _____ reactance, while capacitive reactance is a _____ reactance.

Q6-89. A circuit with an inductive reactance of 100 ohms and a capacitive reactance of 25 ohms has a total reactance of _____ ohms.

Q6-90. The inductive vector is always drawn _____ and the capacitive vector is drawn _____.

SERIES RESONANT CIRCUITS

Every combination of inductance and capacitance will have a *resonant frequency;* that is, one frequency at which the values of inductive reactance and capacitive reactance will equal each other. Because these reactances are equal but opposite to each other, they will cancel each other.

Analysis of Resonant LCR Circuit

A special case arises when the capacitive reactance and the inductive reactance are equal. Fig. 6-76 shows that as frequency increases, X_C decreases; it also shows that as frequency increases, X_L increases. At the point where X_L and X_C cross, or equal each other, the resonant frequency of that LC combination has been reached.

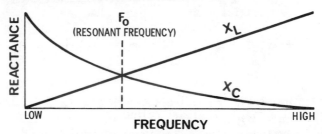

Fig. 6-76. Inductive-capacitive reactance curve.

Fig. 6-77 shows impedance and current plotted against frequency. Notice that both below and above the resonant frequency, impedance is high; consequently, the circuit current is low. Below the resonant frequency, the circuit acts

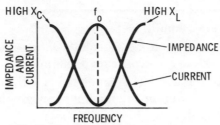

Fig. 6-77. Series LCR impedance-current curve.

capacitively and above the resonant frequency the circuit acts inductively. At the resonant frequency, however, impedance is at its minimum value; consequently, circuit current will be at its maximum value.

At the resonant frequency the voltage across both the inductor and capacitor can exceed the applied voltage. Because X_L and X_C counteract each other, resistance is the only opposition to circuit current, therefore current is high. However, the voltage across both L and C are a function of current times reactance (IX). Fig. 6-78 shows that the current times the inductive reactance (IX_L) and current times the capacitive reactance (IX_C) drops can exceed E applied.

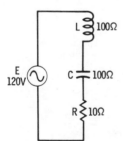

1. AT RESONANCE X_L EQUALS X_C, CANCELING EACH OTHER.

2. CIRCUIT CURRENT IS DETERMINED BY E APPLIED AND R.
   $I = \frac{E}{R} = \frac{120}{10} = 12$ AMPS.

3. CURRENT THROUGH BOTH L AND C IS 12 AMPS.

4. E ACROSS BOTH L AND C IS DETERMINED BY $I \times X_L$ AND $I \times X_C$.
   $E = I \times X_L = 12 \times 100 = 1200V$

Fig. 6-78. Series LCR resonant circuit characteristics.

Q6-91. When the value of X_L equals X_C in a series LCR circuit, a condition called _____ occurs.

Q6-92. At the resonant frequency, circuit current is at its _____ value; impedance is at its _____ value.

Q6-93. Below the resonant frequency a series LCR circuit acts _____; above the resonant frequency, _____.

Your Answers Should Be:

A6-91. When the value of X_L equals X_C in a series LCR circuit, a condition called **resonance** occurs.

A6-92. At the resonant frequency, circuit current is at its **maximum** value; impedance is at its **minimum** value.

A6-93. Below the resonant frequency a series LCR circuit acts **capacitively;** above the resonant frequency, **inductively.**

Resonant Frequency Formula

Every combination of inductance and capacitance will have a resonant frequency. Fig. 6-79 shows the formula used

$$f_o = \frac{1}{2\pi\sqrt{LC}}$$

RESONANT
FREQUENCY
(HERTZ)

Fig. 6-79. Resonant-frequency formula.

to determine this resonant frequency. Notice that the values of L and C must be known in order to determine the frequency.

Power in Series LCR Circuits

No power is consumed in a purely inductive or capacitive circuit. In a series LCR circuit the only power consumed will be resistive power. Fig. 6-80 shows the relationship between inductive, capacitive, and resistive voltage, current, and power. Current I, which is in phase with the applied a-c voltage, flows through all three components, L, C, and R. During the first quarter-cycle of each sine wave, the inductance is returning energy to the circuit and the capacitance is taking energy from the circuit at the same rate. During the second quarter-cycle, the situation is reversed—the capacitor is returning energy, and the inductor is taking it out. This sequence occurs during each cycle.

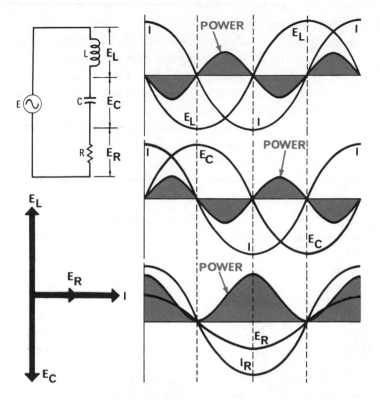

Fig. 6-80. Power in series LCR circuits.

The voltage across the capacitance is equal and opposite to the voltage across the coil at all times, and the two cancel. One voltage (E_C) is 90 degrees behind the current and the other voltage (E_L) is 90 degrees ahead.

Q6-94. The resonant frequency of a series LCR circuit containing a 2H inductor, 2-mfd capacitor, and a 100-ohm resistor is _____ Hz.

Q6-95. The power dissipated by a series resonant LCR circuit with an applied voltage of 120V, 1000 ohms X_L, 1000 ohms X_C, and 100 ohms R is _____ watts.

Q6-96. In a series LCR resonant circuit inductive voltage and capacitive voltage are _____ degrees out of phase.

211

Q of a Series LCR Circuit

The *Q or quality* of a series resonant LCR circuit is the ratio of either X_L or X_C to resistance in the circuit. Either X_L or X_C can be used at resonance because both will be the same value. At frequencies below resonance, Q is the ratio of X_C to R, and above resonance, Q is the ratio of X_L to R. Fig. 6-81 shows the formulas for determining the Q of a series LCR circuit.

$$\text{``Q''} \quad \frac{X_L}{R} = \frac{1000\Omega}{10\Omega} = \frac{100}{1} \text{ (HIGH ``Q'')}$$

$$\text{``Q''} \quad \frac{X_C}{R} = \frac{1000\Omega}{100\Omega} = \frac{10}{1} \text{ (LOW ``Q'')}$$

Fig 6-81. Series LCR circuit Q formulas.

It can be seen that the value of R in series with L and C will determine the Q of the circuit. If the value of R is low, the ratio of R to X_L (or X_C) will be high, or the Q of the circuit will be high. If on the other hand the value of R is high, the Q of the circuit will be low. Fig. 6-82 shows that it is the value of resistance that determines the total circuit current at resonance. At frequencies either below or above resonance, circuit current is determined by the reactance of either inductor or capacitor, and the resistor.

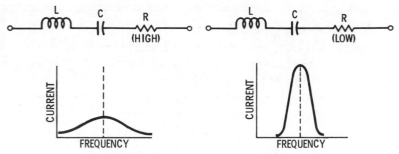

Fig. 6-82. Effect of resistance on circuit Q.

Therefore, the value of resistance will determine the amount of current primarily at the resonant frequency, and current will drop gradually on either side of the resonant frequency.

Series LCR circuits are normally given three broad Q ratings as shown in Fig. 6-83. A low-Q circuit, with a high value of resistance, will have low current and a very broad slope from minimum to maximum current. The medium-Q circuit has a higher current and a more rapid drop from minimum to maximum current. The high-Q circuit has a large resonant current and a very sharp drop on either side of resonance.

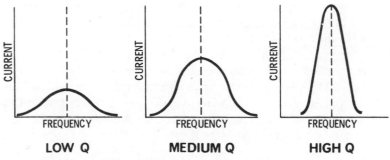

Fig. 6-83. Low-, medium-, and high-Q response curves.

Q6-97. An LCR circuit with an inductance of 0.5 henry a resistance of 10 ohms, and resonant at 1 kHz will have a Q of _____.

Q6-98. A series LCR resonant circuit with a very high current is called a _____-Q circuit.

Q6-99. Q is a ratio of inductive or capacitive reactance to _____.

PARALLEL LCR CIRCUITS

The parallel LCR circuit consists of a capacitor in parallel with a resistor-inductor combination. In many instances, the resistance shown is not a physical resistor, but represents the d-c resistance of the inductor.

Analysis of a Parallel LCR Circuit

When an a-c voltage is applied to a parallel LCR circuit, each of the two branches shows reactance. As shown in Fig. 6-84, the capacitive reactance in the capacitor branch is high at low frequencies, and decreases as the frequency increases. Similarly, the inductive reactance of the inductor branch is low at low frequencies, and increases with the frequency.

The capacitor has a high reactance and the inductor a low reactance at frequencies below resonance. Consequently, most of the current is through the inductive branch and lags the applied voltage. Similarly, if the frequency is above resonance, most of the current is in the capacitive branch and will lead the applied voltage.

At some particular frequency the two reactances in a parallel resonant circuit are exactly equal. Since there is an a-c voltage applied across each branch, two kinds of current are present—an inductive current in the inductive branch and a capacitive current in the capacitive branch. At resonance the two currents are equal. But, because one of the currents leads the applied voltage by 90 degrees and the other lags the voltage by 90 degrees, the two currents are 180 degrees out of phase with each other. This means that they will cancel (add up to zero).

The applied voltage was kept constant as the frequency was varied. Since current is a minimum throughout the circuit at resonance, a parallel circuit has a higher impedance at its resonant frequency than at any other frequency.

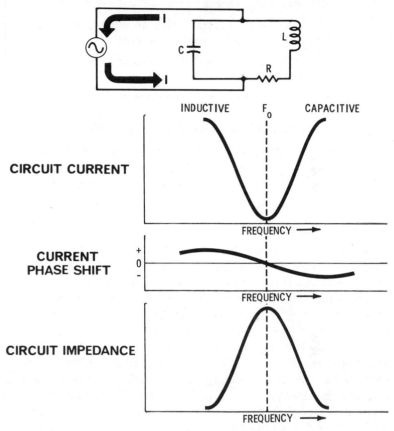

Fig. 6-84. Parallel LCR circuit analysis.

Q6-100. A parallel LCR circuit at a low frequency will act _____.

Q6-101. The impedance of a parallel LCR circuit at the resonant frequency is _____.

Q6-102. The circuit current of a parallel LCR circuit at the resonant frequency is _____ _____.

Action Within the Parallel LCR Loop

The action within the parallel LCR circuit or loop formed by L and C will be just the opposite of the external circuit. Fig. 6-85 shows that the two large currents, inductive and capacitive, still exist, but only inside the loop. Energy alternately flows from capacitor to inductor and back again,

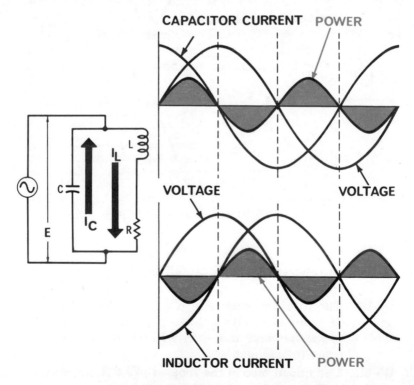

Fig. 6-85. Parallel LCR loop circuit analysis.

twice each cycle. The capacitor alternately charges and discharges, first in one direction and then in the other. The inductive magnetic field alternately builds up and collapses, changing polarity twice each cycle. But all this flow back and forth is contained in the loop, and none appears in the external circuit. The outside circuit only has to replenish the energy lost in any resistance the inductor has, and this constitutes the entire external current.

The Q of the circuit, just as in the series resonant circuit, is the inductive reactance at resonance divided by the resistance of the inductor $\left(\dfrac{X_L}{R_L}\right)$. In a parallel-resonant circuit the loop current between inductor and capacitor is Q times the external (resistive) current.

Impedance Formula for Parallel LCR Circuits

Fig. 6-86 shows the formula that can be used to determine the total impedance of parallel LCR circuits. It can be seen from the formula that the total circuit impedance will grow as X_L or X_C becomes greater relative to resistance. Impedance will decrease as R increases and draws more current.

$$Z_O = \frac{X_L \times X_C}{R}$$

(IMPEDANCE)

Fig. 6-86. Parallel LCR impedance formula.

Q6-103. In the parallel LCR circuit the loop current at resonance is _____.

Q6-104. The total impedance of a parallel LCR circuit at resonance with a 1-henry inductor, a 1-mfd capacitor and a d-c resistance of 1 ohm is _____.

Q6-105. The impedance in the loop or parallel LCR circuit at resonance is _____ _____.

Your Answers Should Be:

A6-103. In the parallel LCR circuit the loop current at resonance is **high**.

A6-104. The total impedance of a parallel LCR circuit at resonance with a 1-henry inductor, a 1-mfd capacitor and a d-c resistance of 1 ohm is **1 megohm**.

A6-105. The impedance in the loop or parallel LCR circuit at resonance is **very low**.

SUMMARY QUESTIONS

1. When there is current through a conductor, a magnetic field expands around the conductor. This field produces a counter emf as the current changes direction. The applied voltage and the counter emf are 180 degrees out of phase with each other. The current lags the applied voltage by 90 degrees, but leads the counter emf by 90 degrees.

   a. The counter emf is generated by an expanding _____ _____.

   b. The counter emf _____ the circuit current by _____ degrees.

2. Inductance opposes any change in current. The unit of measurement of inductance is the henry. Because the henry is an extremely large value of inductance, it is seldom found in electronic circuits. More common values are millihenrys and microhenrys.

   a. A millihenry is _____ of a henry.

   b. The unit of measurement for inductance is the _____.

3. The three factors that determine the amount of inductance of a coil are the number of turns, coil diameter, and core material. Increasing the number of turns or the coil diameter will increase inductance, and changing core material from air to either iron or powdered iron will increase inductance.

   a. If a coil with 50 turns has an inductance of 200 millihenrys, a decrease to 25 turns will lower the inductance to _____ millihenrys.

b. If a coil with a diameter of .5 inch and an inductance of 1000 millihenrys were doubled in diameter, inductance would increase to _____ millihenrys.

4. An a-c circuit containing only inductance will have a phase difference between the applied voltage and the circuit current of 90 degrees, with current lagging the voltage. This phase difference can be shown simply by the use of vectors.

  a. In an inductive circuit, the voltage _____ the current by _____ degrees.

  b. When using vectors, the length of each vector represents _____.

5. When inductors are connected in series, the total value of inductance is determined by adding the values of the individual inductors. When inductors are connected in parallel, either the *like* method, used for equal value inductors, or the *product-over-sum* method is used to determine total inductance. Total inductance of series-parallel connected inductors is determined by finding the inductance of the series and parallel branches. The same methods used to determine total resistance apply to finding total inductance.

  a. If two inductors connected in series have a total inductance of 650 millihenry, when L1 is 250 millihenrys, L2 inductance is _____ millihenrys.

  b. If total inductance is lower than the inductor with the lowest value, they are connected in _____.

6. Inductive reactance, represented by X_L is the opposition offered to alternating current by an inductor. X_L is measured in ohms. Inductive reactance differs from resistance in that when the frequency of the applied a-c voltage changes, the X_L changes. The lower the frequency, the lower the X_L; the higher the frequency, the higher the X_L.

  a. The amount of X_L of an inductor is dependent on the frequency of the applied a-c voltage and _____.

  b. Inductive reactance is measured in _____.

7. Inductors are frequently used in circuits called filters, which allow only certain frequencies to pass through them and block all others. The names of the various filter circuits describe their actions. The low-pass filter

passes only low frequencies and blocks high frequencies. The high-pass filter has the opposite effect. The band-pass filter passes only a band of frequencies and blocks frequencies on both sides of that band.

   a. In a low-pass filter circuit, the inductance is in _____ with the input-output terminals.

   b. In a high-pass filter circuit, the inductance is in _____ with the input-output terminals.

8. A transformer is a device that consists of a primary and secondary winding and is used to transfer power from one voltage-current level to another voltage-current level. The three general classes of transformers are air core, iron core, and powdered iron core. When power is transferred from primary to secondary, the frequency of the a-c voltage remains the same, but the secondary voltage and current are 180 degrees out of phase with primary voltage and current. The amount of voltage and current in the secondary is determined by the turns ratio between the transformer primary and secondary. A step-up transformer will have a higher secondary voltage and lower secondary current, the amount being determined by the turns ratio. A step-down transformer will be just the opposite; a lower secondary voltage and higher secondary current, with the amount determined by the turns ratio.

   a. Transformer secondary current will be greater than primary current in a step-_____ transformer.

   b. Transformer secondary voltage will be greater than primary voltage in a step-_____ transformer.

   c. A transformer with five turns on the secondary for every primary turn and with 120 volts applied, will have a secondary voltage of _____ volts.

9. When an a-c circuit contains both inductance and resistance, the total opposition to alternating current is called impedance. Impedance can be determined by using vectors to represent both phase and amount of inductive reactance and resistance, or by using the impedance formula.

   a. When using the impedance formula, total impedance can be found by determining the square root of _____ _____ and _____ _____ _____.

b. The impedance of an RL circuit with 3 ohms resistance and 4 ohms inductive reactance is _____ ohms.

10. The amount of power consumed by a purely inductive circuit is practically zero. When current is increasing, inductance converts energy into a magnetic field. When the current is decreasing the magnetic field collapses, returning the energy to the circuit. Energy is borrowed, but none is used. The only power consumed is that which is used by the very small d-c resistance of the inductor.

    a. The amount of power consumed by an inductive circuit is practically _____.

11. When a pulse voltage is applied to an RL circuit the length of time required for circuit current to reach 63 percent of maximum is called the time constant. Time constant is determined by dividing the value of R in ohms the value of L in henrys. The resulting waveshapes across R and L are distorted with respect to the pulse input voltage. The inductor voltage is called the differentiated voltage. and the resistor voltage is called the integrated voltage. Five time constants are required for circuit current to reach its maximum value. The universal time constant chart can be used to calculate voltage or current value at any instant of time.

    a. The time constant of an RL circuit can be determined by dividing _____ by _____.

    b. In an RL circuit the resistor voltage waveform is called the _____ voltage, and the inductor voltage waveform the _____ voltage.

12. The time constant-to-period ratio is a ratio of time duration of the RL circuit to pulse time. This ratio determines the waveshapes of the voltages across both the resistor and the inductor. The most common TC-to-P ratios used are short, very short, extra short, intermediate, long, and very long.

    a. The period of a pulse is determined by dividing the _____ of the pulse into 1.

    b. All of the input voltage appears across the inductor during the input pulse _____ _____.

13. Capacitance is the property of an electrical circuit that opposes any change in voltage. The capacitor consists of

two conducting plates separated by an insulating material called the dielectric. The two types of capacitors are fixed and variable. A capacitor will block direct current, but will appear to pass alternating current due to the alternate charging and discharging of the capacitor plates. The unit of measurement for capacitors is the farad, although the more commonly used values are microfarad and picofarad (micromicrofarad).

a. The dielectric is the _____ material between the plates of a capacitor.

b. Capacitance is the property that opposes a change in _____.

c. A capacitor is charged when it has the _____ number of electrons.

14. The three factors that affect the value of capacitance are the area of the plates, the separation or distance between the plates, and the type of dielectric material used. The larger the area of the plates, the greater the capacitance; and the smaller the distance between the plates, the greater the capacitance. The higher the dielectric constant of the insulating material between the plate, the greater the capacitance.

a. If a .01-mfd capacitor has its plate area enlarged three times, its capacitance will be _____ mfd.

b. If the distance between the plates of a capacitor is doubled capacitance will be _____ its original value.

15. When capacitors are connected in series, parallel, or series-parallel, the methods used to determine total capacitance differ from those used for resistors or inductors. The methods used for determining total parallel resistance or inductance, that is the *like* or the *product-over-sum*, are used to determine total series capacitance. Capacitors add in parallel, as do resistors and inductors in series. With series-parallel connected capacitors the circuit is broken into individual series or parallel branches, then analyzed the same as a resistor or inductor circuit.

a. If a .05-mfd, a .01-mfd, and a .025-mfd capacitor are connected in parallel, total capacitance will be _____ mfd.

b. If three .03-mfd capacitors are connected in series, total capacitance will be _____ mfd.

16. The relationship between voltage and current in a capacitive circuit is just the opposite of their relationship in the inductive circuit. In a capacitive circuit current leads voltage by 90 degrees. Again, vectors can be used to show this current-voltage relationship.

   a. In a capacitive circuit the vector representation of voltage is shown 90 degrees _____ the current vector.

17. The opposition offered by a capacitor to alternating current is called capacitive reactance, or X_C and it is measured in ohms. Capacitive reactance differs from resistance in that when the frequency of the applied a-c voltage changes, the X_C changes.

   a. If the current in a capacitive circuit is high at a high frequency, and the frequency of the applied voltage is lowered, the current will _____.

   b. The value of X_C depends on the value of capacitance and the _____ of the applied voltage.

18. When an a-c circuit contains both capacitance and resistance, the total opposition to alternating current is called impedance. The total circuit impedance can be determined by using a vector analysis to represent the phase and amount of capacitive reactance and resistance, or by using the impedance formula.

   a. When using the impedance formula, total impedance can be found by determining the square root of _____ _____ and _____ _____.

   b. The impedance of an RL circuit with 9 ohms resistance and 12 ohms X_C is _____ ohms.

19. When a pulse voltage is applied to an RC circuit the length of time required for the capacitor to charge to 63 percent of the applied voltage is called the time constant. The time constant is found by multiplying the value of R in ohms by the value of C in farads. The waveshape of the pulse input voltage appears distorted across R and C. The resistor voltage is called the differentiated voltage, and the capacitor voltage is called the integrated voltage. Five time constants are required for the capacitor to charge to its maximum voltage level, or

for the resistor voltage to drop to its minimum value.

    a. The time constant of an RC circuit can be determined by multiplying _____ times _____.

    b. In an RC circuit the resistor voltage waveform is called the _____ voltage, and the capacitor voltage the _____ voltage.

20. The time constant-to-period ratio is a ratio of the time duration of the RC circuit to the input pulse voltage time. The TC-to-P ratio determines the waveshape of the voltage across both the resistor and the capacitor. The most common TC-to-P ratios used are extra short, very short, short, intermediate, long, very long.

    a. A very long TC-to-P ratio will provide an almost perfect reproduction of the input pulse voltage across the _____.

    b. When the leading edge of a pulse voltage is applied to an RC circuit, all of the voltage will appear across the _____.

21. A series LCR circuit, or one that contains resistance, inductance, and capacitance, assumes the characteristic of the predominant reactance. Since X_L and X_C have opposite characteristics, a condition called resonance occurs when the two reactances are equal and cancel each other. The following circuit conditions apply to a series LCR circuit:

    1. The circuit acts capacitively at frequencies below resonance, and inductively at frequencies above resonance. At resonance, the circuit is resistive.

    2. Circuit impedance is at its maximum value both below and above resonance, but at its minimum value at resonance.

    3. Circuit current is at its minimum value both below and above resonance, but at its maximum value at resonance.

        a. The only opposition to current in a series LCR circuit at resonance is that offered by the _____.

        b. The series resonant circuit that has the greatest amount of current will be the one with the _____ Q or quality.

22. A parallel LCR circuit exhibits properties that are in most respects the opposite of the series LCR circuit. The

following circuit conditions apply to a parallel LCR circuit:

1. The circuit acts capacitively at frequencies below resonance, and inductively at frequencies above resonance. At resonance, the circuit is resistive.

2. Circuit impedance is low at frequencies below and above resonance, but is at its maximum value at resonance.

3. Circuit current is at a high value at frequencies below and above resonance, but at its minimum value at resonance.

4. Loop current, or current within the LC circuit, is minimum at frequencies below and above resonance and maximum at resonance.

   a. Within the loop or LC circuit the impedance at the resonant frequency is _____.

   b. Current to and from the voltage source in a parallel LCR circuit at resonance is at its _____ value.

SUMMARY ANSWERS

1a. The counter emf is generated by an expanding **magnetic field**.

1b. The counter emf **lags** the circuit current by 90 degrees.

2a. A millihenry is **one-thousandth** of a henry.

2b. The unit of measurement for inductance is the **henry**.

3a. If a coil with 50 turns has an inductance of 200 millihenrys, a decrease to 25 turns will lower the inductance to 50 millihenrys.

3b. If a coil with a diameter of .5 inch and in inductance of 1000 millihenrys were doubled in diameter, inductance would increase to **4000** millihenrys.

4a. In an inductive circuit, the voltage **leads** the current by **90** degrees.

4b. When using vectors, the length of each vector represents **magnitude**.

5a. If two inductors connected in series have a total inductance of 650 millihenrys, when L1 is 250 millihenrys, L2 inductance is **400** millihenrys.

5b. If total inductance is lower than the inductor with the lowest value, they are connected in **parallel**.

6a. The amount of X_L of an inductor is dependent on the frequency of the applied a-c voltage and **inductance**.

6b. Inductive reactance is measured in **ohms**.

7a. In a low-pass filter circuit, the inductance is in **series** with the input-output terminals.

7b. In a high-pass filter circuit, the inductance is in **parallel** with the input-output terminals.

8a. Transformer secondary current will be greater than primary current in a step-**down** transformer.

8b. Transformer secondary voltage will be greater than primary voltage in a step-**up** transformer.

8c. A transformer with five turns on the secondary for every primary turn and with 120 volts applied, will have a secondary voltage of **600** volts.

9a. When using the impedance formula, total impedance can be found by determining the square root of **resistance squared** and **inductive reactance squared**.

9b. The impedance of an RL circuit with 3 ohms resistance and 4 ohms inductive reactance is 5 ohms.

10a. The amount of power consumed by an inductive circuit is practically **zero.**

11a. The time constant of an RL circuit can be determined by dividing **L** by **R.**

11b. In an RL circuit the resistor voltage waveform is called the **integrated** voltage, and the inductor voltage waveform the **differentiated** voltage.

12a. The period of a pulse is determined by dividing the **frequency** of the pulse into 1.

12b. All of the input voltage appears across the inductor during the input pulse **rise time.**

13a. The dielectric is the **insulating** material between the plates of a capacitor.

13b. Capacitance is the property that opposes a change in **voltage.**

13c. A capacitor is charged when it has the **maximum** number of electrons.

14a. If a .01-mfd capacitor has its plate area enlarged three times its capacitance will be **.03** mfd.

14b. If the distance between the plates of a capacitor is doubled, capacitance will be **one-half** its original value.

15a. If a .05-mfd, a .01 mfd, and a .025 mfd capacitor are connected in parallel, total capacitance will be **.085** mfd.

15b. If three .03-mfd capacitors are connected in series, total capacitance will be **.01** mfd.

16a. In a capacitive circuit the vector representation of voltage is shown 90 degrees **behind** the current vector.

17a. If the current in a capacitive circuit is high at a high frequency, and the frequency of the applied voltage is lowered, the current will **decrease.**

17b. The value of X_C depends on the value of capacitance and the **frequency** of the applied voltage.

18a. When using the impedance formula, total impedance can be found by determining the square root of **resistance squared** and X_C **squared.**

18b. The impedance of an RL circuit with 9 ohms resistance and 12 ohms X_C is **15** ohms.

19a. The time constant of an RC circuit can be determined by multiplying **R** times **C.**

19b. In an RC circuit the resistor voltage waveform is called

- the **differentiated** voltage, and the capacitor voltage the **integrated** voltage.

20a. A very long TC-to-P ratio will provide an almost perfect reproduction of the input pulse voltage across the **resistor**.

20b. When the leading edge of a pulse voltage is applied to an RC circuit, all of the voltage will appear across the **resistor**.

21a. The only opposition to current in a series LCR circuit at resonance is that offered by the **resistor**.

21b. The series resonant circuit that has the greatest amount of current will be the one with the **highest** Q or quality.

22a. Within the loop or LC circuit the impedance at the resonant frequency is **minimum**.

22b. Current to and from the voltage source in a parallel LCR circuit at resonance is at its **minimum** value.

FINAL TEST

1. The transistor is a _____-controlling device.
   a. voltage
   b. current
   c. power
   d. impedance

2. The nucleus of an atom contains _____ and _____.
   a. protons, electrons
   b. electrons, neutrons
   c. protons, neutrons
   d. photons, neutrons

3. Atoms are electrically neutral when they have the same number of _____ and _____.
   a. protons, electrons
   b. electrons, neutrons
   c. protons, neutrons
   d. photons, neutrons

4. A material through which electrons can pass readily is called a(an) _____.
   a. insulator
   b. field
   c. vacuum
   d. conductor

5. _____ poles of a magnet repel and _____ poles of a magnet attract.
   a. like, unlike
   b. like, like
   c. unlike, unlike
   d. unlike, like

6. A difference in potential is measured in units called _____.
   a. amperes
   b. coulombs
   c. joules
   d. volts

7. A car battery converts _____ energy to _____ energy.
   a. light, electrical
   b. mechanical, electrical
   c. chemical, mechanical
   d. chemical, electrical

8. Maximum current is induced in a wire when it moves at an angle of _____ to the magnetic lines of force.
   a. 0°
   b. 30°
   c. 45°
   d. 90°

9. If the period of a sine wave is 25 μsec, the frequency is _____.
   a. 25kHz
   b. 25MHz
   c. 4kHz
   d. 40kHz

10. The power in a circuit may be found by _____.
    a. $E \times I$
    b. $E \div I$
    c. $E \div R$
    d. $I \times R$

11. A resistor with the following colors: yellow, purple, and green (from left to right) has a value of _____.
    a. 470K
    b. 4.7Meg
    c. 570K
    d. 47Meg

12. The incorrect equation is _____.
    a. $E = I \times R$
    b. $I = E \div R$
    c. $R = E \div I$
    d. $E = I \div R$

13. As the resistance in a circuit is increased the current in a circuit _____.
    a. increases

b. decreases

c. remains the same

14. A resistor whose colors are brown, red, yellow, and silver may have a maximum value of _____.

    a. 144K
    b. 132K
    c. 126K
    d. 13.2K

15. With a current of 2 amperes through a resistance of 12 ohms, the power dissipated is _____.

    a. 24 watts
    b. 3 watts
    c. 48 watts
    d. 288 watts

16. When 12 volts are applied to a circuit whose resistance is 6Kohms the current will be _____.

    a. 2 amperes
    b. 0.2 amperes
    c. 20 ma
    d. 2 ma

17. When 3 μamps flows through an 18Kohm resistor the voltage drop will be _____.
    a. 54 volts
    b. 54 millivolts
    c. 54 microvolts
    d. 6 millivolts

18. When a current of 20 ma is due to a voltage of 40 volts, the resistance in the circuit is _____.

    a. 20K
    b. 2K
    c. 200 ohms
    d. 20 ohms

19. A 12K resistor in series with a 6K resistor results in a total resistance of _____.

a. 18K
b. 9K
c. 6K
d. 4K

20. The total resistance of a circuit containing a 240-ohm resistor in parallel with an 80-ohm resistor is _____.
    a. 320 ohms
    b. 160 ohms
    c. 60 ohms
    d. 40 ohms

21. Three 15K resistors in parallel result in a resistance of _____.

    a. 45K
    b. 30K
    c. 15K
    d. 5K

22. There are three paths for current at a junction, (paths A, B, and C). If path A supplies 5 ma to the junction, and path B has a current of 8 ma leaving the junction, then path C has a current of _____ ma (entering, leaving) the junction.
    a. 13 ma leaving
    b. 13 ma entering
    c. 3 ma leaving
    d. 3 ma entering

23. A device that offers more impedance to current in one direction than in the other is a (an) _____.
    a. transistor
    b. diode
    c. inductor
    d. capacitor

24. A variable resistor is called a _____.
    a. varactor
    b. variometer

c. potentiometer
d. varistor

25. As the temperature in a resistor is increased, its resistance _____.
    a. increases
    b. decreases
    c. remains the same

26. The resistance of a wire may be increased by (increasing, decreasing) its length and (increasing, decreasing) its cross-sectional area.
    a. increasing, increasing
    b. increasing, decreasing
    c. decreasing, increasing
    d. decreasing, decreasing

27. In order to exist in a stable orbit in a given shell an electron must have a certain _____ level.
    a. energy
    b. valence
    c. potential
    d. conduction

28. The device whose atomic arrangement falls into the cubic lattice system is the _____.
    a. conductor
    b. semiconductor
    c. insulator
    d. inductor

29. The sharing of an electron by adjacent atoms of a semiconductor is known as _____ bonding.
    a. covalent
    b. valence
    c. nuclear
    d. atomic

30. A crystal without impurities is known as a (an) _____ crystal.

a. face-centered
b. body-centered
c. ionic
d. intrinsic

31. N-type germanium is formed by doping it with a _____ material.
    a. pentavalent
    b. tetravalent
    c. crystalline
    d. ionic

32. When the positive terminal of a battery is connected to the N-type region of a PN junction it is said to be _____.
    a. inverted
    b. forward-biased
    c. reverse-biased
    d. diffused

33. The process by which an a-c signal is converted into pulsating direct current is known as _____.
    a. amplification
    b. rectification
    c. inversion
    d. conversion

34. A constantly changing current in a wire results in a (an) _____.
    a. counter emf
    b. inductance
    c. conductance
    d. voltage

35. The property of a circuit that tends to oppose a change in current is called _____.
    a. capacitance
    b. resistance
    c. conductance
    d. inductance

36. The value of an inductor may be increased by (increasing,

decreasing) the number of turns and (increasing, decreasing) the coil diameter.
a. decreasing, decreasing
b. decreasing, increasing
c. increasing, decreasing
d. increasing, increasing

37. In an inductive circuit the current _____ the voltage by _____ degrees.
a. leads, 90
b. leads, 180
c. lags, 90
d. lags, 180

38. The total inductance of a circuit containing a 6-mh inductor in series with a 3-mh inductor is _____.
a. 18 mh
b. 9 mh
c. 3 mh
d. 2 mh

39. The parallel combination of a 36-μh inductor and a 12-μh inductor is equivalent to a _____ inductor.
a. 48-μh
b. 24-μh
c. 9-μh
d. 6-μh

40. The inductive reactance of a circuit may be increased by (increasing, decreasing) its inductance and (increasing, decreasing) the frequency of the applied voltage.
a. increasing, increasing
b. increasing, decreasing
c. decreasing, increasing
d. decreasing, decreasing

41. A device that allows only low frequencies to pass is known as a _____.
a. high-pass filter

b. bandpass filter
c. low-pass filter

42. If 20 volts are applied to the primary of a transformer having a turns ratio of 5:1, the voltage in the secondary will be _____.
a. 100V
b. 20V
c. 4V
d. 1V

43. In a step-up transformer the voltage is (stepped-up, stepped-down) and the current is (stepped-up, stepped-down).
a. stepped-up, stepped-up
b. stepped-up stepped-down
c. stepped-down, stepped-up
d. stepped-down, stepped-down

44. The impedance of a circuit containing a 6-ohm resistor in series with an 8-ohm inductive reactance is _____.
a. 100 ohms,
b. 48 ohms
c. 14 ohms
d. 10 ohms

45. In an RL circuit the time required for the current to reach 63 percent of its maximum value is known as the _____.
a. critical value
b. time constant
c. time factor
d. time vector

46. When a square wave is applied to an LR circuit the waveform across the inductor is _____.
a. integrated
b. differentiated
c. truncated
d. inebriated

47. A device that opposes a change in voltage in a circuit is called a (an) _____.
  a. resistor
  b. capacitor
  c. inductor
  d. transistor

48. A 48-mfd capacitor and a 16-mfd capacitor are connected in parallel, the total capacitance is _____.
  a. 64 mfd
  b. 32 mfd
  c. 24 mfd
  d. 12 mfd

49. Capacitance may be decreased by (decreasing, increasing) the plate area and (decreasing, increasing) the distance between the plates.
  a. decreasing, decreasing
  b. decreasing, increasing
  c. increasing, decreasing
  d. increasing, increasing

50. The capacitive reactance in a circuit may be increased by (increasing, decreasing) the capacitance in the circuit and (increasing, decreasing) the frequency applied to the circuit.
  a. increasing, increasing
  b. increasing, decreasing
  c. decreasing, increasing
  d. decreasing, decreasing

51. A 20-mfd capacitor in series with a 100K resistor results in a time constant of _____.
  a. 20 seconds
  b. 5 seconds
  c. 2 seconds
  d. 0.5 seconds

52. In an RC circuit the current (leads, lags) the voltage by _____ degrees.

  a. leads, 90
  b. leads, 180
  c. lags, 90
  d. lags, 180

53. The voltage across the capacitor in an RC circuit is _____.
  a. integrated
  b. differentiated
  c. desegregated
  d. obliterated

54. The ratio used to determine the shape of a waveform across a component is known as _____.
  a. L-to-R
  b. R-to-C
  c. TC-to-f
  d. TC-to-P

55. In an LCR circuit the total reactance is equal to the _____ X_L and X_C.
  a. sum of
  b. difference between
  c. product of
  d. ratio between

56. In a series-resonant LCR circuit X_L is _____ X_C.
  a. greater than
  b. equal to
  c. less than
  d. in phase with

57. In a series LCR circuit power will be consumed in _____.
  a. L and C only
  b. L only
  c. C only
  d. R only

58. The Q of a resonant circuit is the ratio of _____.
  a. X_L to X_C
  b. X_L to R
  c. X_C to X_L
  d. R to X_C

59. The impedance of a series resonant circuit is _____.
    a. maximum
    b. equal to X_L
    c. equal to X_C
    d. minimum

60. The impedance of a parallel circuit is _____.
    a. maximum
    b. equal to X_L
    c. equal to X_C
    d. minimum

ANSWERS TO FINAL TEST

1.	b	21.	d	41.	c
2.	c	22.	d	42.	c
3.	a	23.	b	43.	b
4.	d	24.	c	44.	d
5.	a	25.	a	45.	b
6.	d	26.	b	46.	b
7.	d	27.	a	47.	b
8.	d	28.	b	48.	a
9.	d	29.	a	49.	b
10.	a	30.	d	50.	d
11.	b	31.	a	51.	c
12.	d	32.	c	52.	a
13.	b	33.	b	53.	a
14.	b	34.	a	54.	d
15.	c	35.	d	55.	b
16.	d	36.	d	56.	b
17.	b	37.	c	57.	d
18.	b	38.	b	58.	b
19.	a	39.	c	59.	d
20.	c	40.	a	60.	a

Index

FOOD-BORNE ILLNESSES

Karen F. Balkin, *Book Editor*

Bonnie Szumski, *Publisher*
Scott Barbour, *Managing Editor*
Helen Cothran, *Senior Editor*

GREENHAVEN
PRESS®

San Diego • Detroit • New York • San Francisco • Cleveland
New Haven, Conn. • Waterville, Maine • London • Munich

THOMSON
———————✳———————™
GALE

LIBRARY OF CONGRESS CATALOGING-IN-PUBLICATION DATA

Food-borne illnesses / Karen F. Balkin, book editor.
    p. cm. — (At issue)
Includes bibliographical references and index.
ISBN 0-7377-1334-8 (lib. : alk. paper) — ISBN 0-7377-1335-6 (pbk. : alk. paper)
    1. Food-borne diseases. 2. Food poisoning. 3. Food—Microbiology. I. Balkin, Karen F., 1949– . II. At issue (San Diego, Calif.)
RC143.F657 2004
615.9'54—dc22   2003066265

Printed in the United States of America

Contents

Page

Introduction

Laws in place today make meat processing the most highly regulated sector of the American food industry. Because contaminated meat has the potential to cause serious illness and even death among thousands of consumers, the development of an effective, federally regulated meat inspection program was a critical step in the prevention of food-borne illness in the United States. Indeed, America is now widely considered to have the safest meat supply in the world.

Beginning in the late 1800s, when exported salt pork and bacon were subject to inspection for trichinosis, federal laws have mandated the inspection of meat to prevent the spread of food-borne illnesses. Because meat is subject to contamination at many points during processing, careful inspection is necessary to ensure that consumers purchase a wholesome product free from food-borne pathogens. While the benefits to public health are undeniable, the passage of federal meat inspection laws has been surrounded by social, political, and scientific controversy for more than a century.

Heated debate followed the passage of the Meat Inspection Law of 1891. According to economist E.C. Pasour of North Carolina State University, this landmark legislation was not enacted to protect consumers from disease caused by contaminated meat. Rather, it was passed in response to unfounded charges by small meat packers that the large packers of the day—Swift, Armour, Morris, and Hammond—were selling unsafe beef. Pasour maintains that smaller slaughterhouses could not compete with larger houses and thus started rumors that the larger companies were selling tainted meat. The stories of unsafe beef frightened domestic buyers and ultimately harmed the export market. Soon, large and small meat packers alike were clamoring for federal meat inspection to prove to consumers that beef was safe to eat. The passage of the Meat Inspection Act of 1891, Pasour argues, was the federal government's political response to an economic problem, not a public health issue.

Less than twenty years after the Meat Inspection Act of 1891 was passed, an obscure Socialist writer published a novel depicting the supposed human degradation, animal cruelty, corruption, and filth associated with meatpacking. The novel stimulated cries for more government regulation of the industry. Upton Sinclair had hoped that his book, *The Jungle*, would focus attention on the evils of capitalism and the plight of oppressed workers. Instead, readers were appalled by the few pages he devoted to a description of the gory and unsanitary conditions under which meat was processed. "I aimed at the public's heart," Sinclair later wrote, "and by accident I hit it in the stomach." Demand for beef dropped as the book became increasingly popular. Beef exports were hurt as well. Winston Churchill, not yet prime minister of Great Britain, said that *The Jungle* "pierces the thickest skull and most leathery heart."

Most historians and Sinclair biographers agree that he spent little time in the Chicago slaughterhouses he called "Packingtown" and did not witness or even speak with people who experienced the horrors about which he had written. Whether *The Jungle* was an accurate description of slaughterhouses or not, it stimulated a public outcry that resulted in a congressional investigation of the meatpacking industry—and ultimately led to passage of the Meat Inspection Act of 1906. Then-president Theodore Roosevelt, who ordered the investigation, was skeptical of Sinclair and wrote in a letter to William Allen White in July 1906, "I have an utter contempt for him. He is hysterical, unbalanced, and untruthful. Three-fourths of the things he said were absolute falsehoods. For some of the remainder there was only a basis of truth." Despite his contempt for Sinclair and *The Jungle*, Roosevelt signed the Meat Inspection Act along with the Pure Food and Drug Act (which banned adulterated food and unsafe patent medicine) on June 30, 1906.

Lawrence W. Reed of the Mackinac Center for Public Policy argues that the Meat Inspection Act of 1906, like the act passed in 1891, had less to do with public health and more to do with profits. He writes: "When the sensational accusations of *The Jungle* became worldwide news, foreign purchases of American meat were cut in half and the meatpackers looked to new regulations to give their markets a calming sense of security." Nevertheless, despite the fact that the new legislation was passed mainly out of economic considerations and cost the taxpayers of the day $3 million, it did provide for more meat inspectors, new regulations for smaller slaughtering operations, and stricter regulations for larger facilities. Consumers were satisfied that Roosevelt had responded to the will of the people and used the power of the federal government to ensure a safer meat supply.

The Poultry Products Inspection Act of 1957 (which added the inspection of interstate-bound poultry to the list of federal inspection responsibilities) and the Wholesome Meat Act of 1967 and the Wholesome Poultry Act of 1968 (both involved scrutiny of plant facilities and processes, not just carcasses) marked the only changes in meat inspection laws for the next ninety years. Trained inspectors continued to rely on their experience and the "poke and sniff" method to determine the wholesomeness of meat. If meat moving down a slaughterhouse packing line looked fresh and wholesome, did not smell as if it were spoiled, or feel spongy or slimy, it was given a U.S. Department of Agriculture (USDA) approval stamp. Unfortunately, the "poke and sniff" method could not detect the presence of *Salmonella* or *E. coli*, two food-borne pathogens that can sicken and even kill consumers.

The inherent limitations of the "poke and sniff" inspection method eventually had fatal consequences. A deadly outbreak of *E. coli* in 1993 was traced to undercooked hamburgers eaten at a Jack in the Box restaurant in the Pacific Northwest. Hundreds of people in the area became ill and several children died. USDA guidelines and consumer education materials were revised, now recommending that processed beef be cooked at a higher temperature to kill *E. coli*. However, consumer organizations like Safe Tables Our Priority (STOP), an activist group started by the mothers of children who had died in the Jack in the Box *E. coli* outbreak, demanded more. According to STOP, "After numerous, substantive contacts with USDA officials . . . S.T.O.P. became a key player in facilitating the first meat and poultry inspection reforms in over 90 years; reforms that included microbial testing for animal fecal contamination [the source of *E. coli*]."

The federal government again responded to a public outcry for safer meat, and in 1996, then-president Bill Clinton made the Hazard Analysis and Critical Control Points (HACCP) system part of a new inspection law. The HACCP system involves identifying points in a processing plant where contamination is most likely to occur and finding methods to prevent it. Each plant can design its own HACCP system but must meet certain federal standards. Then-secretary of agriculture Dan Glickman said, "Rather than catching problems after they occur, we will now focus on preventing problems in the first place." A key point in the HACCP system involves microbiological tests of raw meat and poultry to detect *E. coli* and *Salmonella*. Clinton said at the time, "These new meat and poultry contamination safeguards will be the strongest ever. They are flexible and they do challenge the private sector to take responsibility. They also use the most up-to-date science to track down invisible threats."

Although the HACCP system represented a vast improvement over the Meat Inspection Act of 1906, critics insisted that it did not go far enough. Under the HACCP, company workers were expected to keep records of how well the system was working. For example, companies were required to test for *E. coli*, but no federal inspector would oversee the tests or the final results. In a June 30, 2000, decision (*American Federation of Government Employees et al., v. the U.S. Department of Agriculture et al.*), the U.S. Court of Appeals for the District of Columbia Circuit ruled that it was the duty of federal employees—USDA employees not meatpacking plant employees—to determine whether a product was adulterated or unadulterated. The Court of Appeals ruled unanimously that federal inspectors have a statutory duty to examine meat and poultry carcass-by-carcass.

The passage of federal meat inspection laws over the past century represents the government's most significant effort at preventing food-borne illnesses. In *At Issue: Food-Borne Illnesses*, authors consider the causes of and evaluate possible solutions to this ongoing public health threat.

1

Food-Borne Illnesses: An Overview

Rick Linsk and Gita Sitaramiah

Rick Linsk and Gita Sitaramiah are reporters for the Pioneer Press *in Minnesota.*

Nationally, two out of every five cases of food-borne illness begins with restaurants or caterers. The poor hand-washing practices of restaurant employees spread many types of illness, such as hepatitis A. The presence of other disease-causing organisms such as *E. coli, Salmonella*, and *Listeria*, is usually the result of fecal contamination of meat during processing. Poor food-handling procedures, such as not cooking meat at a temperature high enough to kill pathogens or failing to keep food cold enough to prevent bacteria growth, also cause food-borne illnesses.

Tracie Eckstrom's friends still rib her: She should have had a beer. Relaxing at the Hoggsbreath Bar & Restaurant in Little Canada, [Minnesota] after a softball game in March [2000], Eckstrom was the only team member who drank a glass of ice water. And she was the only one in her group who got hepatitis A.

Thanks to an infected cook who used the bathroom and failed to adequately wash his hands, Eckstrom and 38 other people contracted the virus, which causes nausea, fever, stomach cramps and malaise. An estimated 2,000 people were exposed at the popular sports bar, and more than 800 lined up for protective shots.

Outbreaks of food-borne illness are becoming increasingly familiar.

About 25 times a year on average, public health agencies in Minnesota hear about groups of people getting sick after eating at restaurants, catered events, church picnics, schools, private parties and other venues. The rate is about the same in Wisconsin.

Government-investigated outbreaks barely scratch the surface of food-borne illness in the United States. Most of the estimated 76 million people who get sick annually from something they ate, including 500,000 in Minnesota, never become known to public health agencies.

Still, a look at the records of known outbreaks provides insights into where and how Americans are getting sick, and what can be done about it.

Trends suggest cause for concern, even as public health agencies wield sophisticated new tools to trace and stamp out food-borne disease. For example:

Minnesota's reported outbreaks have increased sharply in recent years. Better detection techniques are one reason, but experts also point to new or evolving germs taking advantage of changes in our diets, the way food is produced, and a more vulnerable population. Some health researchers fear the United States is on the verge of a food-borne illness epidemic.

Restaurants and catered events—not backyard picnics or grocery stores—are the most common places where reported outbreaks start. Many are caused by restaurant employees who come to work sick or handle food improperly.

Most food-borne illness victims suffer for only a few days, but some cases end in tragedy. In July [2000], a 3-year-old South Milwaukee, [Wisconsin] girl died from kidney failure in an *E. coli* outbreak that investigators linked to contaminated ground beef. Last year [1999], a Rochester [Minnesota]–area man died in an outbreak involving deli meats contaminated with *Listeria*.

Most outbreaks remain hidden from the public, meaning you may walk into a restaurant and not know others have been ill. State and local officials say they announce outbreaks only when there's a risk that illnesses still are spreading.

Health investigators from Minnesota, Wisconsin and the federal government have traced outbreaks to a variety of weak links in the food chain, from contaminated ingredients to malfunctioning equipment to mistakes by kitchen workers. Outbreaks can strike at well-run restaurants whose employees make one crucial mistake, or at dirty establishments rife with unsafe practices. Home cooks can unwittingly start outbreaks in their own kitchens or at community events, too.

In Minnesota and Wisconsin, half the outbreaks in recent years began with restaurants or caterers. They were the leading source nationally as well, starting two of every five reported outbreaks from 1988 to 1997, according to the U.S. Centers for Disease Control and Prevention. Cooks at home were to blame one of every five times, the CDC said. Experts believe the numbers may be skewed because food-borne illness victims are more likely to complain about a restaurant than about themselves, their church or a private club.

Loyalty tested

"DRINKIN DANCIN EATIN," announces the sign outside the Hoggsbreath. Another near the front door warns against parking motorcycles on the sidewalk. The Rice Street sports bar might not be associated with gourmet food, but its devoted clientele reminds people of the television show "Cheers": a place where everyone knows your name.

Just a few months ago on a typical day, 400 to 500 people came for breakfast, lunch, dinner, live music or to hang out after sports, as Tracie Eckstrom did. That, however, was before the outbreak that nearly put an end to owners Tom and Jocelyn Duray's business of 24 years.

The trouble began on March 10 [2000], when a manager at Hoggsbreath sent home a cook who was not feeling well. But the cook returned to work a few days later after an emergency room doctor misdiagnosed the problem as a respiratory condition.

It was a mistake that would eventually have serious consequences for Eckstrom, the Durays and hundreds of other Hoggsbreath customers.

The next week, the cook—still not feeling well—developed jaundice, a noticeable yellowing of the skin. This time, a doctor ordered lab tests. On March 20, four days after Eckstrom ate her fateful dinner of a submarine sandwich and a glass of water, the results confirmed that the cook was infected with hepatitis A.

Some health researchers fear the United States is on the verge of a food-borne illness epidemic.

Hepatitis A can make someone sick up to seven weeks after exposure, and hundreds of people had been exposed.

Health officials announced the outbreak to the public on April 14, and more than 800 people lined up in the next few days for protective immune globulin shots at a special public health clinic.

For Tracie Eckstrom, the shots, which are only effective if given within two weeks of exposure, came too late. During Easter weekend in late April, she came down with the classic symptoms of hepatitis A: a 102-degree fever, malaise, nausea, and cramps, followed by jaundice. A lab test confirmed she had the virus, leaving her in tears.

A computer-support technician who has no sick-pay benefits, Eckstrom was out of work for two weeks and says she remained fatigued for six weeks. She joined a class-action lawsuit against Hoggsbreath.

"I never want to see a business go out of business. . . . But maybe they should've been a little more aware of what they were doing," she said.

Hoggsbreath co-owner Tom Duray makes no excuses for the outbreak. "As a business owner, you're responsible for your employees and what happens in your establishment," he said.

By all accounts, the Durays have worked hard to repair the damage to customers' loyalty. After the outbreak, the establishment's future was questionable, but business is now back to about 60 percent of normal. The restaurant's insurance company covered many customers' medical expenses. Workers now wash their hands whenever they enter the kitchen and wear latex gloves as a second line of defense, Tom Duray said. Health officials add that the owners were extremely cooperative with them throughout the outbreak and investigation. Jocelyn Duray herself was ill with the virus for about 10 days.

The cook, meanwhile, left the Hoggsbreath for another restaurant job. Citing privacy laws, health officials refused to identify him.

Unclean hands

It's unlikely anyone will ever know exactly how Eckstrom or others got the virus at Hoggsbreath.

But because of the way that the virus is transmitted—excreted in the feces of infected people—officials are certain that the cook must have accidentally contaminated food.

When a cook or server fails to properly wash hands after using the bathroom, even a microscopic amount of fecal matter can spread bacteria or viruses to food, plates, silverware, co-workers or customers. It happens more than you might realize.

"Our society in general (does) a very poor job" of washing hands, said Kirk Smith, state Health Department epidemiologist. "I notice it in public restrooms. A three-second hand-washing is not going to do the job."

Ill or infected food workers figured in one of every three outbreaks in Minnesota from 1989 to 1998, according to a *Pioneer Press* analysis of 200 confirmed outbreaks. Likewise, a Minnesota Health Department study found that infected food workers were associated with more than half the outbreaks of viral gastroenteritis—the so-called stomach flu—in the past two decades. Sometimes the food handlers themselves had been sick; in other cases, they had household members who were ill. Viral infections are the leading cause of outbreaks in Minnesota.

Three different Subway shops in Minnesota had viral outbreaks that investigators tied to infected employees—in Redwood Falls in January 1996, a month later in Bloomington, and in 1998 in Minneapolis. In the Bloomington case, 21 members of a men's chorus reported getting sick about a day after sharing three six-foot sandwiches. An employee who made the sandwiches had a child ill with diarrhea the week before.

In 1998, investigators concluded an infected food handler had contaminated the seafood bowtie salad, starting an outbreak of *shigella* bacteria among 30 people at Ciatti's Restaurant in Edina [Minnesota]. In July, a Hennepin County jury ordered the restaurant's former ownership—it has changed since the outbreak—to pay $140,000 to lawyer Cecil Schmidt and his wife Barbara. Schmidt's son Jeffrey was hospitalized and settled a separate lawsuit.

Sick workers should not even be in a restaurant. Minnesota law requires restaurants to excuse employees who are ill with vomiting or diarrhea, or infected with *salmonella, shigella, E. coli* or hepatitis A. But there are powerful incentives for restaurant workers—often low-paid and lacking benefits like sick pay—to come to work ill. Some sick employees, like the cook at Hoggsbreath, are infectious before their symptoms appear.

Painful mistakes

After sick workers, unsafe food handling is the next most common cause of outbreaks. In one of every four cases, outbreaks stemmed from undercooking meat, not maintaining food at proper temperatures, crosscontaminating foods with bacteria from raw meat or poultry, or other poor practices.

Health officials investigating a *salmonella* outbreak at the Perkins Family Restaurant in Eagan, [Minnesota] in 1997 found eggs stored above recommended safe temperatures. Investigators detected *salmonella* on a cutting board, near a cooking area, in a pork chop, and in the stool samples of three employees. They theorized the illnesses came from ill employees or contaminated food-preparation surfaces. *Salmonella*, commonly found on raw or undercooked meats, poultry and in eggs, is the bacteria most often associated with outbreaks nationwide.

At a Perkins in Alexandria, [Minnesota] inspectors discovered numerous problems after 25 employees and 25 patrons tested positive for the *salmonella heidelberg* bacteria in July 1999. Employees did not routinely wash their hands between handling frozen raw chicken and making salads, and the hand washing sink was not near the cook line, according to a state report. The restaurant made several changes, replacing worn cutting boards and using pasteurized eggs for omelets.

Vivian Brooks, a spokeswoman for Perkins, said the chain operates every day, around the clock, at 500 restaurants in 35 states, with high standards and happy customers.

In about one of every 10 [food-borne illness] outbreaks studied, illnesses stemmed from contaminated foods.

"These situations that you're describing are not typical," she said.

Lantern House, a Chinese restaurant in Duluth, [Minnesota] had the misfortune in 1998 of making some important people sick: four employees of the St. Louis County Public Health Department, who became ill about six hours after eating at the buffet-style restaurant.

Investigators noted "extensive" violations of food-safety standards and blamed the illnesses on *bacillus cereus*, a pathogen that grows when foods, especially rice, are not kept hot enough. In fact, as the health officials reported after two inspections, "No food item was properly cooled or heated." Authorities closed the restaurant as a health emergency, and it never reopened.

Private events started 33 outbreaks in the period studied, including three at community potluck dinners.

Health officials believe food-handling practices are riskier at the potlucks than at restaurants. But earlier this year [2000], state legislators passed a new law to exempt publicly advertised potluck dinners from licensing and inspection rules. Proponents said they were defending a Minnesota tradition from overzealous bureaucrats.

Publicity rare

Outbreaks can destroy restaurants, which is one reason government agencies do not routinely tell the public about them. Aggie Leitheiser, an assistant commissioner for the Minnesota Health Department, said outbreaks are publicized when officials believe illnesses still may be spreading, as in the Hoggsbreath case.

Craig Hedberg, a former epidemiologist for the state Health Department and now a professor at the University of Minnesota's School of Public Health, said restaurant operators and employees are more likely to cooperate with investigators if they don't fear being stung by bad publicity.

Tom Day, government affairs director for Hospitality Minnesota, a restaurant trade group, said publicizing outbreaks as they occur doesn't do anyone any good. The industry would not oppose an annual report listing where outbreaks had occurred.

"I think they could be publicized on an informational basis after all the facts and findings are known," Day said. "I don't think it's fair to hang a restaurant before everything is known."

Tainted on delivery

In about one of every 10 outbreaks studied, illnesses stemmed from contaminated foods.

In some of those cases, careful measures might have prevented illnesses. When a kitchen worker made salads without washing the lettuce last August [1999] at Clyde's on the St. Croix, a Bayport [Minnesota] restaurant, an estimated 100 to 150 diners became ill with a food-borne virus. The worker did not wash the lettuce because a label on the produce box "purportedly stated this item was a pre-washed lettuce," said a report by Washington County health investigators.

Earlier this year [2000], an *E. coli* outbreak among students at a Minneapolis middle school was traced to a casserole of ground beef, pasta and tomato sauce. State health officials said the meat probably was undercooked. As much as 80 percent of the raw hamburger in the United States is contaminated with *E. coli* bacteria, but cooking to 160 degrees can kill it.

In a few instances, outbreaks occurred despite precautions. Hundreds of Minnesotans in 1998 were caught up in an international series of outbreaks from parsley. The parsley, contaminated with *shigella* at a farm in Mexico, survived washing by restaurants. Some restaurants also innocently made matters worse by chopping the parsley, spreading the bacteria further.

In at least two of the eight seafood-related outbreaks documented in Minnesota since 1989, diners were made ill by hard-to-detect toxins. Four diners got *ciguatera* poisoning in 1997 from hogfish at Bluepoint Restaurant in Wayzata. The same year, five people were sick from *scombroid* poisoning, also known as histamine poisoning, from Indonesian tuna served at Billabong's Restaurant in Bloomington.

Perhaps the most alarming, though rare, are the outbreaks associated with processed, nationally distributed products.

In 1998, *Listeria*-tainted hot dogs and lunch meats from a Sara Lee plant in Michigan killed 21 people in the United States and sickened 80 more.

Last year [1999], a 55-year-old chemistry professor died and four other people became ill after ingesting *Listeria* in cold-cut deli meats purchased from a HyVee grocery store in Rochester, [Minnesota].

What frightens and challenges public health officials is the way that food-safety mistakes these days can become crises of immense proportions.

Six years ago, 224,000 people nationwide were infected with *salmonella* after eating Schwan's ice cream, shipped from Minnesota in tanker trailers that had previously carried nonpasteurized eggs.

Dr. Michael T. Osterholm, the former Minnesota state epidemiologist and an internationally recognized expert in infectious diseases, called the outbreak "a harbinger of things to come."

2

Mad Cow Disease Is a Threat to American Meat

Peter Lurie

Peter Lurie is a physician, public health researcher, and the deputy director of Public Citizen's Health Research Group.

The United States has not been aggressive enough in the fight against mad cow disease. Unless the government becomes more vigilant, the disease will likely find its way into America's food supply. Immediate action by the Food and Drug Administration (FDA) is required to regulate dietary supplements, which may contain infected bovine materials imported from countries where mad cow disease has been diagnosed. The FDA must also insist on stricter compliance with the ban against commingling feed intended for ruminants (cattle, goats, and sheep) with feed intended for nonruminants. Feeding ruminant parts to ruminants was how the mad cow disease epidemic spread in England. Finally, the U.S. Department of Agriculture should test the brain tissue of more cows exhibiting neurological symptoms at the time of slaughter.

While the U.S., to the best of our knowledge, remains free of both Bovine Spongiform Encephalopathy (BSE), otherwise known as "Mad Cow Disease," as well as its human counterpart, variant Creutzfeldt-Jacob Disease (vCJD), the experiences of European countries that grew complacent and now are suffering from epidemics of BSE and, in some cases, vCJD should make us more vigilant than we are at present. The agent that causes BSE has often found a way to pierce small chinks in the public health armor. For this reason, it is critical not only to maintain our defenses but also to strengthen them in the several areas I will highlight in this testimony.

I will address four areas:
1. How the agent that causes BSE might enter the country;
2. How the agent, if it entered the country or arose spontaneously within the country, could spread;
3. Whether the U.S. is doing enough testing to detect the disease; and

Peter Lurie, testimony before the Senate Commerce, Science, and Transportation Committee, Subcommittee on Consumer Affairs, Foreign Commerce, and Tourism, Washington, DC, April 4, 2001.

4. Whether there are medical practices that might spread the disease. How could the BSE agent enter the country?

How the agent that causes BSE might enter the country

We have serious concerns about the ability of customs inspectors to adequately police the borders. With the dramatic increase in global trade, the workload of these inspectors is only likely to grow. Transhipments between countries can make determining the origin of meat and bone meal quite difficult. This is, of course, an issue that extends well beyond BSE to encompass broader issues of food safety.

An issue of particular concern is that of dietary supplements. In 1994, the government, unwisely, essentially deregulated the dietary supplement industry. Whereas, prior to the Dietary Supplement, Health and Education Act (DSHEA), the industry had the burden of demonstrating the safety of its products, now the Food and Drug Administration (FDA) must demonstrate that a particular dietary supplement is unsafe before it can take action. Moreover, this now-$14 billion industry is not required to prove the efficacy of its products and the FDA has still failed to issue Good Manufacturing Practice (GMP) regulations for dietary supplements four years after the agency commenced rulemaking on this issue and seven years after DSHEA. Manufacturers are not required to register with the FDA and the agency only inspects approximately 1% of imported items subject to its jurisdiction, a fraction that may be still lower for dietary supplements. The agency has issued an Import Alert for materials sourced from BSE countries, but compliance is voluntary.

For BSE, this means that an unscrupulous manufacturer could literally take a British cow brain, crush it, dry it out, formulate it into a dietary supplement and export it to the U.S. Indeed, a letter by Dr. Scott Norton in the *New England Journal of Medicine* mentions a product available in the U.S. with 17 cow organs including brain, pituitary, and pineal gland. Due to DSHEA, the FDA is limited in what it can do. Instead of claiming that its regulatory authority over dietary supplements is adequate, as it often does publicly, the agency should be coming back to the Congress to undo the damage done by DSHEA. The best option would be to simply repeal DSHEA. In the alternative, we recommend a variety of improvements, including a mandatory adverse event reporting requirement for all dietary supplement manufacturers, mandatory risk warnings, requirements for company and product registration, and identification of the raw ingredients and the source (by country) for each of the ingredients in each product. This is, of course, a problem that goes well beyond the risk of vCJD; over 100 people have been killed by ephedra, and the agency seems essentially powerless to act. Releasing the GMP regulations for dietary supplements is necessary, but will not suffice to adequately protect American consumers from vCJD that might be caused by these products.

If the BSE agent entered the country, how might it spread?

A. Feeding Practices Since 1997, the FDA has had a ban on the feeding of mammalian parts to ruminants (e.g., cows, goats, sheep), the main route by which the BSE epidemic occurred in Britain and would be amplified in the U.S. This ban requires that manufacturers take action to prevent the commingling of two types of feed: those intended for ruminants, and those intended for nonruminants (e.g., pigs, fish, chickens which can be fed material from mammals).

FDA inspections to date provide evidence that this commingling is possible. The March 2001 FDA inspection report findings (http://www.fda.gov/cvm/index/updates/bsemar3.htm), while improved from the January 2001 findings, still shows that 14% of renderers and 13% of FDA licensed feed mills do not have adequate procedures to prevent mammalian parts from entering ruminant feed: i.e., cows could still be recycled and fed to other cows. (This is precisely what happened in the Purina Mills plant in Texas in which, purely through the voluntary admission of the company, the FDA learned that cow parts had entered cow feed. One thousand, two hundred and twenty-two cows had to be removed from the food chain.) Moreover, 23% of renderers and 63% of FDA-licensed feed mills have still not been inspected for compliance with the feed restrictions and some 6,000 to 8,000 feed mills are not even required to register with the FDA. Of the 1,829 non-FDA licensed feed mills that handle material prohibited from use in ruminant feed, 18% do not have adequate procedures to prevent the recycling of mammalian parts as feed for ruminants. If the industry does not come into better compliance with the mammal-to-ruminant ban, the FDA should consider whether a mammal-to-mammal ban is justified.

Current USDA procedures permit deer and elk from a herd with a proven case of CWD to enter the food chain.

In addition, the FDA feed ban contains an exemption that should be ended. Despite U.S. Department of Agriculture (USDA) objections, the FDA permits the feeding of so-called plate waste (leftover food that has been prepared and/or served to humans) in feed for ruminants. The European Union, Canada and Mexico have banned such practices and so should we.

Finally, there is the issue of Chronic Wasting Disease (CWD), a Transmissible Spongiform Encephalopathy (TSE) of wild and captive elk and deer. While there exists no evidence that humans have become infected from eating deer or elk, current USDA procedures permit deer and elk from a herd with a proven case of CWD to enter the food chain. The problem is that deer and elk are exempt from the USDA's Meat Inspection Act, under which the packer has the burden of demonstrating the safety of his or her product. Instead, deer and elk would have to be restricted under the FDA's Food, Drug and Cosmetic Act, which places the burden upon the agency to demonstrate potential harm and provides no funds to compensate farmers if their herd is seized. This creates an incentive for farmers not to be forthcoming about CWD in their herds. This could be addressed either by a specific regulation excluding CWD-affected herds from the food chain and providing for compensation for the rancher or by bringing deer and elk under the Meat Inspection Act, which does provide for compensation.

B. Meat Processing The processes of slaughtering and processing are not, by their nature, extremely precise ones. Infectious material from the most infectious parts of the cow, the brain and spinal cord, may spread to other parts of the animal.

Pneumatic stunning devices, which stun the animal prior to slaughter by injecting a bolt and compressed air into the head, have been shown to spread potentially infectious brain tissue to other parts of the body. Although the industry appears to be reducing its use of pneumatic stunning devices, this should be given the force of federal regulation and banned. These devices are now banned for use in cattle in Europe.

European countries require that the brain and spinal cord be removed carefully in the slaughtering process. However, in the United States, processes vary widely and are not effectively regulated. We therefore support a regulation that would require the removal of the brain and spinal cord before further processing, since these organs contain the highest levels of infectious material.

Two other meat processing methods have also come under scrutiny. In one, mechanically separated product (MSP), bones with attached muscle are crushed and pushed through an extruder to create a paste. Bone fragments are removed by a sieve-like mechanism. Both spinal cord and dorsal root ganglia (nerve tissue next to the vertebrae), which have demonstrable BSE infectivity, can enter MSP. In the other processing method, advanced meat recovery (AMR), muscle fragments are also removed from bone; this material can become part of ground beef. Early AMR machines used a belt to shave meat off bones, but later AMR machines use a "bone press" that differs from MSP only in degree. While MSP inherently involves the crushing of bones and is thus more likely to introduce nerve tissue into the product than AMR, 1997 USDA inspection records obtained by the Government Accountability Project through the Freedom of Information Act clearly demonstrate that spinal cord can be part of the material generated by AMR. Four of 34 AMR samples sent by USDA inspectors to a USDA laboratory because they were suspected of containing spinal cord tissue turned out to actually contain central nervous system tissue. It is possible that AMR machines could be redesigned to minimize the probability of crushing bones and thus including spinal cord. The USDA began such a rulemaking procedure three years ago, but the rule has still not been finalized. To prevent vCJD, we therefore support a ban on the production of MSP from vertebrae and the issuance of a final rule for better-designed AMR processes that would prevent the inclusion of spinal cord.

Is the U.S. doing enough testing to detect the disease?

To date, the U.S. surveillance efforts for BSE have been quite inadequate. Only 11,954 cow brains had been examined by the USDA in the ten-year span ending in 2000. (Some 40 million cattle are slaughtered annually in the U.S.) By comparison, France, a country which, importantly, has a proven BSE epidemic, is now testing about 20,000 brains per week.

Under current USDA procedures, all cows with neurological symptoms are supposed to be tested for BSE and, regardless of the result, excluded from the food chain. Cows that are unable to ambulate, so-called downer cows, are only occasionally tested. The USDA did not begin testing downer cows until 1993 but has now increased such testing to about 1,900 in 2000 (http://www.aphis.usda.gov/oa/bse/bsesurvey.html). This represents about 1% of all downer cows brought to slaughter in the U.S. The USDA has promised to increase such testing to 5,000 per year in 2001, a move we fully support. Testing of healthy cows does not seem justified in the U.S. at present as the prevalence of disease would most certainly be lower than in downer cows or those with neurological symptoms. . . .

To date, U.S. surveillance efforts for BSE have been quite inadequate.

Testing for the presence of BSE in cow brain can be very time-consuming. However, while three rapid tests for BSE are on the market in Europe, none are on the market in the U.S. It is imperative that these tests be evaluated by the FDA and that test performance characteristics be made public.

Surveillance for human CJD and vCJD is coordinated through the Centers for Disease Control and the National Prion Disease Pathology Surveillance Center at Case Western Reserve University. The Center has examined the brains of about 300 patients with CJD in the past four years. This represents an estimated 39% of patients with CJD in 2000, whereas in Germany and Britain the brains of almost all patients with CJD are examined by pathologists. Canada has recently revamped its surveillance system and provides much more funding for such efforts than does the U.S.

The U.S. government also needs to do more to increase the overall hospital autopsy rate in this country, which has declined from over 40% after World War II to under 10% at present, as well as to increase the rate of examination of brain material specifically. Currently, hospitals and families bear the costs of autopsies, including transportation costs; they should be reimbursed for these costs. The government should also consider creating a network of regional pathology centers to do brain examinations for CJD and needs to do more to contact all neurologists to inform them of the current surveillance system.

Are there medical practices that might transmit BSE and vCJD?

In weighing whether products that are transfused or transplanted into humans should be restricted, the essential questions are: 1. What is the probability of transmission of infection?; 2. Are there suitable alternatives to the material?; and 3. Would the restriction of the material produce a shortage of a vital medical product?

While there has never been a documented case of CJD or vCJD transmitted by blood transfusion, the agent is present in white blood cells (inevitably present to some extent in even red blood cell transfusions) and, in an experiment, a sheep was recently infected by transfusion from a cow with BSE. In 1999, the FDA's TSE Advisory Committee recommended a ban on blood donations from potential donors who had spent more than a total of six months in Britain between 1980 and 1996. The Committee determined that the impact on the blood supply would be manageable and data collected since the restriction on British donors confirm that the supply of blood remained stable after the ban was enacted. In January 2001, with cases of vCJD in France and of BSE in Europe mounting, the Committee extended this recommendation to include France, Portugal and Ireland, although with a 10-year cumulative residency requirement, since BSE and vCJD case rates are lower in those countries than in Britain. The FDA should adopt the Committee's recommendation.

For the public to be adequately protected [against mad cow disease], government will have to take forceful action . . . and not simply depend upon voluntary actions by industry.

Similar travel restrictions should be placed on cadaveric cornea donors, especially because as many as three cases of CJD due to corneal transplantation have been documented. Due to the existing shortages of other transplantable organs such as heart and bone marrow, and the failure to document CJD transmission associated with their transplantation, a travel restriction on such organ donors is not justified. On the other hand, because the U.S. is a net exporter of cornea, we are not concerned that there would be a shortage of cornea were a travel restriction to be implemented.

The issue of vaccines

In 1993, the FDA wrote to the manufacturers of FDA regulated products and in a voluntary Guidance instructed manufacturers to no longer source materials for their products from BSE-affected countries. It repeated the admonition in 1996. Nonetheless, at least six manufacturers simply ignored the Guidance, which does not have the force of a regulation, and continued to source bovine materials for the production of vaccines from BSE-affected countries. The FDA only learnt that its recommendation had been disregarded in early 2000. By then, millions of doses of vaccines such as polio and diphtheria, tetanus, and pertussis (DTP) were injected into Americans, including small children. At a TSE Advisory Committee meeting in July 2000, Committee members agreed that the risk of disease transmission through these vaccines is extremely small and that there is no evidence that vCJD has been spread through this route. Nonetheless, this event was a reminder of the dangers presented by agencies that fail to regulate and industries that act in arrogant disregard of the government.

The lesson of the vaccine debacle applies more broadly to our efforts to reduce the risks of BSE and vCJD: for the public to be adequately protected, government will have to take forceful action—regulations, not guidelines—and not simply depend upon voluntary actions by industry.

3

The Threat of Mad Cow Disease in the United States Has Been Exaggerated

Abigail Trafford

Abigail Trafford is a health columnist for the Washington Post.

The risk of contracting mad cow disease in the United States is minimal. Americans are more likely to contract bacterial types of food-borne illnesses, such as *Listeriosis* or *Salmonella*, than they are mad cow disease. Even if a cow—the main transmitter of the disease—did become sick, officials would isolate the animal long before it could become part of the food chain and a risk to humans. People need to put the potential risk from mad cow disease in perspective and not allow irrational fear to cloud their judgment about whether or not to continue to eat beef.

The man at a dinner party leans over and asks: "Are you worried about 'mad cow' disease? Should we stop eating steak?"

I laugh. Earth to Chicken Little! The sky is not falling on steak. Not here, anyway. Of all the things to worry about, getting mad cow disease from a nice juicy filet mignon is not one of them. Not yet, anyway.

I go through the obvious arguments. Not a single case has occurred in the United States in man or beast. [In December 2003 a cow in Washington state was diagnosed with mad cow disease.] Precautions are in place to prevent the disease from spreading to this country. Feed made from certain animals—the suspected culprit in Europe—is prohibited here. Beef and beef products from affected countries are banned. Even in Europe, fewer than 100 people have succumbed to the strange malady since the outbreak began four years ago [1998]. Those cases have been confined to Britain, Ireland and France where—statistically speaking—people are five times more likely to be killed by a bolt of lightning than by mad cow disease.

If you're going to worry about what you eat, there are bigger food-borne killers. For starters, listeriosis (from contaminated meats, dairy products, raw vegetables) and salmonella (from contaminated raw eggs) each cause 500 deaths a year in this country. *E. coli*, which is most associated with eating contaminated ground beef, kills 61 people a year. Why worry about something that hasn't killed anybody in this country?

The expression on the dinner guest's face goes from polite disagreement to pity. I must sound like a victim of *"Animal Farm"* propaganda from the agri-medical establishment. He doesn't believe a reassuring word I've said.

Why should he? Europe is in a panic over mad cow disease. Overall consumption of beef dropped 27 percent from October to December [of 2000]. The cattle industry has been crushed and governments are shaken. Instead of promoting the national staple of *le steak et pommes frites*, French farmers are throwing stones at their prime minister.

Fear of mad cow disease is unfounded

The fear is spreading to these shores: Cattle in Texas quarantined after eating bone meal. Elk in Oklahoma diagnosed with a chronic wasting disease. Suspect mad cow candy on sale in New York City.

Mamba fruit chew, banned in Poland, is made with a beef-based gelatin produced in Germany, where about 20 cows have been found to be infected with bovine spongiform encephalopathy (BSE), the scientific name for mad cow disease. In the ensuing public-relations meltdown, the company announced it would switch from beef gelatin to vegetable starch.

Of all the things to worry about, getting mad cow disease from a nice juicy filet mignon is not one of them.

Call that Mad Cow Panic Syndrome (MCPS). Tests have shown that the disease cannot be transmitted in gelatin, even from infected cattle, says George Gray, director of the program for food safety and agriculture at the Harvard School of Public Health's Center for Risk Analysis in Boston. "It's a nonissue," he says. "This situation takes on a life of its own."

The perception of risk is wildly out of proportion to the actual risk. "When I have a hamburger, I worry much more about *E. coli* than a chance of BSE," Gray says. Even if an animal in the United States shows up sick one day, there would be no immediate threat to people. Tightened surveillance would prevent the spread to other animals and keep the infected animal from reaching the human food chain. "It's not going to be a big public health risk," Gray continues. But if that day comes, he adds, "we'll go bonkers."

People fear mysterious diseases

Mad cow bonkers. All of us from Henny Penny to Goosey Loosey have a hard time dealing with risks. Certain kinds of hazards, no matter how rare, grab our imagination so that we fear the worst. They usually share these characteristics:

Mysterious. Just what causes mad cow disease is not known. The prime suspect is a prion, an aberrant protein that attacks the central nervous system. Scientists are used to bacteria and viruses, but prions are a new kind of infectious agent. The theory is that herds in Britain were infected from contaminated bone meal. BSE crossed from animals to people, causing a variant of the rare degenerative brain disorder called Creutzfeldt-Jakob disease. There is no evidence, points out Harvard's Gray, that the prions get into muscle meat—in other words, into steak. Greatest concern is focused on brain and bones and mixed meats such as sausage.

Lethal. The disease is horrible and invariably fatal. About 300 Americans die of the classic form of Creutzfeldt-Jakob disease a year, which strikes seemingly at random. There is no effective treatment. With listeriosis, for example, an estimated 2,500 Americans get very sick, but they can be treated with antibiotics and most of them recover. Mad cow disease is a death sentence, and victims are generally younger than those who succumb to the classic form of the brain malady.

Unpredictable. The infection in cattle peaked in 1993. Since then, Britain has slaughtered infected herds and tested cattle to make sure they are healthy. Last year [2000], the European Union banned the use of remnant parts mammal feed to reduce the chances of contamination. At the same time, the incubation period in people for this disease could be anywhere from two to 20 years. Health officials don't know if the number of cases will level off. Or whether the current toll represents the tip of an epidemic iceberg of many more people who harbor the infection. "We don't know how many people are infected. We don't know the size of the risk," says psychologist Baruch Fischhoff of Carnegie Mellon University.

To date, mad cow disease is not a crisis in public health; but it's becoming a crisis in public trust.

There is not a lot people can do to reduce their personal risk. You can avoid lightning by staying indoors in a thunderstorm (about 300 deaths in the United States annually) and prevent head injuries on a bicycle by wearing a helmet (about 800 deaths a year). You can avoid salmonella by cooking eggs and listeriosis by sticking to pasteurized cheese.

But it's hard to control your exposure to all the theoretically possible avenues to mad cow disease—even when there is no evidence of a problem. Just last week [early February 2001], the headlines screeched that five major drug companies had used ingredients from cattle in affected European countries to manufacture vaccines given to millions of American children—contrary to recommendations of the FDA. Animal-based gelatin is also used in supplements with little government oversight.

The prions are falling! In a world of medical globalism, neither diseases nor drugs recognize national boundaries. To date, mad cow disease is not a crisis in public health; but it's becoming a crisis in public trust.

4

America's Food Supply Is Threatened by Terrorism

Katrina Woznicki

Katrina Woznicki is a science writer for United Press International, a worldwide news service.

The September 11, 2001, terrorist attacks put every aspect of American life in jeopardy, including the safety of the nation's food supply. Within two weeks of the attacks, the Food and Drug Administration, Centers for Disease Control and Prevention (CDC), Environmental Protection Agency, U.S. Department of Agriculture, and National Food Processors Association created a food security plan. They developed simple recommendations to help protect the nation's food supply. For example, they encourage food companies to light property to discourage break-ins, lock up food products, and limit access to food products to employees. Further, the CDC is ready to respond immediately to identify and isolate any outbreaks of food-borne illness should they occur.

A mericans already know what it is like to fear lethal anthrax lurking in their mail, but when they go to take a bite out of a sandwich or sit down to a family dinner, how can they be sure they are not about to ingest these deadly microorganisms?

Since [the September 11, 2001, terrorist attacks], bioterrorism became the federal government's number one priority. The subject includes food security—protecting the nation's food supply from a bioterrorism attack.

"I don't think a year ago we were very concerned about possibilities of food terrorism," Dr. Charles Sizer, director of the National Center for Food Safety and Technology in Chicago, Ill. told United Press International (UPI). "This is going to be a long-term, evolving, type of issue. It's a new reality that we have live to with."

Not since 1984 when cult followers of an Indian guru used *salmonella* as a weapon to spike salad bars at 10 restaurants in an Oregon town have Americans even been worried about deliberate food contamination with bacteria. The Oregon case sickened 750 people.

Eighteen years later, advanced technology and a decentralized food supply make it possible for terrorists to contaminate the U.S. food supply and sicken or even kill thousands of citizens.

For example, could a cow be intentionally contaminated with bovine spongiform encephalopathy or mad cow's disease and slipped into the nation's meat supply? On April 22, [2002,] Food and Drug Administration Deputy Commissioner Lester M. Crawford told the Consumer Federation of America, "That is a threat we're watching very closely."

Or could fresh produce be laced with harmful microbes? Although FDA declined to provide possible scenarios it's preparing for—a spokesperson told UPI, "It is FDA's policy not to discuss potential threats"—experts say no one knows what could happen so it is best to be prepared for anything.

"I don't think we know the worst possible case," said Helen Jensen, a member of the National Research Committee, part of the National Academy of Sciences that helped review food security protocol and an economics professor at Iowa State University in Ames, Iowa. "Based on our experience in the last six months, we're seeing things we never expected to see."

To respond to this potential threat, FDA is expected to use $98 million of its $1.727 billion proposed budget for Fiscal Year 2003 specifically for food security.

Since [the September 11, 2001, terrorist attacks], bioterrorism became the federal government's number one priority. The subject includes . . . protecting the nation's food supply from a bioterrorism attack.

Meanwhile, FDA has wasted no time. Since January 10, [2002,] it already has hired 250 food safety inspectors whose jobs it will be to monitor the food distribution process, including checking every single step in food's progress from the farm to someone's dinner plate.

"FDA has been authorized to hire approximately 650 new field personnel" for inspections, Robert E. Brackett, food safety director of the FDA's Center for Food Safety and Applied Nutrition, told UPI. "Although the recent security concerns have accelerated hiring plans, it has been recognized for years that FDA's food inspection capacity needs to be enhanced as part of its normal food safety effort."

These inspectors will be responsible for going through food safety checklists, for both imported and domestic products, to ensure food never gets into the wrong hands or deviates from its scheduled distribution. Random screenings for food pathogens also will be conducted, explained Rhona Applebaum, executive vice president for scientific and regulatory affairs for the National Food Processors Association (NFPA), an organization working closely with FDA on food security.

Preventing food terrorism from the top down

Most Americans do not know where their food comes from because the source of the nation's food supply is so varied and vast. "It's no longer like you know the butcher that's in your local community," Jensen said. This makes coordinating food terrorism prevention an effort starting at the federal level and trickling all the way down to the small farmer or restaurant chain.

Experts . . . cannot even forecast the likelihood of a terrorism attack in food. They just know that after Sept. 11, the country needs to be on guard all the time.

Applebaum said her office contacted FDA Sept. 12, [2001,] about co-ordinating a food security protection plan. The Washington, D.C.–based NFPA met with not only FDA, but also the Centers for Disease Control and Prevention [CDC], the Environmental Protection Agency and the U.S. Department of Agriculture to design guidelines for those involved in the American food chain, including restaurants and food suppliers and distributors big and small. All comprise the Security for Food Alliance, formally created two weeks after the terrorist attacks.

Although some food companies have boosted their surveillance technology to better monitor the facility and employees, the guidelines involve "very low technology," Sizer said.

"Light it, lock it and limit access to it," Applebaum said. Meaning: light the property to reduce the chance of break-ins, lock up the food products, and know the personnel working at the food facility and limit the people with access to the product.

"What you want to make sure you do whether it's a restaurant or a processing plant is that you want to make sure you have some information on the people working for you," Applebaum explained. This can be a challenge, particularly in low-paying restaurants or plants where employee turnover can be high. But Applebaum said if security checklists are fully followed, the guidelines work.

"The more hurdles we put between a person focused on doing evil and the consumer, the less likely it would be for a major (terrorism) event," Applebaum said.

The guidelines may seem simple, but they were designed to allow smaller companies with smaller budgets to be able to participate in national food security efforts.

The CDC is vital

How would federal officials be able to discern a foodborne illness outbreak from a terrorist attack?

"FDA relies upon its sister agency, the Centers for Disease Control and Prevention, and similar state agencies for surveillance and outbreak detection," Brackett said. "Epidemiologists in these agencies are trained to analyze disease patterns and would be the first to detect the source and cause of an outbreak."

Experts concede it might not be possible to know the difference between the two scenarios immediately, but that doesn't affect the initial response, which is to remove contaminated food from the food supply immediately and isolate those who have been sickened, especially if the pathogen is contagious. The fact that responding to a food bioterrorism attack would be similar to responding to a foodborne illness outbreak works in public health officials' favor.

"We have decades of experiences and literally daily experience in dealing with this," said Dr. Jeremy Sobel, a medical epidemiologist with CDC in Atlanta.

When it comes to food bioterrorism, communication is key. CDC already has in place a technologically sophisticated surveillance system allowing real-time electronic correspondence connecting CDC headquarters, state health departments and other local health departments so any foodborne illness or attack can be quickly identified, tracked, quarantined and followed throughout the country.

"In the case of bioterrorism," Sobel explained, this electronic network is crucial in "identifying the perpetrator and getting him off the market too."

CDC also has a genetic fingerprinting system at all state health departments based on collections of previous foodborne pathogens taken from patient and food samples. Having this database of food microbes on hand helps epidemiologists quickly identify any genetic differences in food contaminants.

This could help scientists distinguish an attack from an outbreak and rapidly detect if contaminants have a common source should simultaneous multiple attacks or outbreaks occur throughout the U.S.

Experts said they cannot even forecast the likelihood of a bioterrorism attack in food. They just know that after Sept. 11, the country needs to be on guard all the time.

"We know it's a possibility," Applebaum said. "We don't know what the probability is."

5

Food-Borne Illnesses Are Declining in the United States

Centers for Disease Control and Prevention

The Centers for Disease Control and Prevention (CDC) is part of the U.S. Department of Health and Human Services. It is the federal agency responsible for protecting the health and safety of Americans.

Salmonella and *Campylobacter*, two of the most common causes of food-borne illness in the United States, have declined significantly in recent years. A science-based inspection system of meat and poultry processing plants is credited with the decrease in disease. The system, Pathogen Reduction and Hazard Analysis and Critical Control Point (HACCP), requires that processing plants develop preventative controls and meet pathogen reduction performance standards for *Salmonella*. Periodic inspection ensures that plants meet these standards.

The Department of Health and Human Services today released preliminary data from the Centers for Disease Control and Prevention (CDC) that show a decline in the overall incidence of *Salmonella* and *Campylobacter* infections, two of the most common causes of foodborne disease in the United States. The data come from the Foodborne Diseases Active Surveillance Network (FoodNet).

"These new findings are encouraging and show that our intensified fight against foodborne illness is paying off," said HHS Secretary Donna E. Shalala. "However, we still have work to do. Foodborne disease remains a substantial public health burden that affects millions of people every year. I urge Congress to support our efforts to expand food safety programs throughout the Department."

The data show a 13 percent decline in the number of *Salmonella* infections between 1996 and 1998 and a 44 percent drop in the incidence of *Salmonella* enteritidis, a subtype of *Salmonella* infection associated with egg contamination that has been a major food safety problem since the

Centers for Disease Control and Prevention, "*Salmonella* and *Campylobacter* Illnesses on the Decline," www.cdc.gov, March 11, 1999.

1980s. The data also indicate a 15 percent decline between 1997–1998 in the number of illnesses caused by *Campylobacter*, the most common bacterial foodborne pathogen in the United States. The preliminary findings were collected from five FoodNet sites in California, Georgia, Connecticut, Minnesota, and Oregon and published in the March 12 issue of *Morbidity and Mortality Weekly Report (MMWR)*.

The data show a 13 percent decline in the number of Salmonella *infections between 1996 and 1998.*

"The Administration's new, science-based inspection system requires meat and poultry plants to take steps to prevent contamination by *Salmonella* and other potentially dangerous pathogens," said Agriculture Secretary Dan Glickman. "Our new system has resulted in a sharp decrease in *Salmonella* contamination of raw meat and poultry and, we believe, contributed to this decline in foodborne illnesses."

FoodNet data can be used to document the effectiveness of new food safety control measures such as USDA's [U.S. Department of Agriculture] Pathogen Reduction and Hazard Analysis and Critical Control Points (HACCP) Rule as well as HACCP programs undertaken by the Food and Drug Administration (FDA) for seafood and other food products.

Under the HACCP system, plants must develop a system of preventive controls and meet pathogen reduction performance standards for *Salmonella* set by USDA. Testing occurs to ensure that plants are meeting these tough standards.

Increased prevention efforts are working

"These reported declines in foodborne disease are encouraging and suggest that the stepped up prevention efforts of the USDA and the FDA may be working," said CDC director Dr. Jeffrey Koplan. "However, the reasons for these declines are not fully understood and more study is needed."

The incidence of *E. coli* 0157:H7 went from 2.7 cases per 100,000 population in 1996 to 2.3 in 1997 and then up to 2.8 per 100,000 in 1998. The fluctuation could be a normal variation. CDC continues to gather data about which specific foods caused the illnesses; however, previous studies have linked *E. Coli* infection to milk, drinking water, roast or ground beef, apple cider, lettuce and venison, among other foods, and even to swimming in pools and lakes.

FoodNet is a joint effort by HHS, the USDA, and state health departments to capture a more accurate and complete picture of trends in the occurrence of foodborne illness. Within HHS, the network involves the CDC and the FDA.

At FoodNet sites, public health officials frequently contact microbiology laboratories and other data sources for illness that may be caused by different foodborne pathogens on an active, ongoing basis using standardized data collection methods. Each case is reviewed and strains of the organisms are collected and analyzed. Special case control studies are conducted in order to identify the major risk factors for disease. Data are then electronically submitted to CDC for analysis.

FoodNet sites began collecting data in 1996. Currently sites are located in California, Connecticut, Georgia, Maryland, Minnesota, New York, and Oregon. The total population of these sites is 20.5 million (7.7% of the total U.S. population). Additional FoodNet sites will be added to the program; Tennessee is scheduled to begin collecting data in 1999.

CDC is currently using incidence and community survey data from FoodNet as well as other data sources to improve the estimates of total foodborne illness in the United States. These estimates, soon to be published, will provide the best information to date on the burden of foodborne disease in the United States.

6

Food-Borne Illnesses Are a Threat to Europe

World Health Organization

The World Health Organization is the United Nations' specialized agency for health.

Food-borne illnesses have increased markedly in eastern and western Europe in the past decade. As many as one person in three in industrialized countries may be affected by food-borne diseases every year. Most illness is bacterial, caused by *Salmonella* and *Campylobacter* pathogens, or the result of contamination from chemical sources, such as lead or dioxin. Differences in national food safety and quality policies across Europe make it difficult to uniformly protect the health and well-being of consumers in the region. All countries should have science-based risk assessment and management systems in place to minimize the dangers posed by food-borne illnesses.

Food safety and quality need to be improved in all European countries because foodborne diseases have increased considerably in the region in the past decade, the UN Food and Agriculture Organization (FAO) and the World Health Organization (WHO) said in a joint statement issued today. On the rise in particular are diseases from microbiological hazards such as *Salmonella* and *Campylobacter* and cases of foods contaminated by chemical hazards, such as dioxin, lead and cadmium, according to the two UN agencies.

The statement was issued on the opening day [February 25, 2002] of the *First Pan-European Conference on Food Safety and Quality* in Budapest [Hungary]. Food safety experts from more than 40 countries, including food producers and consumers' associations from Western, Central and Eastern Europe and other countries in transition are meeting in Budapest to discuss how to improve food safety and strengthen consumer confidence after recent food scares.

The meeting is jointly organized by FAO and WHO. It is co-sponsored by the European Community and some FAO/WHO member countries.

"While food has never been safer than it is today in Europe, this should not lead us to complacency. Better monitoring systems are revealing more and more cases of food-borne illness. The number of people suffering from food-borne diseases or even die from them is still far too high," said Hartwig de Haen, FAO Assistant Director-General.

"WHO estimates that, worldwide, thousands of millions of cases of food-borne disease occur every year. As many as one person in three in industrialized countries may be affected by foodborne illness each year, resulting in human suffering and economic losses running into billions of US dollars. Particularly at risk are children, pregnant women, the sick, the poor and the elderly," said Dr David Nabarro, WHO Executive Director.

Food safety and quality need to be improved in all European countries because foodborne diseases have increased considerably in the region in the past decade.

"The consumer has the right to safe food in all European countries. Food safety 'from farm to fork' needs to be ensured throughout the region. To save costs and prevent contamination, food safety must begin with good agricultural practices," de Haen added.

National policies and regulations on food safety and quality are still very diverse in Europe, according to de Haen. "Food safety control systems in Central and Eastern Europe as well as in Central Asian Republics are very different from the EU [European Union], and also vary among each other. Europe is certainly not aiming for a single standard diet. The challenge is: harmonisation in diversity. We need to bring different food safety and quality policies across Europe closer together to protect the health and well-being of consumers. Different food safety systems need to become comparable and fully transparent."

National and international agencies must work together

"Problems with food safety over the last decades have been aggravated by lack of collaboration between different authorities at the national level. WHO, together with FAO and our Member States are working hard to develop new, evidence-based, preventative strategies to lower risk of disease. This work focuses on the whole food production chain. We promote a dialogue with consumers. We encourage interdisciplinary collaboration all the way from farm to table. Different authorities at the national level and different international organizations will have to work together and coordinate their efforts for this to work," noted Nabarro.

Salmonella is still the most frequently reported causal agent of food-borne disease outbreaks in East and West European countries, according to FAO/WHO. Outbreaks occur in private homes and in mass catering kitchens in restaurants, cafeterias, catering services, schools, kindergartens and hospitals.

In addition, *Campylobacter* is currently the most commonly reported gastrointestinal pathogen in many countries, including Denmark, Finland, Iceland, Ireland, the Netherlands, Norway, Sweden, Switzerland and the United Kingdom. Campylobacteriosis is a bacterial infection that affects the intestinal tract.

The contamination of food by chemical hazards is another major public health concern. In Central and Eastern Europe food contamination arises largely from industrial contamination of air, soil and water. One of the hot spots is the Aral Sea area. For almost 30 years the use of water for irrigation of cotton monoculture and the heavy use of insecticides, pesticides and herbicides has created a critical situation for the health of the local population.

FAO/WHO recommended that all countries have science-based risk assessment and management systems in place to deal with microbiological and chemical hazards in food. In some countries, infrastructure needs to be strengthened to achieve a higher level of protection. "Agriculture and health institutions must work together to ensure food safety," de Haen said.

Currently FAO and WHO are performing a number of microbiological risk assessments, the first ever to be performed at the international level. The food-pathogen combinations that have been identified through various expert consultations as deserving immediate attention are *Listeria* in ready-to-eat foods, *Campylobacter* in poultry, *Vibrio* in seafood, and *Salmonella* in eggs and poultry. "These risk assessments will provide templates for Member States to adapt them to their national situation and to assist them in addressing the threats of these pathogens in the most efficient way," Nabarro said.

FAO and WHO stressed the many advantages of safer and high quality food. "Safer food means lower incidence of foodborne diseases, lower public health costs, fewer barriers to international trade, lower productivity losses and better competitiveness."

7

Food-Borne Illnesses Are Costly

Economic Research Service

The Economic Research Service (ERS) is the main source of economic information and research from the U.S. Department of Agriculture. The mission of ERS is to inform and enhance public and private decision making on economic and policy issues related to agriculture, food, natural resources, and rural development.

Costs associated with food-borne illnesses in the United States are estimated to be about $6.9 billion annually. These estimates include medical costs, productivity losses from missed work, and an estimate of the value of premature death. In addition to causing immediate symptoms, food-borne diseases often result in chronic illnesses that affect the joints, nervous system, kidneys, or heart, and lead to additional lifelong medical costs or premature death.

F oodborne diseases are caused by ingesting bacteria, fungi, parasites, or viruses through contaminated food or water, or through person-to-person contact. The Centers for Disease Control and Prevention (CDC) estimates that foodborne diseases cause approximately 76 million illnesses, 325,000 hospitalizations, and 5,000 deaths in the United States each year. ERS has estimated the annual U.S. economic costs incurred for the major bacterial pathogens: *Escherichia coli* O157 and other STECs [Shiga toxin-producing *Escherichia coli*] (an associated hemolytic uremic syndrome), *Campylobacter* (an associated Guillain-Barré syndrome), *Listeria monocytogenes*, and *Salmonella*. In addition, ERS has developed outcome trees for the illnesses caused by those pathogens, showing the costs incurred and the number of cases by the severity of disease: no physician visit, hospitalization, premature death, and chronic complications.

In 2000, ERS estimated that the costs associated with five major pathogens amount to at least $6.9 billion annually. The cost estimate includes medical costs, productivity losses from missed work, and an estimate of the value of premature death that takes into account the age distribution of those taken ill. The estimate excludes travel costs in obtaining

Economic Research Service, "Economics of Foodborne Disease: Overview," www.ers.usda.gov, February 7, 2003.

medical care, lost leisure time, and so forth. Estimates for *Salmonella* were updated in 2003.

ERS also evaluated the pros and cons of the two principal methods of estimating the monetary benefits of reducing foodborne diseases: cost-of-illness and willingness-to-pay. In addition, ERS looked at the pros and cons of three other methods (risk-risk analysis, health-health analysis, and cost-effectiveness analysis) that try to avoid assigning a monetary value to human life and health.

Foodborne diseases are acute and chronic

Pathogens are disease-causing microorganisms that include bacteria, fungi, parasites, and viruses. Most cases of foodborne illnesses are classified as "acute." These are usually self-limiting and of short duration, although they can range from mild to severe. Gastrointestinal problems and vomiting are common acute symptoms of many foodborne illnesses. Deaths from acute foodborne illnesses, while rare, are more likely to occur in the very young, the elderly, or patients with compromised immune systems (such as those suffering from AIDS or cancer). However, the U.S. Food and Drug Administration (FDA) estimates that 2 to 3 percent of all acute cases develop secondary long-term illnesses, called "chronic sequellae."

Chronic sequellae of foodborne illness can occur in any part of the body and subsequently affect the joints, nervous system, kidneys, or heart. These chronic illnesses may afflict the patients for the remainder of their lives or result in premature death. For example, *Campylobacter* infections are estimated to be responsible for 20 to 40 percent of Guillain-Barré syndrome (GBS) cases (a major cause of paralysis unrelated to trauma) in the United States. About 1.5 percent of *E. coli* O157 disease patients develop hemolytic uremic syndrome (HUS), which usually involves red blood cell destruction, kidney failure, and neurological complications, such as seizures and strokes.

Actions by the food industry, consumers, and the public health sector influence how food is produced, marketed, prepared, and consumed. These actions influence the probability that a food item contains pathogens. People who consume contaminated food have some probability of becoming ill. Foodborne illness generates costs that are borne by the food industry, households whose members become ill, and/or the public health sector.

Foodborne diseases cause approximately 76 million illnesses, 325,000 hospitalizations, and 5,000 deaths in the United States each year.

ERS estimates of the costs of foodborne disease are limited to estimating the impact on households. Thus, ERS is underestimating the impact of foodborne illness on society. In fact, we estimate only the medical costs, productivity losses, and the value associated with premature death for a selected number of microbial foodborne health risks. The ERS cost estimates undervalue the household's cost of foodborne illness because some costs are omitted, such as travel to obtain medical care, time lost from work caring for sick children, lost leisure time, pain and suffering, and the costs of certain other chronic complications, such as reactive arthritis in the case of *Salmonella.*

ERS cost estimates are calculated from the number of acute and chronic foodborne-illness cases and deaths caused by each pathogen each year. These costs include medical costs, lost productivity costs, other illness-specific costs (such as special education and residential-care costs), and an estimate of the value of premature deaths.

Societal costs have not been estimated for the vast majority of complications associated with foodborne illnesses. The Centers for Disease Control and Prevention (CDC) estimates that out of a total of 76 million cases of foodborne disease each year in the United States, as many as 62 million cases are of unknown origin. We do, however, cover the following chronic complications in our cost estimates: GBS following *Campy-lobacter* infections, HUS following *E. coli* O157 infections, and chronic disability or impairment following congenital and newborn infections from *Listeria monocytogenes.*

Medical costs

For each foodborne illness, cases are generally divided into five severity levels: 1) those who do not visit a physician, 2) those who visit a physician, 3) those who are hospitalized, 4) those who developed chronic complications, and 5) those who die prematurely because of their illness.

For each severity group, medical costs are estimated for physician and hospital services, supplies, medications, and special procedures unique to treating the particular foodborne illnesses. Such costs reflect the number of days/treatments of a medical service, the average cost per service/treatment, and the number of patients receiving such service/treatment.

In 2000, ERS estimated that the costs associated with five major pathogens [causing food-borne illnesses] amount to at least $6.9 billion annually.

Beginning with estimates released in 2000, ERS cost estimates use a "labor market approach", incorporating information about the wage premiums for high-risk occupations. Cost estimates also use information about the age distribution of deaths to adjust this value to account for the age at death.

In essence, the labor market approach values the economic cost of premature deaths based on the risk premium revealed by the higher wages paid for dangerous jobs. Under this approach, the value of a statistical life equaled $6.5 million in August 2000 dollars after updating the original 1990 estimate of $5.0 million to account for inflation. The labor market approach assumes that risk preferences observed in job choices are indicative of risk preferences for food safety.

ERS modified the labor market approach by taking the age distribution of deaths from each pathogen into account, in effect treating the value of life as an annuity paid over the average U.S. life span at an interest rate of 3.0 percent. Following age-adjustment, the assumed cost of each death was five times higher for individuals who died before their first birthday than for individuals who died at age 85 or older.

Since the five microbial pathogens have different health outcomes for different age groups, adjusting for the age of death raises the cost of some foodborne illnesses and lowers the cost of others. For example, the estimated annual cost of foodborne illnesses caused by *Salmonella* decreased because over two-thirds of the deaths from salmonellosis occur among people over 65 years of age. Adjusting foodborne illness costs for *E. coli* O157 by age at time of death increased the estimate because most deaths are children under the age of five.

Productivity losses

One difficult issue is assigning a value to the productivity losses associated with individuals who become ill and are unable to return to work, or for those illnesses that result in a lifetime of disability (such as prenatal exposure to *Listeria monocytogenes*). ERS currently measures the productivity losses due to nonfatal foodborne illnesses by the value of forgone or lost wages, regardless of whether the lost wages involved a few days missed from work or a permanent disability that prevented an individual from returning to work. Using the value of lost wages for cases resulting in disability probably understates an individual's willingness to pay to avoid disability because it does not account for the value placed on avoiding pain and suffering. The willingness to pay measure derived from labor market studies that ERS uses to value a premature death is not an appropriate measure of willingness to pay to avoid disability because it measures the higher wages paid to workers to accept a higher risk of premature death, not disability. Methods have been suggested to adjust willingness to pay to reduce the risk of premature death downward to estimate willingness to pay to avoid disability, such as the approach based on measuring "Quality Adjusted Life Years" (QALY). As yet, there is no consensus among economists about how to use these methods to value willingness to pay to avoid the disability, pain, and suffering associated with foodborne illnesses. ERS's conservative estimates of the annual costs due to foodborne illnesses (particularly the chronic conditions associated with *Campylobacter*) would be substantially increased if willingness to pay to avoid disability, pain, and suffering were also taken into account.

8

Genetically Modified Food Causes Food-Borne Illnesses

Physicians and Scientists for Responsible Application of Science and Technology

Physicians and Scientists for Responsible Application of Science and Technology is an organization of professional scientists and laypeople who are concerned about the conditions that are hampering impartial comprehensive, interdisciplinary evaluations of the safety of new applications of science and technology—particularly the genetic modification of plants and animals used for food.

A considerable increase in the rate of food-borne illnesses occurring in the United States from 1994 to 1999 can be traced directly to an enormous rise in the consumption of genetically engineered (GE) foods during the same time period. One explanation for the link between an increase in food-borne illnesses and the use of GE foods is the creation of new viruses during the engineering of these foods. Because GE food plants contain virus genes that are similar to human virus genes, genetic mutations can occur creating new viruses. These new mutated viruses can cause illness in people who eat GE food. In addition, *Bacillus thuringiensis* (Bt)—common in GE food—is responsible for intestinal irritation which may cause acute as well as chronic gastrointestinal illnesses. Moreover, bacterial DNA sequences present in almost all GE foods may increase the likelihood of intestinal inflammation, as well as other inflammatory diseases such as rheumatoid arthritis. Thus, the increase in food-borne illnesses may indeed be linked to GE foods.

In [the] USA, between 1994 and 1999, the rate of illnesses caused by food has doubled for some kinds of diseases and increased tenfold for other kinds. As a comparison, the rate in Sweden in 1999 was about the same as it was in the US in 1994.

Mae-Wan Ho, director of the Institute of Science in the Society, and an expert on food biotechnology notes in a recent report that there is a very pronounced difference between Sweden and the US in one respect—

the rate of virus-caused illnesses. While in Sweden, viruses were the cause in only 9% of the cases, they were so in 80% of the cases in the USA.

The reason for this increase is unknown. But Mae-Wan Ho points out that *the use of genetically engineered foods has increased enormously in the US since 1994.* By comparison, in Sweden, almost no GE [genetically engineered] foods were used in 1999.

GE crops can generate new viruses

Ho suspects that a possible reason might be that GE foods may give rise to new viruses. This has been well established scientifically (even the biotech firm Monsanto has acknowledged this). The reason is that every cell in GE plants contains parts of virus genes that can combine with the genes of infecting viruses. In a very large proportion of GE crop varieties, the virus genes come from a virus (Cauliflower Mosaic Virus—CaMV) related to human viruses. Therefore some scientists have warned that GE plants may give rise to new human viruses.

New bacterial pathogens?

Ho has warned that so called vector DNA used in all GE crops may also be a culprit. This DNA comes from virus and bacteria and facilitates the combination of genes of unrelated species. Thereby it might promote the emergence of new bacteria.

How GE foods cause illness

We agree that the large scale cultivation of GE crops brings with it a definite risk for the emergence of new viruses. But if this were the cause of a major part of foodborne disease increase, it should also have caused a considerable increase of virus diseases affecting other organs. We are not aware that this has happened. So we assume that, if new viruses have contributed to the increase of foodborne diseases, it is likely to be to a minor extent.

The large scale cultivation of GE crops brings with it a definite risk for the emergence of new viruses.

We propose another explanation how GE foods might be the cause. It is based on the remarkable fact that 82% of the foodborne diseases and 25% of the death cases were caused by "unknown pathogens" in the American study that Ho refers to.

In addition, in practical medicine, the diagnosis of "virus GE disorder" mostly occurs through exclusion as it is costly and not useful to detect all the potential viral pathogens (as there is no specific therapy for viral diseases, specific diagnosis is of no help). So when, in a case of pronounced diarrhoic disease, the common pathogens, like *salmonella, shigella* etc., have been excluded, it is often assumed that the disease is viral.

We suggest that part of the foodborne diseases of unknown origin as well as of the "virus disorders" may perhaps have been caused by GE foods in two possible ways:

1. By a known toxin common in genetically engineered food. It is the *Bacillus thuringiensis* (Bt) toxin.
2. By bacterial DNA used for genetic engineering in almost all GE foods.

1. Major GE crops have been genetically engineered to produce the Bt toxin for its insecticidal ability.

Professor Joe Cummins has recently pointed out that an Egyptian study indicates that the Bt toxin causes intestinal irritation which may cause acute as well as chronic gastrointestinal illness. This study found that mice, fed with genetically engineered potatoes, developed significant intestinal changes indicating an irritative effect of the toxin.

We suggest that part of the foodborne diseases of unknown origin as well as of the "virus disorders" may perhaps have been caused by GE [genetically engineered] foods.

As the Bt-toxin demonstratedly affects mouse intestines, it cannot be excluded that it might cause disturbances in humans as well, manifesting as "foodborne disease with unknown origin". Biotech proponents assert that this toxin is degraded by stomach acid (although it is actually quite acid resistant). People may have a low level of gastric acid because of disease or because of the very common use of Losec or similar potent antacid preparations. In addition, there may exist a genetic variability in the susceptibility to the toxic effect, so that a minority of the population is especially sensitive. As the foods are not labelled as GE, the connection is not apparent to the consumer. According to Cummins, no studies have been done that reliably exclude this possibility.

2. Professor Joe Cummins has pointed out that certain bacterial DNA sequences present in practically all GE crops may increase the risk for inflammatory disorders. These so called CpG sequences are found in the DNA used for enabling gene insertion (vectors) and in many of the primary crop protection genes including Bt and most herbicide tolerance genes. This bacterial DNA contains considerable amounts of the CpG sequence (higher forms of life, so called eukaryocytes, have little of this sequence and it is in a different state). This sequence induces inflammation and may adversely affect autoimmune diseases like rheumatoid arthritis. It also acts as a promoter of lymphoma, a malignant blood disease.

Inflammation induced in the bowel by this bacterial DNA in GE foods might perhaps mimic foodborne diarrhea. As Cummins points out, it might also induce or worsen other inflammatory conditions.

There are two conceivable ways in which GE foods may cause gastrointestinal disturbances in addition to those proposed by Ho. It is through the presence of the common Bt toxin and through the very common presence of the CpG DNA sequence that induces inflammation. The large increase of assumed "virus foodborne" diseases and the large proportion of diseases with unknown cause justify a consideration of these alternatives.

9

Genetically Modified Foods Do Not Cause Food-Borne Illnesses

AgBiotechNet

AgBiotechNet is an online news service that publishes information about agricultural biotechnology for researchers, policy makers, and the agriculture industry worldwide.

There is no credible evidence that food from genetically modified (GM) plants causes food-borne illnesses in humans. The claim that individuals who eat GM foods will suffer allergic reactions is unsubstantiated, as is the assertion that GM foods lack nutritional value. Further, the risk of GM foods transmitting harmful viruses to people—which can cause food-borne illnesses—is negligible. Thus, consumers' fears about the safety of GM foods are unfounded.

C laims that foodstuffs containing ingredients from genetically modified [GM] plants are inherently less safe than their non-GM conventional counterparts remain unproven, according to a UK [United Kingdom] Royal Society policy statement.

In two submissions to the UK government-sponsored GM Science Review, the Royal Society argues that the potential for GM ingredients to reduce the nutritional quality of foods or to cause allergic reactions is in principle no different to that for non-GM ingredients. It says there is no credible evidence that human health can be damaged by eating DNA sequences created by the genetic modification of foodstuff ingredients. The statement suggests that any risks through allergenicity or inadvertant change in nutritional status would be equivalent to those encountered through traditional breeding. It also argues that health risks associated with specific viral DNA sequences[1] in GM plants are "negligible" and that DNA consumption from a wide variety of sources "poses no significant risk

---

1. Some consumers are concerned that specific viral DNA sequences in GM plants will combine with human DNA and produce new viruses that could cause foodborne illnesses.

AgBiotechNet, "No Evidence GM Foods Unsafe, Says Royal Society," www.agbiotechnet.com, May 8, 2003. Copyright © 2003 by Cabi Publishing. Reproduced by permission CAB International.

to human health, and that additional ingestion of GM DNA has no effect".

Patrick Bateson, Vice-President and Biological Secretary of the Royal Society, said: "We conducted a major review of the evidence about GM plants and human health [2002], and we have not seen any evidence since then that changes our original conclusions. If credible evidence does exist that GM foods are more harmful to people than non-GM foods, we should like to know why it has not been made public."

No evidence of health risks

He added: "The public have been told for several years that GM foods are inherently unsafe to eat. Most people would like to know what evidence exists to back up such claims. We have examined the results of published research, and have found nothing to indicate that GM foods are inherently unsafe. If anybody does have convincing evidence, get it out in the open so that it can be evaluated."

"The public have a right to decide whether they want to buy GM foods, and are entitled to have access to sensible and informed advice, based on sound science. It is disappointing to find a group like Greenpeace stating on its website that 'the risks are enormous and the consequences potentially catastrophic,' without offering any solid reasons to support such a claim."

DNA consumption . . . "poses no significant risk to human health, and . . . additional ingestion of GM DNA has no effect."

Bateson continued: "Undoubtedly some important questions need to be answered about the potential impact, good or bad, of GM crops on the environment. But these should be addressed without a smokescreen of unfounded claims about their threat to human health."

He noted that a recent opinion poll showed that the majority of the UK public is opposed to GM foods. "Many consumers have been made anxious by unsubstantiated claims about the safety of GM foods," he said. "The developers of GM products also have not successfully demonstrated to consumers what benefits they offer compared to conventional foods."

The Society's submissions also draw attention to some areas of food regulation that it believes should be addressed to ensure that all foods, including those containing GM ingredients, are assessed properly. Bateson said: "The public expect regulations to keep abreast of new developments in the way food is made, and to be just as effective for both GM and non-GM foods. We understand that the Food Standards Agency has taken on board the recommendations we made in our report [in 2002] and is taking action to address the issues we highlighted."

10

Irradiation Helps Improve Food Safety

Randall Lutter

Randall Lutter is a fellow with the American Enterprise Institute (AEI)–Brookings Joint Center for Regulatory Studies. The American Enterprise Institute and the Brookings Institution established the AEI–Brookings Joint Center for Regulatory Studies to provide analyses of existing regulatory programs and new regulatory proposals.

Food irradiation can help reduce food-borne illnesses. All major international public health organizations have endorsed food irradiation as a risk-free, practical method for improving food safety, yet the U.S. Department of Agriculture and the Food and Drug Administration have been slow to approve the process. Criticism of food irradiation by several public interest groups and reluctance by grocers to offer irradiated foods are also barriers to making irradiated foods available in the United States. Despite those barriers, test marketing has shown that irradiation is well accepted by consumers.

Food-borne pathogens cause thousands of deaths and tens of millions of cases of food-borne illness each year in the United States. Although most food-borne illness involves only nausea and diarrhea, many people develop serious complications, including rheumatoid, cardiac, hepatic, and neurological problems. Food-borne disease is declining little if at all, despite major new food safety initiatives. The best way to prevent a substantial part of those deaths and illnesses is food irradiation, which all major international public health organizations have endorsed because it is safe and effective.

Irradiation is extremely effective at reducing pathogens. Irradiation of frozen ground meat products with a 7-kilogray (kGy) dose—a dose already approved by the U.S. Food and Drug Administration (FDA)—could eliminate *Escherichia coli* 0157:H7, a particularly hazardous pathogen. Irradiation destroys *Staphylococcus aureus* and *Campylobacter jejuni*, which are together responsible for more than 2.6 million food-borne illnesses per year,

Randall Lutter, "Food Irradiation—the Neglected Solution to Food-Borne Illness," *Science*, vol. 286, December 17, 1999, pp. 2275–76. Copyright © 1999 by the American Association for the Advancement of Science. Reproduced by permission.

as effectively as it reduces *E. coli* 0157:H7. Reductions in numbers of viable organisms would be dramatic for other important pathogens: irradiation of meat reduces *Salmonella* levels by factors of 10 billion to 100 trillion. It is also effective for seafood, eggs, precooked meats, and produce.

Irradiation of food does not pose risks to consumers. The World Health Organization (WHO) has advised that "as long as sensory qualities of food are retained and harmful microorganisms destroyed, the actual amount of ionizing radiation applied is of secondary consideration." At high doses, irradiation can cause some loss of vitamins, but at currently permitted doses "—there's less vitamin degradation than you get with microwaving or cooking." Almost two decades ago, the WHO concluded that "irradiation of food up to an overall average dose of 10 kGy produced no toxicological hazard and introduced no special nutritional or microbiological problems." In 1997, WHO added that "food irradiation is perhaps the most thoroughly investigated food processing technology." It concluded that ". . . one can go as high as 75 kGy, as has already been done in some countries, and the result is the same—food is safe and wholesome and nutritionally adequate." Joining the WHO in endorsing food irradiation to improve food safety are the Codex Alimentarius Commission, the American Medical Association, the American Dietetic Association, and the health authorities of approximately 40 countries.

Market data in the United States suggest many informed consumers prefer irradiated foods. In retail trials, irradiated chicken had a market share of 43% when sold at the same price as other chicken. When sold for a 10% premium—a markup much greater than the costs of irradiation—its share of the market was about 25%. Indeed, many different types of medical, pharmaceutical, and consumer products are already irradiated.

Two government agencies are responsible

In the United States, two separate government agencies are responsible for regulation of food. The U.S. Department of Agriculture (USDA), through its Food Safety and Inspection Service, has responsibility for all meat and poultry and related products, whereas the Food and Drug Administration, part of the Department of Health and Human Services, regulates all other foods. According to the Federal Food, Drug, and Cosmetic Act, irradiation of food, including meat and poultry, is prohibited without a determination by the FDA that food irradiation at particular doses and for particular uses is safe. This dual, overlapping responsibility for irradiation of meat and poultry has contributed to delays in bringing irradiation of these foods to market.

Despite the well-established benefits of irradiation, federal regulations now permit irradiation to control pathogens only for poultry and spices. The USDA's regulations restrict poultry irradiation: it is permissible only at a dose of 3 kGy and with labeling statements that consumers can mistake for warnings. The USDA has proposed to allow meat irradiation and is expected to announce regulations this month.[1] Regulatory decisions to approve irradiation of seafood, precooked meats, and eggs, all of which are linked to food-borne illnesses and death, are years from com-

1. Meat irradiation regulations were approved in January 2001.

pletion. Faster government action could prevent illness and death associated with those foods.

Congress is partly responsible for delays in bringing food irradiation to market. The Federal Food, Drug, and Cosmetic Act defines sources of irradiation used to treat food as "food additives" and prohibits the use of food additives without an explicit determination of their safety. That definition delays the marketing of irradiated foods. In effect the Act directs FDA to address the wrong question—whether irradiation is safe—rather than whether food irradiation reduces risks to public health, taking into account both the reduced incidence of food-borne illness and any loss of safety from increased irradiation.

The regulatory agencies have also delayed the benefits of food irradiation by creating a redundant and complicated two-step approval process that is avoidable under current law. The first step is a determination by the FDA that food irradiation at particular doses is safe for particular uses. The second step is a determination by the USDA that the use of irradiation is in compliance with applicable FDA requirements, does not render the product adulterated or misbranded or otherwise out of compliance with the requirements of the Federal Meat Inspection Act, is functional and suitable for the product, and is permitted only at the lowest level necessary to accomplish the stated technical effect as determined in specific cases. The second step is required not by the Federal Food, Drug, and Cosmetic Act, but by USDA's interpretation of its own regulations, which prohibit use of a "substance" in the preparation of any meat product unless such a determination is made.

That two-step process, while arguably sensible for additives that do not improve public health, substantially delays delivery of the benefits of food irradiation to consumers. The FDA approved irradiation of meat 3 years after receiving a petition; however, the USDA, which must also approve, has taken two more years to issue its own rule. In their recent rulemakings about meat irradiation, the agencies do not cite any recent scientific discoveries confirming the safety of irradiation. Instead, they cite safety evidence most of which is 20 years old.

Anti-irradiation groups slow approval process

The slow pace of government approval of irradiation has causes more complex than bureaucratic inertia and lack of interagency leadership. Cautionary or critical positions taken by several public interest groups play a role. Food and Water, a stridently anti-irradiation group, has paid for advertisements and organized telephone and letter campaigns against food irradiation. Consumers Union, the publisher of *Consumer Reports*, has been studiously neutral on the subject. Other influential groups, including Center for Science in the Public Interest, National Consumers League and Consumer Federation of America take a slightly more supportive stand, but still manage to impede improvements in public health by advocating conspicuous labeling and even increased testing of irradiated foods. Such views, because they are presented by "public interest" groups, can deter agencies that seek to regulate by consensus from implementing regulatory changes that would promote public health, unless there is strong political leadership.

Industry has also been slow to irradiate poultry, although the USDA allowed it in 1992. The market share of irradiated poultry is only about 1%. Why isn't irradiated poultry found in supermarkets today, given that market trials suggest it could sell at a profit? One possible reason is that grocers may be reluctant to stock "safer" poultry because it would raise questions about the safety of their other poultry products. In addition, their contracts with major poultry suppliers may include volume discounts that discourage the introduction of new products that hurt established brands. Those explanations are not fully satisfactory, but they suggest that factors limiting market share include market barriers, as well as restrictions on labeling and dose. More creative marketing may be needed to bring irradiated foods to U.S. consumers.

Irradiation of meat, when approved by USDA, may become more widespread than poultry irradiation, because people like rare hamburgers. Many restaurants have already stopped selling medium-rare hamburgers because of safety concerns.

USDA must speed up approval

Although the USDA has recently proposed to allow irradiation of meat, the USDA's rulemaking is late and should have been expedited. Millions of illnesses and thousand of deaths per year could be avoided by irradiation of meats, and the USDA's delays postpone these benefits.

Furthermore, the USDA proposal is too limited. It would unnecessarily restrict producers' ability to market irradiated meats by mandating the content and placement of certain statements on food labels and by offering no guidelines for labeling claims like "*Salmonella*-free." It takes no steps to promote irradiation of precooked meats, eggs, and seafood. It would leave in place redundant testing requirements and performance standards for *Salmonella*.

There are several ways the government can improve its regulation of food irradiation. First, the USDA should not require any labeling that could be misinterpreted as a warning; instead, it should require only that irradiation be identified as food preservatives are now. In addition, the USDA should allow labels that inform consumers how irradiated foods reduce the risk of food-borne disease and death. Second, the USDA should revise its rules so that firms that irradiate at a given dose would be exempt from redundant requirements to test for pathogens on those products. Third, the FDA—which under the Act must determine the safety of irradiation at particular doses for particular purposes—should allow irradiation of precooked meats, eggs, and seafood.

Regulatory agencies will have to become much more supportive of food irradiation if consumers are to enjoy all the health benefits that it promises. The FDA should promptly determine that irradiation of any food is generally recognized as safe, based on the findings of the World Health Organization and other scientific and public health organizations. In addition, the White House should make up for its recent lack of leadership on this issue and demonstrate the benefits of irradiated food by serving irradiated turkey at the next state dinner.

11

Food Irradiation Is Dangerous and Ineffective

John M. LaForge

John M. LaForge is codirector of Nukewatch, an antiwar group, and editor of its quarterly newsletter, the Pathfinder. *His articles have appeared in* Z Magazine, Earth Island Journal, *and the* Progressive.

Irradiation of food has not been proven to be a safe, effective method of reducing food-borne illnesses. It does not kill all disease-causing pathogens, especially viruses, and no studies of long-term effects of eating irradiated foods have been conducted. Further, irradiation destroys B vitamins and changes the taste and aroma of meat. Because food irradiation uses cesium-137, a hazardous radioactive waste material, it endangers the workers who handle it and presents a potential risk of environmental contamination. For all these reasons, the government should prohibit irradiation of food until the safety of the process and the wholesomeness of irradiated food can be guaranteed.

The same folks that brought you open-air bomb testing, human radiation experiments, Three Mile Island,[1] and Chernobyl[2] are promoting the food irradiation process. Ever since 1986, the FDA [Food and Drug Administration], the nuclear industry, and the meat industry have moved to expose almost the entire food supply to nuclear irradiation. But staunch citizen opposition has generally kept the business out of use. For 14 years, Food & Water,[3] and thousands of individuals have kept poultry, fruits, and vegetables free of irradiation. But the struggle is on to keep the meat supply out of this risky business.

According to an August 1997 "CBS News" poll, 73 percent are against irradiation and 77 percent say they wouldn't eat irradiated food.

1. The accident at the Three Mile Island nuclear power plant near Middletown, Pennsylvania, on March 28, 1979, was the most serious in U.S. nuclear power plant history.   2. The accident at the Chernobyl nuclear power plant in the Ukranian republic of the former Soviet Union on April 26, 1986, was the worst in the history of nuclear power. Over two hundred thousand people were evacuated from the area.   3. Food & Water is a national nonprofit organization that educates the general public about various threats to the food and water supply.

John M. LaForge, "Food Irradiation and Nuclear Weapons," *Z Magazine*, vol. 13, October 2000, pp. 36–39. Copyright © 2000 by John M. LaForge. Reproduced by permission.

How irradiation works

Food is irradiated using radioactive gamma ray sources, usually radioactive cobalt-60 or cesium-137, or high-energy electron beams. After packaging and being put into large metal boxes, the foods are placed on conveyor belts that move past the radiation sources. The materials are hit with the equivalent of 30 million X-rays, (according to the Spring 1998 *Food & Water* journal). The industry now uses cobalt-60 supplied by the Canadian company Nordion International, Inc. But the only isotope available in sufficient quantities for large-scale irradiation is cesium-137. When not in use the cobalt or cesium is lowered into cooling ponds.

In the process, which takes about 20 to 30 minutes, the gamma radiation passes through the food, killing all bacteria (helpful as well as harmful) and slowing decay but not leaving the food radioactive.

Irradiated food "will cost more, contain slightly reduced levels of B vitamins, endanger workers, and risk environmental contamination."

Irradiators are used on the meats at the end of the production line, after it is already sealed in packages. This is particularly important in ground beef, where bacteria can easily get beneath the surface during grinding. However the industry is lobbying for approval of irradiating unpackaged meats as well.

Cesium-137 is radioactive waste left in huge quantities from nuclear weapons production at Hanford in Washington State and Savannah River, South Carolina. A by-product of nuclear reactor operation, cesium-137 is an extremely hazardous isotope that is deadly for 600 years. It is water-soluble, which makes it terribly dangerous in the event of an accident. As radioactive waste, it is extremely expensive to store and keep out of the biosphere.

The Department of Energy admitted to the House Armed Services Committee in 1983: "The utilization of these radioactive materials simply reduces our waste handling problem. . .we get some of these very hot elements like cesium and strontium out of the waste" (Michael Colby, ed., "Food Irradiation: Why it Must Be Stopped and How We Can Do It, An Activist Primer," *Food & Water*, 1998). Dr. Rosalie Bertell (a renowned epidemiologist from Toronto [Canada]) explains that irradiation is a convenient excuse to reprocess spent irradiated fuel rods from weapons production reactors.

FDA spokesperson Jim Greene said in 1986 that using the cesium-137 "could substantially reduce the cost of disposing of nuclear waste" (*Grand Forks Herald*, 28 April 1986).

Irradiation changes nutrient content

The gamma rays break up the molecular structure of food, forming positively and negatively charged particles called "free radicals." The free radicals react with the food to create new chemical substances called "radiolytic products." The radiolytic products unique to the irradiation process are called "unique radiolytic products" (URPs). Some radiolytic products, such as formaldehyde, benzene, formic acid, and quinones are harmful to human health. Benzene is a known carcinogen. Some URPs are completely new chemicals that have not been identified, let alone tested for toxicity. URPs were somehow given a blanket exemption by the FDA from the safety testing required of other food additives.

Although the FDA says irradiation doesn't change nutritional content, the process does destroy nutrients essential to human health, such as vitamins C, E, K, and B-complex. (Vitamin E levels can be reduced by 25 percent after irradiation and vitamin C by 5–10 percent. Irradiation is ineffective against viruses.)

Radiation doses at the levels recommended will not kill all microorganisms. Typically, 90 percent may be destroyed and this means that the food still has to be treated with care otherwise the remaining organisms will reproduce rapidly. While the government and meat industry claim the flavor and aroma of the treated meats doesn't change, taste testers have disagreed.

Food Editor for the *New York Times*, Marian Burrows, writes, "Well-cooked conventional meat still tastes better. A blind tasting of irradiated and conventional ground beef, as well as steaks, pork loin and chicken makes it clear that the meat industry has its work cut out for it . . . all the irradiated meat smelled funny, especially the ground beef . . . barnyard odor . . . like steamed cow" (*New York Times*, December 10, 1997).

There has been no study of the effects of a long-term diet of irradiated foods.

Foods already approved for irradiation include beef, pork, poultry, nuts, potatoes, wheat, wheat flour, fruits, and vegetables, as well as all teas, and 60 dried herbs and spices. The nuclear industry also irradiates medical equipment, food containers, cosmetics, tampons, adhesive bandages, and cleaning solutions for contact lenses. A short chronology of the approval process looks like this:

- In 1953, food irradiation was named part of the so-called "atoms for peace" programs and the Army began research. In 1958 irradiation was classified as a food additive, requiring safety testing.
- In 1963, the FDA approved irradiation for bacon, but later banned it, having learned of "deficiencies" in the Army's research data on which the FDA had based its approval (*Ms Magazine*, November 1985).
- The FDA, in 1968, re-approved the use of irradiation for bacon, for killing insects in wheat and wheat flour, and for the inhibition of sprouting in potatoes.
- In 1983, the FDA approved sterilization of spices with irradiation. Low-dose irradiation can also be used to inhibit sprouting of onions, garlic, and ginger, and to inhibit the ripening of bananas, avocados, mangoes, papayas, and guavas. Hawaii is being pushed hard to open large irradiators for treating these tropical fruits.

- In 1996, the FDA gave permission for the expanded use of irradiation in the U.S. food supply.
- 1997 saw FDA approval of irradiation for beef and other red meats such as lamb (MLWK *Journal* and St. Paul *Pioneer*, December 3, 1997).

Hide the label, they will buy

In 1999, the U.S. Department of Agriculture (USDA) proposed rules and regulations for labeling the food and for licensing the factories that may do the irradiating. The rule-making process brought to light a horrifying series of accidents and contamination.

The meat industry lobbied vigorously for the 1997 bill on irradiation as an alternative to Clinton administration proposals for greater government authority to recall contaminated meat and punish violators. This is why professional critics of the process are so alarmed.

Former Assistant Secretary of Agriculture Carol Tucker Forman writes that irradiation sterilizes dirty meat, "but it doesn't keep meat from being recontaminated. Every time the meat is handled, from packing plant to grocery store to a home stove, it can come into contact with disease-causing bacteria. The meat might pass through a contaminated grinder, or it could be mixed with scraps that have been sitting in the store for a while" (*New York Times*, December 5, 1997).

Michael Jacobson, executive director of the Center for Science in the Public Interest opposes irradiation and writes that irradiated food "will cost more, contain slightly reduced levels of B vitamins, endanger workers, and risk environmental contamination" (letters, *NYT*, December 8, 1997).

The 1997 bill also changed labeling requirements for all foods treated with irradiation, so that the words: "Treated with Irradiation," need be no larger than those of the ingredient list.

However, the FDA requires no labeling of irradiated ingredients, so potato soup made with irradiated potatoes, onions, and spices need not be so labeled. Today, the industry is lobbying hard to eliminate all labeling requirements for irradiated foods.

An illustrative parallel is found in the use of GMOs (genetically modified organisms). In Europe, foods containing GMOs require labeling. This may explain why Europeans are more educated on the subject and why the European Union banned the import of U.S. GMOs. However, in the U.S. where no labeling of GMOs is required nearly 65 percent of foods on supermarket shelves contain ingredients that are genetically modified.

FDA approval is no guarantee of safety

FDA troubles with prescription drugs don't inspire confidence in its "okay" for irradiation. After 80 deaths were attributed to the heartburn medicine Propulsid, the FDA is considering a severe restriction and the manufacturer has withdrawn it. The action came on the heels of the Rzulin scare. FDA ordered it off the market after it was linked to 63 deaths.

There has been no study of the effects of a long-term diet of irradiated foods. The FDA reviewed 441 toxicity studies to determine the safety of irradiated foods. The team leader in charge of the review testified that all 441 studies were flawed. The FDA now claims that only 6 of the 441 were "properly conducted, fully adequate by 1980 standards, and able to stand alone in support of safety."

One of these six showed a statistically significant increase in stillbirth rates among rats fed irradiated wheat. Another reported unexplained deaths and abnormalities in animals given irradiated food, not reaching statistical significance because of the small number of animals in the study. Both studies used irradiation levels well below the proposed levels for human food. Dr. Bertell concludes: "Thus the 'scientific' evidence in support of food irradiation consists of studies with low irradiation dose, small number of animals, short follow-up times, and negative results. No real scientist would accept these studies as establishing the safety of irradiated foods."

With this shabby hobbled-together assurance of just five studies, the FDA approved irradiation for the public food supply.

Food caterers, restaurants, retirement homes, childcare centers, hospitals and schools are not required to inform clients that their foods are irradiated (Minneapolis *Star Tribune*, December 16, 1999).

Without a guarantee of start-to-finish safety, from the handling of radioactive source materials to the long-term consumption of irradiated foods, irradiation should be prohibited.

The facilities that irradiate foods and equipment have caused accidents that must not be repeated. The NRC [National Response Center] has recorded 54 accidents at 132 irradiation facilities worldwide since 1974. Unhappily, expanding irradiation will increase the number of radiation accidents by increasing the handling and high-speed transportation of radioactive "source" materials on railroads and highways. It will expose factory surroundings and industry workers to radioactive spills and leaks. Indeed irradiation's "Three Mile Island" has already happened.

In Decatur, Georgia, Radiation Sterilizers, Inc. (RSI) got 252 21-inch canisters of cesium-137 (which were never designed for use at an irradiation facility) from the Department of Energy. In 1988 RSI began using the cesium-137 to irradiate spices. After only two years, a cesium-137 capsule began leaking into the storage pool. It took federal officials six months to find the leak's source. Contaminated workers took the poison home with them. In 1992, the contaminated building was abandoned, and RSI took the word "radiation" out of its name. Now they're "Sterigenics" (*Food & Water Journal*, Spring 1998).

Neither the FDA nor the nuclear industry has demonstrated an ability to safeguard the public from its deadly man-made radiation. Without a guarantee of start-to-finish safety, from the handling of radioactive source materials to the long-term consumption of irradiated foods, irradiation should be prohibited.

The priorities for governments and their food inspectors should be: (1) improving food harvesting, storage and manufacturing processes; and (2) eliminating or containing the contamination that has found its way into the food chain.

12

Federal Inspection Makes America's Meat Safe

Kerri B. Harris

Kerri B. Harris is executive director of the International HACCP Alliance at Texas A&M University. The International HACCP (Hazard Analysis and Critical Control Point) Alliance helps provide a uniform program to assure safe meat and poultry.

Federal meat inspection laws initiated in the last century and continually updated make the meat industry the most highly regulated food industry in the country. Daily inspections of processing plants and packing establishments by U.S. Department of Agriculture (USDA) and Food Safety and Inspection Service (FSIS) employees ensure the safety of American meat. The Hazard Analysis and Critical Control Point (HACCP) rule, which became part of the federal inspection laws on July 25, 1996, requires the reduction of *Salmonella* and *E. coli* pathogens in meat and the development and implementation of a system to identify food safety hazards. The use of Sanitation Standard Operating Procedures (SSOPs) to prevent direct meat contamination or adulteration was also part of the HACCP rule. Further, FSIS has an ongoing chemical monitoring program to detect and prevent the misuse of chemicals such as antibiotics in livestock production.

The safety of meat products and the protection of public health are primary concerns for the beef industry. Throughout the past few years and even today, there are many food safety challenges facing the industry. The industry has completed and is currently conducting research, identifying new and improved technologies, and exploring all opportunities to strengthen the safety of today's meat supply. The beef industry is dedicated to producing the highest quality and safest beef products for consumers.

Government oversight is not new to the meat industry, but it has continued to change. In 1906, the meat industry was heavily criticized in *The Jungle* written by Upton Sinclair for poor working environments and producing meat under insanitary conditions. Congress responded to the public demands for improved working conditions and better sanitation by passing the Federal Meat Inspection Act (FMIA) of 1906, which was amended in 1967 by the Wholesome Meat Act. In late 1992 and early 1993, there was an outbreak of *Escherichia coli* O157:H7 which caused some people to question the safety of meat products, especially ground beef. Partly in response to the public concern, the United States Department of Agriculture's (USDA) Food Safety and Inspection Service (FSIS) released the 1996 Pathogen Reduction/Hazard Analysis and Critical Control Point (PR/HACCP) final rule, which mandated the implementation of HACCP throughout the meat industry.

Meat inspection

Under the Meat Act the USDA/FSIS inspects all meat sold in interstate commerce and re-inspects imported products to ensure they fulfill all U.S. requirements. As of August 2002, the FSIS had over 9,000 full-time employees serving to ensure that all regulatory requirements are met in approximately 6,200 federally inspected establishments. Unlike the Food and Drug Administration's (FDA) inspection system that has periodic visits by inspectors to food establishments, FSIS inspectors are in the establishments each and every day to ensure that the products are fit for human consumption and in compliance with all Federal laws governing the wholesomeness and safety of meat products. Therefore, the meat industry is truly the most highly regulated food industry in the country.

To provide this extensive oversight, FSIS maintains a comprehensive system of controls, some of which are outlined below.

Humane handling and antemortem inspections

The inspection process starts with the live animal. Antemortem inspection involves a visual and physical evaluation of the live animal prior to slaughter to identify any conditions that may indicate disease or illness. The inspection personnel are responsible for identifying any high-risk animals and making determinations to allow them to enter the food chain or to condemn them from entering. These actions are taken to ensure that meat is safe and wholesome for consumption.

Humane handling has long been of interest to both the Agency and the industry. The beef industry has studied the behavior and movement of cattle and designed pens, walkways and equipment to improve the handling of livestock. In early 2002 the FSIS placed 17 District Veterinary Medical Specialists (DVMS) in the field to deal specifically with the oversight of humane handling issues. Strict guidelines are in place and strongly enforced to prevent the mishandling of animals.

Postmortem inspections

The inspectors are responsible for conducting a thorough examination of the lymph nodes, organs, and entire carcass to identify signs of disease and unwholesome conditions. This inspection process involves all slaughtered animals. The postmortem inspection allows inspectors to further evaluate the carcass and tissues from any animal they suspected to be a high risk during antemortem inspection before a final decision on product use is determined. If any carcass or its parts are identified as diseased or unwholesome then they are condemned and prevented from entering the food supply. This is a complete system to prevent diseased animals from entering the food supply.

Product inspections

The inspection system continues throughout the entire processing segment of the industry, including both raw and fully cooked products. Processing inspectors are responsible for processed meat products and all other ingredients contained in the finished product. These inspectors are responsible for cured and smoked products, frozen dinners, canned meats, and other processed products. They must verify that the establishment is maintaining sanitary conditions and following all procedures and labeling regulations.

Hazard Analysis and Critical Control Point (HACCP) rule

The use of HACCP as a process control for food safety is not new to the food industry or to the meat industry. Many establishments were utilizing HACCP before the release of FSIS' Pathogen Reduction/HACCP final rule on July 25, 1996. However, the release of the HACCP rule is probably the most significant change for meat inspection since the 1967 amendment to the Act.

As the name implies, there are two components to the 1996 rule—1) the reduction of pathogens, and 2) the development and implementation of HACCP systems. The pathogen reduction part of the rule includes the *Salmonella* Performance Standard and the generic *E. coli* testing. The regulation was phased in over a three-year period with the final implementation dates in early 2000. Today, all federally and state inspected establishments are operating under a HACCP system and all new establishments must have a HACCP Inspected Meat system developed before receiving a grant of inspection.

Under the Meat Act the USDA/FSIS inspects all meat sold in interstate commerce and re-inspects imported products to ensure they fulfill all U.S. requirements.

HACCP allows establishments to identify food safety hazards that are reasonably likely to occur in the process or type of product being produced and establish points of control to prevent them from occurring. HACCP is a science-based process control system that focuses on preventing food safety problems. The role of the FSIS inspector in a HACCP system is to verify that the establishment has developed and is implementing the HACCP system as designed. In late 2001, the FSIS introduced the Consumer Safety Officer (CSO) positions that report to the district offices. The CSO is responsible for conducting a comprehensive assessment of the establishment's food safety system to see if it is an adequately designed and supportable program that will control food safety hazards.

Residue and microbiological testing

FSIS has an on-going residue monitoring program to detect and prevent the misuse of chemicals (i.e., antibiotics) during the production of livestock. The Agency is responsible for identifying any high-risk animals and collecting samples for laboratory analysis to determine if violative levels of chemical residues are present. The industry has been working with the Agency to continue to decrease the possibility of chemical contamination by promoting educational programs for livestock producers and implementing quality systems, such as the Beef Quality Assurance (BQA) program. Through the efforts of both the Agency and the industry, the risk of chemical residues in beef will continue to decline.

The meat industry is truly the most highly regulated food industry in the country.

Microbiological contamination is another major issue facing the meat industry. Pathogens such as *Listeria monocytogenes* and *Salmonella* are concerns on fully cooked, ready-to-eat products. The industry has conducted extensive research to learn more about environmental contamination in operations producing ready-to-eat foods to help minimize the risk of *Listeria monocytogenes* and other pathogens on fully cooked products. The FSIS personnel randomly select finished products to test for these pathogens. Any products that are found to be contaminated will be prevented from entering the food supply or will be recalled if already in commerce.

In 1994, FSIS declared that raw ground beef contaminated with the pathogen *E. coli* O157:H7 is adulterated and must be further processed to kill the microorganism or destroyed. This was the first time the presence of bacteria in a raw meat product was defined as an adulterant. FSIS also initiated a microbiological testing program to detect *Escherichia coli* O157:H7 in raw ground beef. As of Oct. 7, 2002, 42 out of more than 5,000 samples collected have tested positive for *E. coli* O157:H7. Inspected establishments and retail outlets are randomly selected for sample collection. Imported ground beef products are also subjected to sample collection by FSIS Import Inspection personnel and ground beef products produced at state inspected establishments are collected by state program personnel.

Sanitation

The HACCP final rule also required the development and implementation of Sanitation Standard Operating Procedures (SSOPs). These programs are intended to prevent direct product contamination or adulteration, and focus on pre-operational and operational activities. Every establishment must develop, implement, and maintain effective SSOPs. Also, the Sanitation Requirements for Official Meat and Poultry Establishments Final Rule became effective on January 25, 2000. This rule established performance standards for sanitation and was designed to consolidate the sanitation regulations into a single rule applicable to both meat and poultry. Section 416.1 of the rule states, "Each official establishment must be operated and maintained in a manner to prevent the creation of insanitary conditions and to ensure that product is not adulterated."

The USDA inspection legend

The USDA's Food Safety and Inspection Service has authority over the production of wholesome and safe meat products. Each federally inspected establishment is granted an establishment number that is placed on the official inspection legend. The inspection legend is stamped onto carcasses at various locations and placed onto product labels of packaged meats. The application of the inspection legend means that the operation has complied with all of the Agency's regulatory requirements.

Meat production is the most highly regulated food industry. The USDA's Food Safety and Inspection Service is responsible for developing rules and regulations for the production of wholesome and safe foods and providing regulatory oversight during the day-to-day production. However, the beef industry understands and accepts its responsibility in producing the safest product possible. The combination of regulatory oversight and the commitment and dedication of the industry should allow consumers to purchase and prepare meat products with confidence in the safety of the product. Food safety begins with the establishment, includes regulatory verification, and ends with the consumer. Working together— the USDA's Food Safety and Inspection Service, the beef industry, and the consumer—we can make a winning team for the safest beef supply in the world.

13

Federal Inspection Does Not Adequately Ensure Meat Safety

Eric Schlosser

Eric Schlosser is an investigative journalist and author of Fast Food Nation: The Dark Side of the All-American Meal, *an exposé of fast-food chains.*

America's federal meat inspection laws are not strict enough to protect consumers from food-borne pathogens such as *E.coli* and *Salmonella*. Further, the U.S. Department of Agriculture (USDA) lacks the ability to enforce those laws. Specifically, the USDA has no power to force a meat packer to recall meat even when high levels of pathogens are found in the company's products; recall of tainted meat is strictly voluntary. Often, as in the case of the ConAgra recall in July 2002, meat packers only take action after people become ill. The USDA cannot effectively carry out its dual and conflicting mandate—to promote the sale of American meat and at the same time protect consumers from unsafe meat. Only the creation of an independent food safety agency with aggressive enforcement powers will protect consumers from food-borne illnesses caused by unsafe meat.

In a summer full of headlines about corporate misdeeds and irresponsibility, ConAgra's massive recall in July [2002] stands apart. The defective product wasn't fiber optic cable, energy futures or some esoteric financial instrument. It was bad meat—almost 19 million pounds of beef potentially contaminated with *E. coli* O157:H7, enough to supply a tainted burger to at least one-fourth of the US population. Unlike other prominent scandals, this one does not seem to involve any falsification of records, shredding of crucial documents or deliberate violation of the law. And that makes it all the more disturbing. The Bush Administration and its Republican allies in Congress have allowed the meatpacking industry to gain control of the nation's food safety system, much as the airline industry was given responsibility for airport security in the years leading up to the September 11, [2001] attacks. The deregulation of food safety makes about as much sense as the deregulation of air safety. Anyone who eats meat these days should be deeply concerned about what our meatpacking companies now have the freedom to sell.

Anyone who eats meat these days should be deeply concerned about what our meatpacking companies now have the freedom to sell.

At the heart of the food safety debate is the issue of microbial testing. Consumer advocates argue that the federal government should be testing meat for dangerous pathogens and imposing tough penalties on companies that repeatedly fail those tests. The meatpacking industry, which has been battling new food safety measures for almost a century, strongly disagrees. In 1985 a panel appointed by the National Academy of Sciences warned that the nation's meat inspection system was obsolete. At the time USDA inspectors relied solely on visual and olfactory clues to detect tainted meat. After the Jack in the Box outbreak in 1993, the Clinton Administration announced that it would begin random testing for *E. coli* O157:H7 in ground beef. The meatpacking industry promptly sued the USDA in federal court to block such tests.

E. coli O157:H7, the pathogen involved in both the Jack in the Box outbreak and the recent ConAgra recall, can cause severe illness or death, especially among children, the elderly and people who are immuno-suppressed. The Centers for Disease Control and Prevention (CDC) estimate that about 73,000 Americans are sickened by *E. coli* O157:H7 every year. An additional 37,000 are sickened by other dangerous strains of *E. coli* also linked to ground beef. At a slaughterhouse these pathogens are spread when manure or stomach contents get splattered on the meat.

Company employees conduct inspections

The USDA won the 1993 lawsuit, began random testing for *E. coli* O157:H7 and introduced a "science-based" inspection system in 1996 that requires various microbial tests by meatpacking companies and by the government. The new system, however, has been so weakened by industry opposition and legal challenges that it now may be less effective than the old one. Under the Hazard Analysis and Critical Control Points plans that now regulate production at meatpacking plants, many food safety tasks have been shifted from USDA inspectors to company employees.

In return for such concessions, the USDA gained the power to test for *salmonella* and to shut down plants that repeatedly failed those tests. *Salmonella* is spread primarily by fecal material, and its presence in ground beef suggests that other dangerous pathogens may be present as well. In November 1999, the USDA shut down a meatpacking plant for repeatedly failing *salmonella* tests. The Texas company operating the plant, Supreme Beef Processors, happened to be one of the leading suppliers of ground beef to the National School Lunch Program. With strong backing from the meatpacking industry, Supreme Beef sued the USDA, eventually won the lawsuit and succeeded this past December [2001] in overturning the USDA's *salmonella* limits. About 1.4 million Americans are sickened by *salmonella* every year, and the CDC has linked a nasty, antibiotic-resistant strain of the bug to ground beef. Nevertheless, it is now perfectly legal to sell ground beef that is thoroughly contaminated with *salmonella*—and sell it with the USDA's seal of approval.

This summer's ConAgra recall raises questions not only about the nation's food safety rules but also about the USDA's competence to enforce them. The USDA conducts its random tests for *E. coli* O157:H7 at wholesale and retail locations, not at the gigantic slaughterhouses where the meat is usually contaminated. By the time the USDA discovers tainted meat, it's already being distributed. On June 17 and 19, [2002] USDA test results showed that beef shipped from the ConAgra slaughterhouse in Greeley, Colorado was contaminated. But the USDA failed to inform ConAgra for almost two weeks. Meanwhile, the bad meat continued to be sold at supermarkets, served at countless restaurants and grilled at outdoor barbecues nationwide. Although the packages said "Freeze or sell by 06 18 02," Safeway supermarkets in Colorado held a two-for-one sale of the questionable ConAgra meat from June 19 to June 25.

ConAgra's recall was "voluntary"

Four days later the USDA informed ConAgra that it had distributed beef contaminated with *E. coli* O157:H7, ConAgra announced a "voluntary recall" of 354,200 pounds. Then health authorities noticed that people were getting severely ill, mainly small children in Colorado. A common symptom was vomiting and defecating blood. After consultations with the USDA, ConAgra expanded the voluntary recall on July 19 to include an additional 18.3 million pounds of beef processed at the Greeley plant between April 12 and July 11. About three dozen illnesses and one death have thus far [September 2002] been linked to ConAgra's meat. Based on previous *E. coli* outbreaks, perhaps twenty times that number of illnesses occurred without being properly diagnosed or reported. According to the most recent tally, less than one-tenth of the 18.6 million pounds of ConAgra's recalled meat has been recovered. The rest has most likely been eaten.

America's food safety system has been expertly designed not to protect the public health but to protect the meatpacking industry from liability.

Throughout the recall, USDA officials praised ConAgra for how well it had cooperated with the government, offering little criticism or explanation of how this company had managed to ship thousands of tons of potentially contaminated meat for months. The USDA also deflected criticism of its own role in the outbreak; a Montana wholesaler had warned the agency in February that beef shipped from ConAgra's plant in Greeley was tainted. Instead of imposing a tough penalty on ConAgra, the USDA often seemed eager to shift the blame and responsibility to consumers. "If people cooked their food correctly," said Elsa Murano, USDA under secretary for food safety, "a lot of outbreaks would not take place."

When most people learn how the meatpacking industry operates, they're appalled.

Although ConAgra apparently violated no laws, its behavior made clear where the real power lies. The recall of its meat was entirely voluntary. In an age when defective Happy Meal toys can be swiftly ordered off the market at the slightest hint of a choking hazard, the government can neither demand the recall of potentially deadly meat nor impose civil fines on companies that sell it. ConAgra has refused to disclose publicly which restaurants, distributors and supermarkets got meat from Greeley; federal law does not require the company to do so. Colorado health officials did not receive a list showing where ConAgra's meat had been distributed until the first week of August—more than a month after the initial recall. Health officials in Utah and Oklahoma did not receive that information from ConAgra until the third week in August. "I know it's here," an Oklahoma public health official told the *Denver Post* at one point, referring to the recalled meat. "But without knowing where it went, there's not a whole lot we can do." In future recalls, ConAgra now promises to do a better job of sharing information with state health authorities—even though the law does not require the company to do so.

Excessive line speeds cause problems

ConAgra's meatpacking operations in Greeley are described at length in my book *Fast Food Nation*, and I've spent a great deal of time with workers there. For years they have complained about excessive line speeds. The same factors often responsible for injuries in a slaughterhouse can also lead to food safety problems. When workers work too fast, they tend to make mistakes, harming themselves or inadvertently contaminating the meat.

America's food safety system has been expertly designed not to protect the public health but to protect the meatpacking industry from liability. The industry has received abundant help in this effort from the Republican Party, which for more than a decade has thwarted Congressional efforts to expand the USDA's food safety authority. According to the Center for Responsive Politics, during the 2000 presidential campaign meat and livestock interests gave about $23,000 to [Democrat] Al Gore and about $600,000 to [Republican] George W. Bush. The money was well spent. Dale Moore, chief of staff for Agriculture Secretary Ann Veneman, was previously the chief lobbyist for the National Cattlemen's Beef Association [NCBA]. Elizabeth Johnson, one of Veneman's senior advisers, was previously the associate director for food policy at the NCBA. Mary Waters, USDA assistant secretary for Congressional relations, assumed the post after working as legislative counsel for ConAgra Foods.

It would be an understatement to say that the Bush Administration has been friendly toward the big meatpackers. During Congressional testimony this past spring [2002], Elsa Murano, USDA chief food safety advocate, argued that her agency does not need the power to order a recall of contaminated meat. Nor did it need, she said, any new authority to shut down ground beef plants because of *salmonella* contamination.

New, tougher legislation

The meatpacking companies don't want any of their customers to get sick. But they don't want to be held liable for illnesses either, or to spend more money on preventing outbreaks. The exemplary food safety system at Jack in the Box increases the cost of the fast food chain's ground beef by about one penny per pound. The other major hamburger chains also require that their suppliers provide meat largely free of dangerous pathogens—and that requirement has not yet driven the meatpacking industry into bankruptcy. Senator Tom Harkin has introduced two pieces of food safety legislation that would help fill some of the glaring gaps in the current system.[1] The SAFER Meat, Poultry and Food Act of 2002 would give the USDA the authority to demand recalls of contaminated meat and impose civil fines on meatpacking companies. The Meat and Poultry Pathogen Reduction Act would place enforceable limits on the amounts of disease-causing bugs that meat can legally contain. Harkin's bills embody a good deal of common sense. Companies that produce clean meat should be allowed to sell it; those that produce dirty meat shouldn't. The Republican Party's alliance with the big meatpackers does not reflect widespread public support. The issue of food safety isn't like abortion or gun control, with passionate and fundamentally opposing views held by millions of American voters. When most people learn how the meatpacking industry operates, they're appalled. The outrage crosses party lines. Democrat or Republican, you still have to eat.

None of the recently proposed reforms, however, would prove as important and effective as the creation of an independent food safety agency with tough enforcement powers. The USDA has a dual and conflicting mandate. It's supposed to promote the sale of American meat— and protect consumers from unsafe meat. As long as the USDA has that dual role, consumers must be extremely careful about where they purchase beef, how they handle it and how long they cook it. While many Americans fret about the risks of bioterrorism, a much more immediate threat comes from the all-American meal. Until fundamental changes are made in our food safety system, enjoying your hamburgers medium-rare will remain a form of high-risk behavior.

---

1. As of August 2003, neither piece of legislation had passed.

14

Private Inspection Would Improve Meat Safety

E.C. Pasour Jr.

E.C. Pasour Jr. is an economist at North Carolina State University.

Private inspection firms driven by market incentives can provide consumers with more effective safeguards against tainted meat than federal inspection. A private firm inspecting meatpacking plants would be profitable only as long as its inspections accurately reflected the quality of the meat. If consumers became ill after eating meat inspected by a particular firm, that firm would soon go out of business. Thus, the profit incentive would stimulate more careful inspection of meat as well as the development of new methods to detect and destroy pathogens.

Last year's [1997] news reports of tainted beef focused public attention on the safety of the meat supply. In August 1997, Secretary of Agriculture Dan Glickman forced Hudson Foods to recall 25 million pounds of hamburger meat produced at the firm's state-of-the-art plant in Nebraska. The nation's largest beef recall occurred after several Colorado consumers became sick from hamburgers linked to *E. coli* contamination.

Examples of illness rooted in unsafe meat are not isolated incidents. Bad or undercooked meat causes an estimated 4,000 deaths and 5 million illnesses annually, according to the federal government's Centers for Disease Control. Moreover, a single incident of contaminated meat has the potential to affect large numbers of people. In 1993, five hundred people became ill and four children died in the Pacific northwest as a result of eating tainted hamburgers.

Illness and death caused by bad meat (whether tainted or undercooked) inevitably evoke calls for more government regulation. It is ironic that increased government intervention is viewed as an antidote to tainted meat, despite the federal government's long-standing responsibility for meat inspection in the United States. Indeed, the Hudson Foods incident occurred only a year after President [Bill] Clinton announced the most sweeping changes in the government's meat-inspection system.

E.C. Pasour Jr., "We Can Do Better than Government Inspection of Meat," *The Freeman: Ideas on Liberty*, vol. 48, May 1998, pp. 290–95. Copyright © 1998 by the Foundation for Economic Education, Inc. Reproduced by permission.

Moreover, a federal inspector was based at the Hudson Foods plant to check the plant's procedures daily.

Chronic problems related to meat inspection and meat safety warrant increased scrutiny of the most appropriate method of inspecting meat. During recent decades, successful deregulation initiatives occurred in a number of areas including banking and transportation. This shows that market forces may provide an improvement over government regulation of economic activity, even when regulations are long-standing and widely accepted.

Is meat inspection different?

Skeptics, including even many market proponents, might say that the conventional analysis doesn't hold for government regulations protecting health—where slip-ups can be fatal. Problems of "government failure," however, may be worse than any market imperfections that government regulation is instituted to remedy. Thus, government failure would have even graver implications for health issues.

Is it possible that the free market could substitute for, and even improve on, the current system of federal meat inspection? The following analysis demonstrates that the problems in government meat inspection are similar to those that plague all other government regulation of economic activity. There is no way for government regulators to obtain the information and realize the incentives of the decentralized market process, whatever the area of economic activity. Thus, market inspection of the U.S. meat industry, when contrasted with the current system of federal regulation, is likely to reduce the incidence of illness associated with the consumption of unsafe meat.

Federal meat inspection—how it began

The Meat Inspection Act of 1891 was a major landmark in federal regulation of meat and, indeed, of federal regulation of economic activity in the United States. A review of the political economy of that era is helpful in understanding the impetus for government regulation. Most government intervention then and now, at least ostensibly, is in response to "market failure"—economic outcomes that fall short of "perfect competition." (All markets fail, of course, when measured against this criterion.)

Moreover, the 1891 act was instituted under false pretenses. It was a solution to a largely nonexistent problem—contaminated meat. There is no reliable evidence that tainted meat was a major factor in the adoption of the legislation. In a political-economic analysis of the era, Gary Libecap concludes that "the record does not indicate that the incidence of diseased cattle or their consumption was very great, and there is no evidence of a major health issue at that time over beef consumption." Government meat inspection, once in place, however, like many other government regulations, was soon viewed as necessary to protect consumers.

There is a great deal of evidence that the political impetus for the 1891 legislation was the consequence of rapidly changing economic conditions. Market dominance by Chicago meat-packers—primarily Swift, Armour, Morris, and Hammond—quickly followed the introduction of refrigeration around 1880. Refrigeration allowed for centralized, large-scale, and lower-cost slaughterhouses because of production, distribution, and transportation advantages. The four large Chicago firms accounted for about 90 percent of the cattle slaughtered in Chicago within a decade after the introduction of refrigeration.

The Chicago packers fundamentally changed demand and supply conditions in the meatpacking industry. Small, local slaughterhouses throughout the country were rapidly displaced because they could not compete with the lower-cost Chicago packers. Local slaughter firms, in response, charged that Chicago packers used diseased cattle and that their dressed beef was unsafe. The disease issue, as bogus as it apparently was, threatened both domestic demand and export markets for U.S. meat. Cattle raisers, especially those in the midwest, backed federal meat inspection to promote demand.

Cattle producers were also concerned about falling prices. Prices fell because the supply of cattle grew rapidly. But producers attributed the fall to their declining market power versus the Chicago packers—a charge that seemed credible because of the packers' size and concentration. Ostensibly to deal with the largely spurious allegations of unsafe meat and collusion by the Chicago packers, cattlemen, and local packers called for federal meat inspection and antitrust legislation. Enactment of the Sherman Act in 1890 and the Meat Inspection Act of 1891 were thus closely tied legislatively.

The Jungle and the Meat Inspection Act of 1906

The famous Meat Inspection Act of 1906 also was heavily influenced by false charges. Ideas have consequences, and public policy can be influenced by a popular book, such as Upton Sinclair's *The Jungle*—regardless of its merits. The muckraking novel focused on greed and abuse among Chicago meat-packers and government inspectors. The characters in *The Jungle* tell of workers falling into tanks, being ground up with animal parts, and being made into "Durham's Pure Leaf Lard."

Sinclair wrote *The Jungle* to ignite a socialist movement on behalf of America's workers. He did not even pretend to have actually witnessed or verified the horrendous conditions he ascribed to Chicago packing houses. Instead, he relied heavily on both his own imagination and hearsay. Indeed, a congressional investigation at the time found little substance in Sinclair's allegations.

> *It is ironic that increased government intervention is viewed as an antidote to tainted meat, despite the federal government's long-standing responsibility for meat inspection in the United States.*

Nevertheless, the sensational allegations dramatically reduced the demand for meat. U.S. exports fell by half. Major meat-packers saw new regulations as the way to restore confidence, and they strongly endorsed the Meat Inspection Act of 1906, which expanded the scope of federal inspection to include smaller competitors.

Economic conditions back then were much different from today's. However, there is a lesson to be learned from that early period concerning government and free-market approaches to meat inspection.

The early legislation, for the most part, was not a response by government to a legitimate public-health threat. Congress enacted the 1891 act in response to political pressure by local meat-packers and cattle growers who felt victimized by the rise in power of the Chicago packers and by lower cattle prices. This legislation along with the Sherman Act and the Interstate Commerce Act, all enacted within a four-year period, represented a significant break with what had previously been considered an appropriate role for the federal government.

The 1906 Meat Inspection Act, too, was largely a response to the meat industry's financial problems rather than to a health threat. The earlier spate of interventionist legislation, however, had provided a new mandate for government regulation of economic activity that facilitated the passage of the 1906 act. Thus, the case of federal meat inspection is yet another example of [Austrian economist and social philosopher] Ludwig von Mises's insight that government intervention almost inevitably leads to further intervention.

Pitfalls of government regulation

Thus government meat inspection, like most other economic regulation, was instituted mainly because of favor-seeking: the use of time and money to harness the power of government for private ends. Favor-seeking is a negative-sum activity. The nation's output of goods and services decreases as resources are used to restrict competition rather than to expand production and exchange. Favor-seeking is just one example of "government failure."

Government intervention often is counter-productive because of information and incentive problems. The crucial economic problem confronting society is how to use people's specialized knowledge to best satisfy consumers. As Nobel laureate F.A. Hayek emphasized, government officials cannot obtain the information that motivates individual choice because that information, much of which is never articulated, is strongly linked to a particular time and place. Consequently, officials must base decisions on something other than the "public interest," if that term means the interests of the people who comprise the public.

Moreover, even if the information could be known, it is unlikely to be used most effectively. Government officials lack appropriate incentives because power and responsibility are separated. Those who make and administer laws do not bear the consequences of their actions, at least not to the same extent as private individuals. As shown below, markets generally are superior to government regulation because they cope better with information and incentive problems.

Related to the incentive problem is another flaw in the current system of meat inspection: the adverse effect of government regulation on innovation. That flaw is found in all alternatives to the decentralized market process.

In the absence of the profit motive, individuals have less incentive to discover and implement new technology in the inspection and handling of meat. No one knows, of course, which new technology will ultimately prove beneficial in meat inspection or in any other area. However, in the marketplace, if an innovation proves to be profitable the person responsible for it will receive a large part of the reward. Things are quite different in a centralized system. Under government regulation, the government employee who discovers or adopts a potentially superior technology is likely to receive only a small amount of additional compensation. On the other hand, if the innovation doesn't pan out, he will lose much less than the entrepreneur in a profit-and-loss system.

Market inspection of the U.S. meat industry . . . contrasted with . . . federal regulation, is likely to reduce the incidence of illness associated with the consumption of unsafe meat.

This fundamental difference between markets and government is highly important to innovation in the meat industry. The heart of U.S. meat inspection continues to be the "poke and sniff" method that relies on the eyes and noses of some 7,400 Department of Agriculture [USDA] inspectors. In 1997 a small Massachusetts company, SatCon Technology Corporation, working with a North Dakota–based group of ranchers, found a way to use lasers to find illness-causing pathogens such as *E. coli* and *salmonella* by scanning animal carcasses in slaughterhouses. Such technological innovation has the potential to revolutionize meat inspection in the United States.

But it is more likely to be adopted in a free market than in a government-regulated market. Since it has the potential to dramatically reduce both the amount of labor currently used in meat inspection and the rationale for government regulation, it is inconsistent with two important goals of any bureaucracy: maintaining jobs and expanding its operation.

Market competition versus government regulation

The experience of government control of economic activity shows why government meat inspection is likely to be inferior to free markets. Private inspection firms, which must meet the market test, have a greater incentive to be effective than do government regulators. A private firm providing information to consumers about meat quality will reap profits when successful and incur losses when not. Thus, if a private meat-grading service were to become lax in satisfying consumers, meat firms no longer would be willing to pay for the service. Consequently, the private firm not only has an advantage in obtaining the necessary information; it also has a greater incentive to use it in the interest of the public weal.

Moreover, profit-seeking firms are likely to have a greater incentive than government regulators to adhere to quality standards. Government inspectors get to know the people operating the plants they regulate. Strict enforcement of standards might create hardship for those people. For example, if meat is considered to be of marginal quality but not to pose a significant health threat, regulators may be inclined to overlook such infractions. In short, when contrasted with market regulation, government regulators have a smaller incentive to enforce safety regulations.

Numerous studies have shown the benefits from privatization. It is quite likely that problems of food safety would be dealt with better through the decentralized market process, which provides a greater opportunity for both business firms and consumers to achieve their goals. Stated differently, the market process provides a greater incentive than government regulation for private firms and consumers to discover, disseminate, and use information about the quality of meat.

For one thing, government regulation gives consumers a false sense of security. It leads them to assume that they are being protected by the government, reducing the incentive to do their own checking. Market methods of inspection, in contrast, give consumers a greater incentive to acquire information about the quality of meat. Consequently, they are likely to be more alert to potential problems of food safety.

It is true, of course, that meat may be contaminated when it appears to be safe. If sellers of meat have more information about quality than consumers do, can consumers look after their interests? Yes; uneven information does not imply that sellers have an incentive to sell unsafe meat. Consumers are protected by the sellers' economic interests.

Private inspection firms, which must meet the market test, have a greater incentive to be effective than do government regulators.

The use of brand names, such as Armour or Swift, is one way that private firms assure quality standards for meat. A brand name enables consumers to identify a firm's meat product and choose it over competitors. Hence, a firm with an established and valuable brand name has a strong financial incentive to adhere to quality standards.

A company responsible for selling contaminated meat can be quickly ruined by adverse publicity about its products. The recall of Hudson beef in 1997 left Burger King branches across the midwest without hamburgers. Following the recall, Burger King canceled their contract with Hudson Foods and announced that it would never buy from the company again— showing that it is strongly in the financial interest of business firms not to sell tainted meat.

Where quality is difficult for consumers to evaluate, little-known firms may benefit from the services of private inspectors to certify safety. There is considerable evidence that market forces can assure product quality without government regulation. Best Western, for example, is a private certification agency that enables travelers to identify motels that meet specified quality standards. Underwriters Laboratories establishes standards for electrical products, and tests them to see if they meet those standards. These examples show that firms frequently are willing to pay to assure customers that their products meet prescribed standards. The success of *Consumer Reports* and similar publications is further evidence that consumers are willing to pay to be informed.

Is meat inspection an exception to the rule that private firms generally perform more effectively than government? There are good reasons to think that market-based inspection of the meat industry could improve on the current system. Illness associated with contaminated meat often occurs with federal meat inspection. There is no way, of course, to prevent all food-related illness. Mistakes on the part of buyers and sellers, and some degree of fraud, are unavoidable whatever the institutional arrangement. The goal in meat inspection, as in other areas of economic activity, is to establish an institutional arrangement that provides and uses information in a way that best serves consumers. The free market generally is more effective than government regulation in doing so.

Why not more market inspection of meat?

We've seen that businesses and consumers are willing to pay to assure product quality. And, as emphasized throughout, it is apparent that private inspection agencies "have a lot going for them." Yet, despite the ostensible advantages of the market approach, there is little reliance on market forces in meat inspection in the United States. Why does the meat industry not rely on market regulation more?

Market-generated information about the quality of meat undoubtedly would be much greater in the absence of government regulation. Government inspection tends to preempt market inspection, much as taxpayer-financed education crowds out privately funded schools, by reducing the incentives of sellers and buyers to look after safety on their own. There is little demand on the part of meat handlers for services that would be provided by private firms in the absence of government inspection. Business firms are, of course, also happy to have the taxpayers pick up the tab for inspection.

Similarly, with assurances by the USDA (and the media) that government regulation is crucial to consumer safety, there is little impetus for consumers to change the current institutional arrangement. Moreover, when problems of meat safety occur, there is no discussion of "government failure." Instead, regulatory officials plead for more power. In the aftermath of the Hudson Foods incident, for example, Secretary Glickman requested additional authority to shut down food-processing plants and to impose fines of $100,000 per day on any plant not obeying his order.

There can be no guarantees when it comes to food safety. Indeed, zero risk is not a reasonable objective in any aspect of human action. There are two approaches to ensuring the safety of meat—market inspection and government regulation. It is ironic that the public expects government regulation, which has more imperfections than the competitive market process, to provide for meat safety. Few people question the appropriateness of government regulation of the meat industry, even when they fault its effectiveness.

No one has a stronger interest in protecting consumers from tainted meat than the businesses in the industry. Ultimately, safety is best assured when rooted in the self-interest of business firms and consumers.

15

Too Much Responsibility for Food Safety Is Placed on Consumers

Sandra B. Eskin, Nancy Donley, Donna Rosebaum, and Karen Taylor Mitchell

Sandra B. Eskin is a writer and consultant on food safety issues. Nancy Donley is president of Safe Tables Our Priority (STOP). Donna Rosebaum is cofounder of STOP and a food safety advocate. Karen Taylor Mitchell is executive director of STOP. STOP is a nonprofit organization that assists victims of food-borne illnesses and advocates for food safety.

Government and food industry officials are sending consumers mixed messages; they insist that America has the safest food in the world and then try to convince consumers that they have to take special precautions in cooking and storing food so it will be safe to eat. Further, inaccurate or incomplete labeling may lead consumers to believe that food is safe and "ready to eat" when cooking may be necessary, particularly for vulnerable consumers—pregnant women, the very old or the very young, and people with compromised immune systems. Finally, too much emphasis is placed on consumer education and the responsibility of consumers to protect themselves from unsafe foods. The best way to reduce the incidence of food-borne illnesses is to keep pathogens from contaminating the food supply before it ever reaches consumers.

Food safety agencies, as well as food industry trade associations, have made extensive investments in consumer education since 1993. In 1998, the government established a website, www.foodsafety.gov, for food safety resources. Food safety messages such as "It's safe to bite when the temperature's right" are appropriate and useful, and academic studies have shown that consumer knowledge regarding certain foods, pathogens, and handling procedures has increased dramatically over the past decade. However, a number of problems exist with current consumer education efforts.

Mixed messages

Government and industry officials at all levels constantly send mixed messages to the public. With government officials and industry leaders incessantly repeating the unsubstantiated mantra, "we have the safest food supply in the world," foodborne illness victims in particular and consumers in general are unprepared to believe that they are at significant risk from pathogenic bacteria in the food they eat. Attempts to change people's behavior are doomed to fail when they are being told there is no problem.

Similarly, consumers are being given mixed messages about what constitutes safe food handling behavior. They read about a product recall but are also told that no illnesses have been associated with it, leading them to question whether a real problem exists. Furthermore, recall information is juxtaposed with information stating that it's safe to eat contaminated product as long as you cook it right. As a result, it is reasonable for consumers to conclude, "It must not be that bad or they'd tell us not to eat it at all." To make matters worse, numerous studies have shown that knowledge of food safety hazards is not translating into behavioral changes sufficient to protect most families from contaminated food.

Government-sponsored consumer education initiatives send mixed messages to the public, and place too much emphasis on the responsibility of consumers to protect themselves from foodborne illness.

Product labels also send mixed messages. Consumers reasonably presume that a product is safe when it is stamped "Inspected by the USDA" [United States Department of Agriculture] on a product label, when this may not be the case. Products that are labeled "ready to eat," are, in fact, not ready to eat, particularly for vulnerable consumers—older persons, pregnant women, and people with suppressed immune systems—who are especially susceptible to *Listeriosis*. Among other products, notably fresh produce, warning and handling labels are conspicuously absent, as is information about the food's origin that could help consumers assess its safety.

Moreover, key messages are either missing from or underemphasized in current consumer education initiatives. The most important of these is the extensive threat posed by cross-contamination. The fact that precious educational resources are targeted at young schoolchildren blatantly ignores the reality that they are not the ones who prepare the food.

Blaming the victim

Most significant here is the fact that the current food-safety strategy followed by both the government and industry places far too much emphasis on consumer intervention. The overemphasis on consumer education fosters the misleading impression that it is consumers' responsibility to make sure that their food is safe, and that, if people get sick, it's their own fault. The contradictory nature of USDA's dual missions—to both market meat and protect the public—is particularly relevant here, as shown by the 1998 USDA Annual Report, which recast the foodborne illness awareness and educational goals of the 1997 Presidential directive as "Raising Consumers' Confidence in Food Safety."

> *Consumer education should not be a substitute for measures that would prevent microbial contamination and its proliferation in food production and transportation.*

An industry-government partnership called FightBac, instituted in 1997, perhaps best demonstrates the educational misfire. A major originator of consumer information, the FightBac campaign delivers the message to consumers to "keep your food safe from bacteria." Yet, this message is more appropriately delivered to the food industry itself. Consumers cannot keep their food safe from most deadly pathogenic contamination; at best they can merely mitigate the effects of prior contamination. To that extent, the government must provide consumers with complete and realistic information about food contamination and foodborne disease in the United States, consistently do all it can throughout the food production chain to "keep consumers safe from bacteria in food," and implement effective behavioral change models to help consumers effectively mitigate risks until preventable contamination is under control.

There is no question that consumers can compound or even create food safety problems through cross-contamination, undercooking, and improper thawing or cooling. However, government-sponsored consumer education initiatives send mixed messages to the public, and place too much emphasis on the responsibility of consumers to protect themselves from foodborne illness. The most direct and effective solution to the problem is to keep the pathogens out of the food supply in the first place. Consumer education should not be a substitute for measures that would prevent microbial contamination and its proliferation in food production and transportation.

Workable recommendations

• Educational messages relating to food safety must be consistent, truthful, and complete, and they must explain the problem as well as promote techniques to minimize risk from foodborne pathogens.

• Research is needed to enhance the effectiveness of food safety education on consumer behavior modification before further resources are expended on efforts which fail to reduce the toll of foodborne disease.

• Special attention should be paid to developing educational initiatives directed at subpopulations with particularly high incidences of severe foodborne illness.

Organizations to Contact

The editors have compiled the following list of organizations concerned with the issues debated in this book. The descriptions are derived from materials provided by the organizations. All have publications or information available for interested readers. The list was compiled on the date of publication of the present volume; the information provided here may change. Be aware that many organizations take several weeks or longer to respond to inquiries, so allow as much time as possible.

American Council on Science and Health (ACSH)
1995 Broadway, 2nd Fl., New York, NY 10023-5860
(212) 362-7044 • fax: (212) 362-4919
e-mail: acsh@acsh.org • website: www.acsh.org

ACSH provides consumers with scientific evaluations of food and the environment, pointing out both health hazards and benefits. It participates in a variety of government and media events, from congressional hearings to popular magazines. It publishes the bimonthly *News and Views*, as well as the booklets *Eating Safely: Avoiding Foodborne Illness, Biotechnology and Food*, and *Modernize the Food Safety Laws: Delete the Delaney Clause*.

Biotechnology Industry Organization (BIO)
1625 K St. NW, Suite 1100, Washington, DC 20006
(202) 857-0244 • fax: (202) 857-0237
e-mail: info@bio.org • website: www.bio.org

BIO represents biotechnology companies, academic institutions, and state biotechnology centers engaged in the development of products and services in the areas of biomedicine, agriculture, and environmental applications. It conducts workshops and produces educational activities aimed at increasing public understanding of biotechnology. Its publications include the bimonthly newsletter *BIO Bulletin*, the periodical *BIO News*, and the book *Biotech for All*.

Campaign for Food Safety (CFS)
860 Hwy. 61, Little Marais, MN 55614
(218) 226-4164 • fax: (218) 226-4157
e-mail: alliance@mr.net • website: www.purefood.org

The Campaign for Food Safety promotes the growth of organic and sustainable agriculture practices. CFS activist strategies include education, boycotts, grassroots lobbying, litigation, networking, direct-action protests, and media events. It publishes the newsletter *Campaign for Food Safety News* as well as the periodic *Action Alerts*.

Center for Science in the Public Interest (CSPI)
1875 Connecticut Ave. NW, Suite 300, Washington, DC 20009
(202) 332-9110 • fax: (202) 265-4954
e-mail: cspi@cspinet.org • website: www.cspinet.org

The Center for Science in the Public Interest is a nonprofit education and advocacy organization committed to improving the safety and nutritional quality of the U.S. food supply. It publishes *Nutrition Action Healthletter*, the largest-circulation health newsletter in the country.

Food and Drug Administration (FDA)
5600 Fishers Lane, Rockville, MD 20857
(888) 463-6332
e-mail: webmail@oc.fda.gov • website: www.fda.gov

The FDA is a public health agency, charged with protecting American consumers by enforcing the Federal Food, Drug, and Cosmetic Act and several related public health laws. To carry out this mandate of consumer protection, the FDA has investigators and inspectors covering the country's almost ninety-five thousand FDA-regulated businesses. Its publications include government documents, reports, fact sheets, and press announcements.

Food Safety Consortium (FSC)
110 Agriculture Building, University of Arkansas, Fayetteville, AR 72701
(501) 575-5647 • fax: (501) 575-7531
e-mail: fsc@cavern.uark.edu • website: www.uark.edu/depts/fsc

Congress established the Food Safety Consortium, consisting of researchers from the University of Arkansas, Iowa State University, and Kansas State University, in 1988 through a special Cooperative State Research Service grant. It conducts extensive investigation into all areas of poultry, beef, and pork meat production. The consortium publishes the quarterly *FSC Newsletter*.

Friends of the Earth (FoE)
1025 Vermont Ave. NW, No. 300, Washington, DC 20005
(202) 783-7400 • fax: (202) 783-0444
e-mail: foe@foe.org • website: www.foe.org

Friends of the Earth monitors legislation and regulations that affect the environment. Its Safer Food, Safer Farms Campaign speaks out against what it perceives as the negative impact biotechnology can have on farming, food production, genetic resources, and the environment. It publishes the quarterly newsletter *Atmosphere* and the magazine *Friends of the Earth* ten times a year.

International Vegetarian Union (IVU)
PO Box 9710, Washington, DC 20016
(202) 362-8349
e-mail: vuna@ivu.org • website: www.ivu.org

The International Vegetarian Union is a nonprofit organization which advocates animal welfare, humanitarian, and health objectives. It publishes the annual *IVU News* and makes available on its website articles concerning food safety issues from affiliate vegetarian organizations.

National Cattlemen's Beef Association (NCBA)
5420 S. Quebec St., Greenwood Village, CO 80111-1905
(303) 694-0305 • fax: (303) 694-2851
e-mail: cattle@beef.org • website: www.beef.org

National Cattlemen's Beef Association is the marketing organization and trade association for America's 1 million cattle farmers and ranchers. Its Food Safety library publishes the quarterly *Food and Nutrition* newsletter, the fact sheet "Progress in Food Safety: Toward a Safer Beef Supply," and the booklet *Plating It Safe.*

National Food Safety Database
University of Florida
3082 McCarty Hall B, PO Box 110287, Gainesville, FL 32611
(352) 846-2270 • fax: (352) 846-1102
e-mail: alla@gnv.ifas.ufl.edu • website: www.foodsafety.org

The National Food Safety Database project is an organization funded primarily by the USDA in order to develop an efficient management system of U.S. food safety databases. Numerous food safety fact sheets, including "Preventing Foodborne Illnesses," "Myths About Food Safety," and "Botulism—It Only Takes a Taste," are available on its website.

Organic Consumers Association (OCA)
6101 Cliff Estate Rd., Little Marais, MN 55614
(218) 226-4164 • fax: (218) 353-7652
website: www.organicconsumers.org

The OCA is a grassroots nonprofit public interest organization that deals with crucial issues of food safety, industrial agriculture, genetic engineering, corporate accountability, and environmental sustainability. The OCA is the only organization in the United States focused exclusively on representing the views and interests of the nation's estimated 10 million organic consumers. The association publishes three newsletters, *Biodemocarcy, Organic Views*, and *Organic Bytes*, as well as fact sheets including "Hazards of G.E. Foods and Crops."

Safe Tables Our Priority (STOP)
PO Box 4352, Burlington, VT 05406
(802) 863-0555 • fax: (802) 863-3733
e-mail: mail@safetables.org • website: www.stop-usa.org

Safe Tables Our Priority is a nonprofit organization devoted to victim assistance, public education, and policy advocacy for safe food and public health. STOP's mission is to prevent unnecessary illness and loss of life from pathogenic food-borne illness. STOP's publications include newsletters, policy statements, testimonies, and press releases. The organization also offers several pamphlets including *What Is Foodborne Disease* and *The Problem Is Unsafe Food*, as well as a report, *Why Are People Still Dying from Contaminated Food?*

U.S. Department of Agriculture (USDA) Food Safety and Inspection Service (FSIS)
1400 Independence Ave. SW, Room 2932-S, Washington, DC 20250-3700
(202) 720-7943 • fax: (202) 720-1843
e-mail: fsiswebmaster@usda.gov • website: www.fsis.usda.gov

The Food Safety and Inspection Service is the public health agency of the USDA responsible for ensuring that the nation's commercial supply of meat, poultry, and egg products is safe, wholesome, and correctly labeled and packaged. It publishes fact sheets, reports, articles, and brochures on food safety topics.

Bibliography

Books

Peter Cerexhe and John Ashton — *Risky Food, Safer Choices.* New South Wales, Australia: New South Wales University, 1999.

Madeline Drexler — *Secret Agent.* Washington, DC: National Academy Press, 2002.

Lawrence J. Dyckman and Erin J. Lansburgh — *Meat and Poultry.* Collingdale, PA: DIANE, 2002.

Thomas W. Frazier and Drew C. Richardson, eds. — *Food and Agricultural Security: Guarding Against Natural Threats and Terrorist Attacks Affecting Health, National Foods Supplies, and Agricultural Economies.* New York: New York Academy of Sciences, 2000.

Robert H. Gates — *Infectious Disease Secrets.* Philadelphia, PA: Elsevier, 2003.

Kathleen Hart — *Eating in the Dark: America's Experiment with Genetically Engineered Food.* New York: Alfred A. Knopf, 2003.

Knut J. Heller — *Genetically Engineered Food: Detection of Genetic Modification.* New York: John Wiley and Sons, 2003.

Rebecca Hohlstein — *Food Fight: The Battle to Protect Our Food and Water Against Terrorism.* Madison, WI: Goblin Fern Press, 2003.

Mick Isle — *Everything You Need to Know About Food Poisoning.* New York: Rosen, 2000.

Bill Lambrecht — *Dinner at the New Gene Café: How Genetic Engineering Is Changing What We Eat, How We Live, and the Global Politics of Food.* New York: St. Martin's Press, 2001.

Warren Leon — *Is Our Food Safe?* New York: Crown/Three Rivers Press, 2002.

Marion Nestle — *Safe Food: Bacteria, Biotechnology, and Bioterrorism.* Berkeley: University of California Press, 2003.

Michael T. Osterholm and John Schwartz — *Living Terrors: What America Needs to Know to Survive the Coming Bioterrorist Catastrophe.* New York: Dell, 2001.

Thomas Peacock — *Is It Safe to Eat Out? How Our Local Health Officials Inspect Restaurants to Assure Food Safety . . . or Do They?* Lincoln, NE: Writer's Showcase Press, 2002.

Peter Pringle — *Food, Inc.: Mendel to Monsanto—the Promises and Perils of the Biotech Harvest.* New York: Simon & Schuster, 2003.

Maxine Rosaler — *Botulism.* New York: Rosen, 2003.

Andrew Rowell   *Don't Worry, It's Safe to Eat; the True Story of GM Food, BSE, and Foot-and-Mouth Disease.* London: Earthscan, 2003.

Eric Schlosser   *Fast Food Nation: The Dark Side of the All-American Meal.* Boston: Houghton Mifflin, 2001.

Maxine Schwartz   *How the Cows Turned Mad.* Berkeley: University of California Press, 2003.

Charlotte A. Spencer   *Mad Cows and Cannibals: A Guide to the Transmissible Spongiform Encephalopatries.* Upper Saddle River, NJ: Prentice-Hall, 2003.

John Stauber   *Mad Cow USA.* Monroe, ME: Common Courage Press, 2003.

Jill Trickett   *The Prevention of Food Poisoning.* Cheltenham, England: Stanley Thornes, 2001.

U.S. Government Printing Office   *The Future of Food.* Washington, DC: U.S. Government Printing Office, 2000.

Periodicals

Joel Bleifuss   "A 21st Century Plague? Britain's Mad Cows May Harbinger the Deaths of Millions," *In These Times*, February 7, 2000.

Edith A. Chenault   "Scientists Charged with Helping to Prevent Food-Borne Illness," *Texas A&M Agricultural News*, February 10, 2000. www.agnews.tamu.edu.

Mary H. Cooper   "Mad Cow Disease," *CQ Researcher*, March 2, 2001. Available from 1414 22nd St. NW, Washington, DC 20037.

Council on Foreign Relations   "Food and Agriculture," *Terrorism Q & A*, 2003.

Environmental Health Perspectives   "The New System for Seafood Safety," October 1998.

Thom Hartmann   "No Place to Escape," *Tikkun*, May/June 1999.

David Hosansky   "Food Safety," *CQ Researcher*, November 1, 2002.

Issues and Controversies On File   "Update: Food Safety," February 20, 1998. Available from Facts On File News Service, 11 Penn Plaza, New York, NY 10001-2006.

Journal of Environmental Health   "Dramatic Decline in Foodborne Illness," December 2002.

Heather Klinkhamer   "Globalization I: How Should the FDA Ensure the Safety of Imported Foods," testimony at the 21st Annual National Food Policy Conference, March 24, 1998. www.stop-usa.org.

Joseph P. Lewandowski   "Food Terrorism Potential Small but Worrisome," *Natural Foods Merchandiser*, January 2002. www.newhope.com.

Kathryn McConnell   "U.S. Regulatory Process Ensures Food Safety, Officials Say," U.S. Embassy, Japan, November 14, 2002. www.tokyo.usembassy.gov.

New Zealand   "Food Borne Illnessess," September 2000.
Ministry of Health   www.moh.govt.nz.

Milford Prewitt   "USDA to Confab: Food Supply Safe from Terror; Veneman Says Pipeline Well Protected," *Nation's Restaurant News*, March 31, 2003.

Bryan Salvage   "Activist Law Firm Lobbying for Hepatitis A Vaccination Program," *Outbreak*, March 15, 2001. www.outbreakinc.com.

Susan Bourque Seward   "Food Service Hand Washing Versus Glove Use: A Food Safety Perspective," *Dietetic Intern*, December 2000. www.dieteticintern.com.

James H. Steele   "Food Irradiation: A Public Health Measure Long Overdue!" *21st* Century, Fall 1999.

Miriam E. Tucker   "AMA Primer to Promote Management, Prevention of Food-Borne Illnesses," *Family Practice News*, February 15, 2001.

University of Georgia   "Food-Borne Illnesses Under Attack," *Return on*
College of Agriculture   *Investment*, 2001. www.agcomm.uga.edu.
and Environmental
Sciences

U.S. Department   "The Animal and Plant Health Inspection Service and
of Agriculture   the Department of Homeland Security: Working Together to Protect Agriculture," *APHIS Factsheet*, May 2003.

U.S. Department   "Consumer Food Safety Behavior: Consumer Demand
of Agriculture   for Food Safety," *Briefing Room*, June 5, 2002. www.ers.usda.gov/Briefing.

U.S. Food and   "FDA Issues Final Two Proposed Food Safety
Drug Administration   Regulations," May 6, 2003. www.cfsan.fda.gov.

Donovan Webster   "The Stink About Pork," *George*, April 1999. Available from 30 Montgomery St., Jersey City, NJ 07032.

World Health   "Terrorists Threats to Food: Guidance for Establishing
Organization   and Strengthening Prevention and Response Systems," 2002. www.who.int/fsf.

Catherine E. Woteki   "Safeguarding America's Meat," *Ripon Forum*, Summer 2001.

Index